# "Feeding To Win"

©
1973
**Equine Research**
PUBLICATIONS
P.O. Box 347
Grapevine, Texas 76051

## ACKNOWLEDGEMENT

My sincerest appreciation to Jerry A. Rheudasil, D.V.M., and Gary Potter, D.V.M., Ph.D., of Texas A & M University for the invaluable assistance rendered the research staff of Equine Research Publications in the writing of this book.

Don M. Wagoner<br>Editor/Publisher

## DEDICATION

For what she is, what she stands for, and for everything she has done for the horse world, this book is fondly dedicated to the beautiful, and gracious "first lady" of racing, Penny Tweedy.

D.M.W.

# TABLE
# OF CONTENTS

# Introduction

The horse, in his present state of evolution, has been known to man for a time pre-dating recorded history. Originally hunted for food, later becoming a beast of burden, a method of transportation, an instrument of war, a power source for farm equipment, a swift and exciting runner, and finally a form of pleasure and recreation. With the turn of the twentieth century, the advent of mechanized farm equipment and transportation shifted much of the emphasis on the horse from work, to pleasure. The horse population declined rapidly, reaching its lowest mark by mid-twentieth century.

No longer a major economic necessity, the horse as a subject of research and scientific study was all but forgotten. Evaluating the nutritional needs of the horse was left largely to the horse owner. Concerned horse owners were faced with the dismal reality of little, if any, scientifically accurate information with which to deal in developing a nutritionally balanced ration for their animals.

In the last two decades an increase in the number of arena, and turf enthusiasts, coupled with the rising popularity of the "pleasure" horse have created dramatic changes in the picture. The horse industry has become a billion dollar twentieth century phenomenon. The horse population is increasing in quantity, and quality at a rapid pace. Suddenly the horse has become an animal too valuable to be ignored. Universities, scientific foundations, and government facilities have begun allocating time and funds to equine research. And, the most neglected field of study, nutrition, has become recognized as a science as well as an art.

In the past, equine nutrition was the "stepchild" of the agriculture industry. Attention and research in the field of nutrition was concentrated in the areas of cattle, swine, sheep, and goats. An owner of animals within one of these favored groups could insist on, and get, the most recent and exact data in formulating rations, and would not consider using outdated techniques or feeds. He could rely on charts and tables which told him exactly what and how much to feed, and feel confident the ration he used had been thoroughly tested and was the best available. The horseman was not so fortunate.

Much of the accepted knowledge of feeding horses was obtained through trial and error, and the scientific data available till now, has been largely borrowed from the cattle industry. Some of these programs were beneficial to the horse but were not necessarily the best available. Others were actually harmful, or of little nutritional value. Knowledge gained from cattle feeding proved to be largely inapplicable, primarily because the horse is a nonruminant, and, unlike the cow, has its fermentation vat, the cecum, at the end of the digestive tract rather than the beginning. Too, the scientific emphasis in bovine nutrition is directed either toward weight gain, or milk production. Discrepancies in nutritional requirements between the cow and the horse have become as obvious as the differences in their uses.

Until recent years, few people have realized the wide ranging effects of the horse's diet on his health. Diseases such as founder, colic, and malnutrition are obviously connected with feeding, but there are many others where the relationship is not so readily noticed. Infertility, susceptibility to fractures, the trauma of parasite infestation, and many other problems are aggravated by poor nutrition.

So much for poor nutrition. We will now discuss mediocre nutrition. A high percentage of today's horses are the victims of the "maintenance diet." And, a high percentage of the horsemen feeding such a diet mistakenly believe their feeding program to be excellent.

The horseman feeding rations of this quality often competes in the arena or at the track, but he rarely carries a blue ribbon, or poses for a "win" picture. This is usually the horseman who learned the principles of equine nutrition either from his grandfather, or from an equally modern and astute source such as some "old time" trainer who once enjoyed an humble but well-discussed measure of local repute.

This is the horseman who would really like to be a winner, but talking him out of his "tried and true" methods and rations is next to impossible. He is usually economy oriented in his feed purchases, and oblivious to all but the least subtle discrepancies in quality. His horses regularly fail to achieve performance and appearance levels sufficient to qualify for the winner's circle. His excuses for their failure to do so however, are always very persuasive.

This book was not written for the benefit of the horseman who wants to "get by" with a maintenance diet for his horses. FEEDING TO WIN was written for the benefit of the serious horseman. The horseman who truly cares for the welfare of his horses will find FEEDING TO WIN to be an invaluable guide to achieving his goals in the horse world. And, it doesn't matter whether these goals include winning a 4H contest, or the Kentucky Derby. In other words, the theory upon which the material in this book is based is: THE QUALITY OF THE FEEDING PROGRAM SHOULD NOT BE DETERMINED BY THE VALUE OF THE HORSE. IT SHOULD BE DETERMINED BY THE SELF-RESPECT OF THE OWNER.

The information in FEEDING TO WIN is presented in definitive scientific terminology, sound enough to satisfy the most competent nutritionist. On the other hand, all topics have been thoroughly explained in a manner designed to satisfy the needs of every horseman.

A summary will appear at the end of each chapter. This is designed for two purposes: one, it makes the text a ready reference when you need information on a particular subject in a hurry; two, it provides the less ambitious reader with sound general knowledge of the subject where reading the entire text is not desirable.

The final chapter of the book (The Art and Science of Feeding), is a practical approach to the previous material. The basic methods of formulating rations for different breeds of horses are given, together with recommended diets and management practices by the recognized leaders from various corners of the horse world. Readers interested only in this applied knowledge will find it by going directly to that chapter. It is advised, however, that the more serious students of equine health and nutrition give themselves the full benefit of the entire text.

FEEDING TO WIN is the most complete and current reference on the subjects of equine health and nutrition. The research staff of EQUINE RESEARCH PUBLICATIONS will be continually investigating all scientific developments in these areas. When sufficient data is available to revise this book, or if it should become outdated in any major respect, a revised edition will be published and purchasers of this edition will be notified of its availability.

This book was intended to provide both a solid foundation for the student of equine nutrition, and the means by which all serious horsemen may improve their competitive edge at the track, or in the arena. But above all, this book was written for the benefit of our grand and noble friend . . . the horse.

Don M. Wagoner
Editor/Publisher

# 1

# The Equine
# Digestive System

This chapter is intended to explain the equine digestive system to a student of nutrition rather than to a student of physiology. For this reason, digestion has been considered from a functional approach. The anatomical details have not been explored more thoroughly than is necessary to understand the needs of the equine digestive system, and the relationship of these needs to specific feeds and diets. The reader who wishes a more detailed explanation should refer to a text on equine anatomy and physiology.

Digestion is the process by which food is broken down by the body into its simplest forms so that it can be absorbed into the bloodstream and provide nutrients for energy, growth, and repair, or be stored for future needs. Digestion takes place through muscular action, enzyme action, and bacterial fermentation. The digestive process is completed when usable nutrients are assimilated and undigested food residues and waste products are excreted.

## The Digestive Tract

The digestive system of the horse consists of a muscular tube called the alimentary canal, which begins at the lips and terminates at the anus, and has several associated organs. The alimentary canal is divided into the mouth, pharynx, esophagus, stomach, small intestine, cecum, large colon, small colon, and rectum. Accessory organs which aid in digestion are the teeth, salivary glands, liver, and pancreas. (See Figure One)

The alimentary canal has a total length of approximately ten times the length of the body, or about one hundred feet in the mature horse. (1) It changes diameter abruptly in several places, enlarging at the stomach, narrowing at the small intestine, and enlarging again at the cecum, and it is coiled and looped many times along its length. The digestive tract is lined with mucous membrane, containing glands which secrete digestive fluids. Food enters the horse at the mouth, is broken down and assimilated as it passes through the tract, and the undigested material continues through the canal to the anus, where it passes out of the body.

The horse is a nonruminant, (does not chew a cud), and has a digestive system which is intermediate between that of the cow (See Figure Two) and the pig (See Figure Three). Cattle, sheep, and goats, which are ruminants, differ from the horse in that they have four compartments to their stomachs. The first compartment, or rumen, contains an active microbial population that initiates fermentation and partial breakdown of roughage, which cannot be acted upon by enzymes in the small intestine. The rumen and its microbes allow this digestion of roughage before it reaches the small intestine, resulting in a much greater utilization of the nutrients in the animal's feed. Also, the stomach capacity of the cow, for example, is from ten to twenty times that of the horse. The large compartmented stomach greatly increases the amount of food which can be ingested at one time. The ruminant can therefore effectively digest a diet which is high in fiber and low in nutrient quality, and can be fed less frequently than the horse.

Swine have digestive systems similar to that of the horse, except that the relative capacity of the cecum and large intestine is limited. They cannot break down cellulose to the extent of the horse, and must be fed a diet low in fiber content and high in nutrient quality for maximum growth and feed utilization.

The horse has less digestive capacity than the cow, but more than the pig. The cecum and large colon of the horse serve some of the same purposes as the rumen in the cow, but they are not quantitatively as effective. Due to the size of these organs and the presence of a microbial population, food moves slowly through the cecum and large colon, and cellulose is broken down by a fermentation process. However, since the cecum follows the small intestine, where the greatest assimilation of nutrients takes place, the utilization of this roughage is less than that in the cow. The horse is also limited by the small capacity of the stomach. Horses therefore do well on a diet which is moderate to low in fiber, has fairly high nutrient content, and is fed frequently.

# HORSE

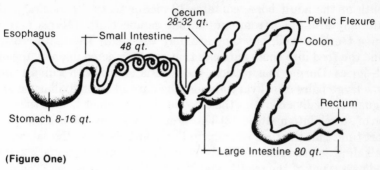

Esophagus

Small Intestine
48 qt.

Cecum
28-32 qt.

Pelvic Flexure

Colon

Rectum

Stomach 8-16 qt.

Large Intestine 80 qt.

**(Figure One)**

# COW

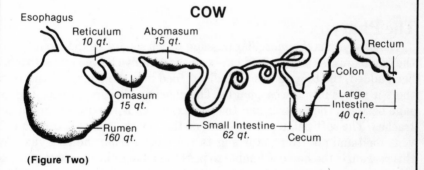

Esophagus

Reticulum
10 qt.

Abomasum
15 qt.

Rectum

Omasum
15 qt.

Colon

Small Intestine
62 qt.

Large
Intestine
40 qt.

Rumen
160 qt.

Cecum

**(Figure Two)**

# PIG

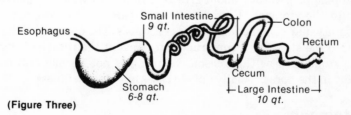

Small Intestine
9 qt.

Colon

Esophagus

Rectum

Cecum

Stomach
6-8 qt.

Large Intestine
10 qt.

**(Figure Three)**

# The Mouth

The digestive process in the horse begins at the mouth. Food is grasped with the lips and incisor teeth, and pulled backwards into the mouth. The mouth of the adult horse contains 12 incisor teeth, 24 molars, and the male may also have from one to four canine teeth. (Mares may have canine teeth as well, but they are only vestigial.) The teeth crush and grind the food into small particles that are then acted upon by the digestive juices. During mastication, the food is mixed with saliva from the three large pairs of salivary glands; the parotid, submaxillary, and sublingual. The saliva contains the enzyme ptyalin, which begins the conversion of starch into maltose. (2) This breakdown of starch is limited by the short time that the food remains in the mouth, because the saliva, which is alkaline, is gradually neutralized by the acid in the stomach after the food passes out of the mouth, and its digestive action ceases. The mature horse secretes as much as ten gallons of saliva each day, or about eighty-five pounds. (3)

# The Pharynx

The pharynx is the muscular passage which separates the mouth from the esophagus. After the food has been thoroughly chewed and saliva has been added, the tongue pushes balls of food into the pharynx, and from there it moves into the esophagus. The pharynx also provides an air passage between the nostrils and the larynx, which is the upper part of the trachea. The soft palate, at the back of the mouth, acts as a trap to prevent food and air from returning to the mouth from the pharynx. For this reason, if the horse is unable to pass food down the esophagus due to obstruction or illness, the food will return through the nostrils rather than through the mouth.

# The Esophagus

The esophagus is a tube about five feet in length which connects the pharynx to the stomach. Food is conveyed through the esophagus by waves of muscular contractions called peristalsis. The opening of the esophagus into the stomach is constructed to prevent the return of ingesta from the stomach. For this reason, vomiting is not normal and occurs only rarely in the horse, usually only in cases of extreme illness.

# The Stomach

The major digestive processes begin in the stomach, which has a capacity of from two to four gallons in the full grown horse. (4) When considering this capacity, however, it must be remembered that the saliva mixed with the food greatly increases the total amount of stomach contents.

In digestion, water passes quickly out of the stomach, through the small intestine, and into the cecum and colon. Solid food is acted upon by digestive juices. In the stomach, these are primarily hydrochloric acid and the enzyme pepsin, which are secreted by the gastric mucosa. Pepsin breaks down proteins into fragments, and hydrochloric acid dissolves the the mineral matter in the food. Digestion by enzymes in the digestive tract is more complete when the stomach is not completely full. The muscles of the stomach walls contract and expand to mix the food with the digestive juices and force the contents gradually into the small intestine. Once the stomach action begins, it continues for as long as food is entering the stomach from the esophagus until the stomach is less than two-thirds full. Unless food is withheld for twenty-four hours or more, the stomach never completely empties. Food may remain in the stomach anywhere from fifteen minutes, up to as long as several days. It should be noted that if the horse ingests large quantities of food at one time, it passes much more rapidly through the stomach, and is not thoroughly digested. For this reason, it is advisable to feed the daily ration in three, (or more) small feedings rather than in one or two large meals. Another point to remember is that the feed which is consumed first, remains in the stomach for the greatest length of time, and is acted on most thoroughly by the digestive juices. This is why it is often recommended that the horseman feed hay, which is hard to digest, before grain, which is highly digestible.

## The Small Intestine and Accessory Organs

The pyloric valve is the juncture of the stomach with the small intestine. The small intestine, located between the stomach and the cecum, is approximately seventy feet long, with a capacity of about twelve gallons. (5) When empty, its diameter is only about two inches at most. This part of the alimentary canal is coiled and looped and doubled back upon itself in many places. It is supported by a double fold of the peritoneum called the mesentery. The mesentery is strong and flexible enough to allow the peristaltic contractions to move freely along the length of the intestine. The part of the small intestine which leaves the stomach is called the duodenum. The central portion is the jejunum, and the final segment which connects with the cecum at the ileocecal valve is the ileum. The liver and the pancreas secrete bile and pancreatic juice which are carried into the small intestine through a common duct. It is in this part of the digestive tract that the major enzymatic breakdown of food occurs.

The liver is the largest gland in the horse's body. It secretes a continuous flow of bile, which aids in digestion of fats, and it also serves as a storage facility for energy in the form of glycogen, or animal starch. Unlike cattle and humans, the horse has no gall bladder for bile storage, so it must use the bile as it is produced by the liver, without a reserve supply.

The pancreas is a large, compound gland. It secretes enzymes in addition to those produced by the gastric and intestinal mucosa. All of these enzymes have been found to be proteins composed of amino acids, and they react to heat and cold in the same manner as other proteins. Each enzyme produced by the body has a specific function in the digestive process, and acts on only one form of nutrient.

In the small intestine, intestinal juice, bile, and pancreatic juice combine to breakdown the remaining mineral matter, and most of the fats, soluble carbohydrates, and proteins in the food. The small intestine is lined with thousands of tiny fingerlike projections called villi. It is through these projections that digested food nutrients are absorbed into the capillaries and lymph system to be carried throughout the body. Most of the dissolved nutrients are absorbed at this point. The remaining food matter, consisting mostly of fiber, is moved by peristaltic action into the cecum and colon.

## The Large Intestine

The cecum is a greatly enlarged pouch through which food moves more slowly than through the rest of the digestive system. The cecum is about four feet long, and holds about ten gallons. Fermentation by microbial action helps to break down some of the roughage and free a portion of the remaining nutrients in the food. The cecum allows the horse to utilize the fiber content of the food to some degree for its nutrient value instead of just for intestinal bulk and peristaltic stimulation. Protein absorption is limited in the cecum, but there is considerable passive absorption of water-soluble nutrients. Recent research also indicates that virtually all of the energy absorption in the forage-fed horse takes place in the cecum.

From the cecum, the food passes to the large colon, where more of the moisture is absorbed. Further bacterial action takes place here, and there is a small amount of nutrient absorption, primarily energy. The large colon is about twelve feet long, holding about twenty gallons, and it is usually distended with food. (6)

In the small colon, most of the moisture in the food is resorbed, and the contents of this part of the intestine are mainly solid waste and indigestible or undigested food. It is here that the feces are formed.

The rectum is a short straight tube about one foot in length, and it holds the waste material until it is passed out of the horse's body through the anal opening. This is the final part of the digestive tract.

## Summary

The digestive system of the horse evolved to meet the specific needs of a grazing animal which ate frequent, small meals. As the horse was domesticated, however, its diet changed. Several limiting factors of the equine digestive system require that diets approximate natural grazing in some respects. These limiting factors are the small size of the equine stomach, and the fermentation gut located after the small intestine. These must always be considered when formulating a ration. When large quantities are fed at one time, improper digestion results, and this is also true when diets high in low-quality fiber are fed. A diet which is designed to meet the specific needs of the equine digestive system and which is fed in frequent small portions will result in better health and freedom from digestive disturbances.

### REFERENCES CITED

1. Jones, William E., D.V.M., Ph.D., Editor, **Anatomy of the Horse.** Caballus Publishers, East Lansing, Michigan, (1972)
2. Morrison, Frank B., **Feeds and Feeding, Abridged, Ninth Edition.** The Morrison Publishing Company, Claremont, Ontario, Canada, (1958)
3. Ensminger, M. E., Ph.D., **Horses and Horsemanship.** Interstate Printers and Publishers, Inc., Danville, Illinois, (1969)
4. Ensminger, M. E., Ph.D., **Op. Cit.**
5. Jones, William E., D.V.M., Ph.D., **Op. Cit.**
6. Simmons, Hoyt, **Horseman's Veterinary Guide.** The Western Horseman, Colorado Springs, Colorado, (1963)

# 2

# Qualitative Nutrient Requirements

The suitability of any ration is determined not so much by the feeds that it includes, but by the nutrients that these feeds supply. In order to prepare a ration which is balanced and will sustain growth, tissue repair, proper body function, good health, and performance, it is necessary to have an understanding of the various nutrients required by horses and their functions in developing and maintaining superior equine athletes.

## Classes of Nutrients

A nutrient is any food constituent or group of food constituents of the same general composition that aids in the support of life. (1) In other words, it is a class of ingredients or building blocks in food which supports a particular function in the body, such as growth, repair, or energy.

There are six distinct classes of nutrient constituents contained in feeds. These are proteins, fats, carbohydrates, minerals, vitamins, and water. When fed in the right combination, they provide all the factors necessary to sustain life and health. Most feeds contain some amount of each of these nutrients. An understanding of the functions of each will show clearly why they are necessary, and knowledge of the basic requirements for each specific nutrient factor will simplify formulation of an adequate, nourishing ration.

## Protein

Proteins are large, complex molecules which contain carbon, hydrogen,

*Equine Research Publication staff photo*

**PRETTY BERMUDA?**

This 8 inch tall Bermudagrass needs mowing, for optimum nutritional value.

oxygen, and nitrogen. In addition, they usually contain sulphur, and some may contain phosphorus or iron. These proteins are composed of amino acids, which are acid compounds which link together to form the protein molecule. It is these amino acids that are important in equine nutrition, since amino acids in feed protein are used to synthesize protein in body tissues of the horse. Combinations of different amino acids are joined to form specific proteins. It has been determined that each type of protein maintains specific proportions of amino acids, so that once the amino acid make-up of a particular feed has been determined, it can be assumed that it will remain constant.

Proteins are essential to life for all plants and animals, since they are the basic component of the cell wall. Gerardus Mulder, a Dutch chemist, gave the name of proteins to these substances because it was derived from a Greek word meaning "to come first". (2) He believed that proteins were the most important of all the nutrients. While it has now been recognized that all of the nutrients are vital to life, and therefore may be considered nearly equal in importance, proteins are essential, and their importance cannot be minimized.

## The Function of Protein

Almost half of the dry weight of a mature animal is made up of protein. (3) Protein forms the skin, hair, muscle, connective tissue, hooves, nervous system, and much of the skeleton of the horse. It forms a portion of the cell wall, and also the nucleus and protoplasm of the cell. Without protein, there would be no growth and repair of body tissue. High level protein intake, particularly in early life, is necessary to develop the muscle strength and stamina of the race or performance horse.

Plants are able to synthesize proteins directly from inorganic compounds in the soil and atmosphere, but horses cannot do this to any great extent. Instead, they break down the existing protein in feeds into its amino acid components, and from these amino acids, they build body proteins. The horse is able to synthesize some amino acids in the cecum, but others can only be obtained in sufficient quantities from feeds. There are known to be at least twenty-four amino acids, and of these, there are approximately ten which can be considered dietary essentials. These ten essential amino acids are synthesized to some degree in the cecum and colon, but not in sufficient quantities to meet body needs. Therefore, when choosing a ration for horses it is necessary to consider protein **quality,** or amino acid make-up, as well as quantity of total protein in the feed. All feedstuffs do not supply the same balance of amino acids. For this reason, a ration which contains only a few ingredients, such as a diet

*photo courtesy of Quarter Horse Journal*

Being the Honor Roll Reining Quarter Horse for 1972 required stamina and versatility on the part of Joe's Red Boy, owned by Marvin Copple of Lincoln, Nebraska. The 8-year-old gelding was hauled more than 83,000 miles during the year, requiring an outstanding feeding program to maintain his top performance record.

of grass hay and oats, is not likely to contain enough different amino acids. It is therefore advantageous to include several different grains and hays in the diet. Fortunately, since different protein feeds have different amino acid components, a feed which may be low in one essential amino acid can be balanced by adding other protein sources to the ration. The oilseed meals are especially good sources of high quality proteins which contain most of the essential amino acids. The amino acids which are considered essential to the horse are arginine, histidine, isoleucine, leucine, lysine, methionine, phenylalanine, threonine, tryptophan, and valine.

## Fats and Related Substances

The term most commonly used in discussing fats and related substances in feeds is **lipids.** This term includes not only fats, but also glycerides, cholesterol, lecithin, chlorophyll, volatile oils, and resins. All of these compounds are found in growing plants, where they provide energy to the growing plant. Chlorophyll, volatile oils, and resins are not actually nutrient when digested by the horse, but they are related to fats in structure, and have similar functions in the plant sources from which they were taken. All lipids contain carbon, hydrogen, and oxygen.

## The Function of Lipids

Lipids serve several functions in the body. First, they are the source of linoleic acid, an essential fatty acid which the body cannot synthesize. Linoleic acid affects growth and skin condition in young animals. However, it takes only a small amount of lipids in the diet to satisfy the requirement for linoleic acids. The remainder of the fats and fat-like substances are used as sources of energy. They are also of importance in forming a portion of the cell membranes. They are constituents of some vitamins and hormones. It is also possible that certain other fatty acids may have a catalytic effect in the body metabolism, increasing the efficiency of feed use, but this has not yet been conclusively determined. (4)

Fats and fat-like substances provide energy in more concentrated form than do other nutrients. The energy content of fat is over nine kilocalories per gram, as compared to about four kilocalories per gram for carbohydrates and proteins. This factor has what is known as a protein sparing effect in some cases. This means that when enough fats are present in the diet, they will be efficiently used to meet the body's energy needs, leaving the protein for muscle development and growth. While protein is not generally fed to meet energy needs, if there is not enough fat and carbohydrate energy in the diet, protein will be used for energy

*photo courtesy of The Blood-Horse*

The legendary Man O' War is pictured in a rare photograph of one of his handy victories. The much talked about, often compared "Big Red" lost but one of his 20 odd races during his career.

instead of building and maintaining tissues. This is an inefficient use of feeds.

While a higher fat content in feeds would seem to be advantageous because of the higher energy value, it is counterbalanced to some degree by a markedly poorer keeping quality. The lipid portion of the feed is the most unstable and perishable. Unless very carefully stored and quickly consumed, feeds with a high fat content may easily become rancid. If this happens, nutrients such as carotene and essential fatty acids are quickly lost. The feed becomes unpalatable, and in some cases, actually harmful.

It is interesting to note that a higher fat content in feeds may increase their palatability for most animals, and that if horses become used to a feed with a high fat content it may be difficult to return them immediately to a ration which is significantly lower in fat without a corresponding loss of appetite. Corn, for example, is a feed with a relatively high fat content. Horses which are used to a diet high in corn may not eat well if suddenly switched to a barley ration, which would be low in fat.

# Carbohydrates

Carbohydrates are substances formed of carbon, hydrogen, and oxygen, with two hydrogen atoms for every one atom of oxygen. Carbohydrates are formed only in plants in a process called photosynthesis, where the chlorophyll in the plant uses energy from the sun to produce carbohydrates from carbon dioxide and water.

# Function of Carbohydrates in the Diet

Carbohydrates, because of their prevalence in feeds, serve as the chief source of energy for the horse. Carbohydrates make up sixty percent or more of most grains and hays. While they do not have as high an energy content as fats, the carbohydrate intake is much greater, because of its natural occurrence. Carbohydrates are also necessary for the digestion of fats, because fat cannot be completely oxidized in the body without pyruvic acid, an organic acid which is formed when carbohydrates are oxidized. Like fats, carbohydrates also have a protein sparing action.

Carbohydrates include sugars, starches, glycogen (or animal starch, the form in which energy is stored in the liver), and cellulose. The sugars and starches are a form of energy and yield pyruvic acid, which is necessary to the metabolic process. Cellulose is the major component of fiber in the ration, and makes up a large portion of plant cell walls. Energy in cellulose is extracted by bacterial action in the large intestine and converted to volatile fatty acids, which are metabolized by the body tissues.

When entering any sort of strenuous competition, each horse should be in its best physical condition. Without a high-quality feeding program, this is not possible.

Lignin, a carbohydrate-like substance, is often found in combination with cellulose, and is prevalent in coarse, stemmy feeds. It is the tough fiber that is found in tree bark and the stalks of plants. It is nutritionally detrimental to the horse because it inhibits normal bacterial action on cellulose in roughage. There are other carbohydrates called hemicelluloses. These are slightly more digestible than cellulose, and are also a part of the plant cell-wall structure. Due to their bulky nature, these substances stimulate normal intestinal peristalsis. The starches and sugars are called nitrogen-free extract, and are most abundant in the grains and concentrates. The celluloses and related substances are classed as fiber, and are most common in hays.

When they are digested by the body, the sugars and starches are eventually converted to glucose, a simple sugar, which is the form of sugar carried in the blood stream. Since this conversion to glucose is simple and readily accomplished by the body, the soluble carbohydrates are classified as highly digestible, in fact, the most highly digestible of the energy sources in feeds.

In the newborn foal, the cellulose in feeds cannot be digested efficiently because there is an insufficient amount of bacteria in the large intestine at birth. These bacteria increase in number as the foal grows older, and the ability to digest cellulose increases correspondingly. Therefore, young horses should be fed predominantly concentrate feeds, while older horses can effectively utilize more of the roughage feeds.

# Water

Water is essential to the life of the horse, as are all of the nutrient substances discussed. Without water an animal can live only a few days, while without other nutrients life can be prolonged for a much longer period. Water helps the cells to maintain their form and structure, and nearly two-thirds of the body's water is contained within the cells. Water helps to regulate the temperature of the horse as it is evaporated through the sweat glands. Water carries vital substances throughout the body, and serves as a carrier for waste products as they are removed. Without water, survival would be impossible. It is therefore essential that a constant supply of clean water be available; at least twelve gallons per day for the mature horse. (5)

The amounts of water consumed have a direct effect on the health of the horse. The quality of water the animal drinks will also affect its health. These considerations are discussed in detail in Chapter Four.

# Vitamins

Vitamins are carbon containing compounds which are necessary for life and growth. Many cannot be manufactured in sufficient quantities by the body and must be contained in the diet. They are found in feeds in the smallest amounts compared to other nutrients, and compose only a minute fraction of the horse's body weight, but they are no less vital.

In the late nineteenth century scientists discovered that combinations of protein, carbohydrates, fats, minerals, and water were not sufficient to support life. There had to be some other substance in foods that contributed to health and growth. This missing factor was given the name **vitamine** in 1912 by a Polish biologist, Casimir Funk. The name was derived from two words: **vita,** because the substance was thought to be vital to life, and **amine,** because he thought the substance had an amine, or nitrogen containing structure. The final **e** was dropped after it was realized that not all vitamins were amine compounds.

The vitamins can be divided into two groups: those which are soluble in fat, and those which are water-soluble. Within these two groups there are a number of different vitamins. Since all of these vitamins have been discovered since 1915, there are several whose exact functions and requirements are not yet known. (6)

Each specific vitamin has certain functions that it performs in the body, and can be found in certain types of feeds. The individual vitamins and their requirements as far as known are discussed fully in Chapter Five.

# Minerals

Minerals are inorganic compounds which remain as ash when the other substances in a feed are burned in a nutrient analysis. Horses are believed to require fifteen different minerals for life and health, and it is possible that more essential minerals will be determined. (7)

Minerals may be found in the body in combination with organic substances, or in pure form. They have two basic nutritional roles. First, they are building substances. They are particularly prevalent in the hard tissues of the body, such as the bones and teeth. They are also present in muscular and nervous tissue. The second major role of the mineral substances is catalytic action and as structural elements in vital body compounds, such as certain vitamins. Minerals help to maintain correct fluid pressure and distribution within cells. They also affect such diverse functions as heartbeat and thirst.

Each of the known essential minerals has a specific function, and in addition, there are some minerals, such as calcium and phosphorus, which work in combination. The role of the individual minerals, including both essential minerals and those which have been found in body tissues and have not yet been proven essential, is discussed fully in Chapter Six.

## Summary

Nutrients are ingredients or components of feeds which support body functions. The nutrients are obtained from proteins, fats, carbohydrates, minerals, vitamins, and water in feed. All of these nutrients must be present to sustain life.

Proteins are composed of amino acids, which are organic compounds. The horse digests protein by breaking it down into its amino acid components and recombining it into body proteins. It is important to remember that different proteins contain different amino acids, and several protein sources should be included in the ration in order to supply all of the essential amino acids.

Fats and the fat-related substances are classed under the term lipids. They are organic compounds that provide the most concentrated energy source for animals. Lipids also yield linoleic acid, an essential fatty acid which is necessary for growth and skin condition, and they are carriers of the fat-soluble vitamins. While fats increase the palatability of feeds for most horses, an excess of fats causes storage problems due to heating and deterioration.

Carbohydrates include sugars, starches, and fiber. The fiber portion of the carbohydrate is necessary for proper intestinal action and cecal bacterial growth. The soluble portion of the carbohydrate, also called nitrogen-free extract, provides the major energy source for horses. While not as concentrated an energy source as fats, nitrogen-free extract is highly digestible and is the major nutrient component of the grains and concentrate feeds.

Water is the nutrient substance found in the greatest proportion in the body of the horse. Water affects body temperature and cell structure, and serves as a medium for food transportation within the body and waste removal from the cells.

Vitamins are dietary essentials which were discovered within the twentieth century. They have a catalytic effect on many body processes. There are two classes of vitamins: those which are soluble in fat, and those which are water-soluble.

Minerals are inorganic nutrients which are used in building tissues, and they may also have a catalytic effect like vitamins. Minerals are present within the body in combination with organic nutrients and in free form.

# REFERENCES CITED

1. Morrison, Frank B., **Feeds and Feeding, Abridged, Ninth Edition.** The Morrison Publishing Company, Claremont, Ontario, Canada, (1958)
2. Wilson, Eva D., Fisher, Katherine H., and Fuqua, Mary E., **Principles of Nutrition.** John Wiley and Sons, Inc., New York, (1965)
3. Pike, Ruth L., and Brown, Myrtle L., **Nutrition: An Integrated Approach.** John Wiley and Sons, Inc., New York, (1967)
4. Crampton, E. W., and Harris, L. E., **Applied Animal Nutrition.** W. H. Freeman and Company, San Francisco, (1969)
5. Ensminger, M. E., Ph.D., **Horses and Horsemanship.** Interstate Printers and Publishers, Inc., Danville, Illinois, (1969)
6. Guthrie, Helen Andrews, **Introductory Nutrition,** The C. V. Mosby Company, Saint Louis, (1971)
7. Ensminger, M. E., Ph.D., **Op. Cit.**

## QUALITATIVE NUTRIENT REQUIREMENTS

## OF

## MATURE HORSES, PREGNANT MARES, AND LACTATING MARES *

(Nutrient Concentration in Ration Dry Matter)

| BODY WEIGHT (lbs.) | DAILY FEED ** (lbs.) | PERCENTAGE OF LIVE WEIGHT | DIGESTIBLE ENERGY (Calories per lb.) | PROTEIN (%) | DIGESTIBLE PROTEIN (%) | CALCIUM (%) | PHOS-PHORUS (%) |
|---|---|---|---|---|---|---|---|
| **Mature Horses at Rest** | | | | | | | |
| 450 | 6.5 | 1.5 | 1250 | 10.0 | 5.3 | 0.26 | 0.20 |
| 900 | 11.0 | 1.3 | 1250 | 10.0 | 5.3 | 0.31 | 0.24 |
| 1,100 | 13.0 | 1.2 | 1250 | 10.0 | 5.3 | 0.33 | 0.25 |
| 1,325 | 15.0 | 1.1 | 1250 | 10.0 | 5.3 | 0.35 | 0.26 |
| **Mature Horses at Light Work (2 hr/day)** | | | | | | | |
| 450 | 8.5 | 1.9 | 1250 | 10.0 | 5.3 | 0.21 | 0.15 |
| 900 | 15.0 | 1.7 | 1250 | 10.0 | 5.3 | 0.24 | 0.18 |
| 1,100 | 17.5 | 1.6 | 1250 | 10.0 | 5.3 | 0.25 | 0.18 |
| 1,325 | 20.5 | 1.5 | 1250 | 10.0 | 5.3 | 0.26 | 0.19 |
| **Mature Horses at Medium Work (2 hr/day)** | | | | | | | |
| 450 | 10.5 | 2.4 | 1250 | 10.0 | 5.3 | 0.19 | 0.14 |
| 900 | 19.0 | 2.2 | 1250 | 10.0 | 5.3 | 0.20 | 0.15 |
| 1,100 | 23.0 | 2.1 | 1250 | 10.0 | 5.3 | 0.20 | 0.15 |
| 1,325 | 27.0 | 2.0 | 1250 | 10.0 | 5.3 | 0.20 | 0.15 |
| **Mares, Last 90 Days of Pregnancy** | | | | | | | |
| 450 | 7.0 | 1.6 | 1250 | 11.5 | 6.9 | 0.33 | 0.25 |
| 900 | 12.0 | 1.4 | 1250 | 11.5 | 6.9 | 0.36 | 0.28 |
| 1,100 | 14.0 | 1.3 | 1250 | 11.5 | 6.9 | 0.38 | 0.29 |
| 1,325 | 16.0 | 1.2 | 1250 | 11.5 | 6.9 | 0.39 | 0.29 |
| **Mares, Peak of Lactation** | | | | | | | |
| 450 | 12.5 | 2.8 | 1250 | 13.5 | 8.7 | 0.61 | 0.41 |
| 900 | 19.5 | 2.2 | 1250 | 13.3 | 8.4 | 0.47 | 0.40 |
| 1,100 | 22.0 | 2.0 | 1250 | 13.1 | 8.3 | 0.47 | 0.37 |
| 1,325 | 24.0 | 1.8 | 1250 | 12.9 | 8.0 | 0.47 | 0.36 |

*Data derived from Nutrient Requirements of Horses, National Research Council, 1973*
**Assume 1250 Calories of digestible energy per lb. of 100% dry feed*

# QUALITATIVE NUTRIENT REQUIREMENTS
## OF
## GROWING HORSES *

(Nutrient Concentration in Ration Dry Matter)

| AGE | BODY WEIGHT | DAILY GAIN | DAILY FEED ** | % OF LIVE WEIGHT | DIGESTIBLE ENERGY | PROTEIN | DIGESTIBLE PROTEIN | CAL-CIUM | PHOS-PHORUS |
|------|------|------|------|------|------|------|------|------|------|
| (mos.) | (lbs.) | (lbs.) | (lbs.) | | (Calories per lb.) | (%) | (%) | (%) | (%) |
| **450 lb. Mature Weight** | | | | | | | | | |
| 3 | 100 | 1.50 | 6.5 | 6.5 | 1250 | 17.9 | 13.0 | 0.59 | 0.37 |
| 6 | 200 | 1.00 | 7.0 | 3.5 | 1250 | 14.9 | 10.2 | 0.53 | 0.34 |
| 12 | 300 | .50 | 6.5 | 2.2 | 1250 | 11.7 | 7.1 | 0.41 | 0.25 |
| 18 | 350 | .25 | 6.5 | 1.8 | 1250 | 10.7 | 6.2 | 0.35 | 0.22 |
| 42 | 450 | .00 | 6.5 | 1.5 | 1250 | 10.0 | 5.3 | 0.29 | 0.20 |
| **900 lb. Mature Weight** | | | | | | | | | |
| 3 | 200 | 2.25 | 8.5 | 4.3 | 1250 | 19.5 | 14.6 | 0.68 | 0.43 |
| 6 | 400 | 1.50 | 10.0 | 2.5 | 1250 | 14.2 | 9.5 | 0.78 | 0.48 |
| 12 | 550 | 1.00 | 11.0 | 2.0 | 1250 | 12.1 | 7.5 | 0.45 | 0.30 |
| 18 | 725 | .50 | 11.5 | 1.6 | 1250 | 11.2 | 6.6 | 0.37 | 0.27 |
| 42 | 900 | .00 | 11.0 | 1.2 | 1250 | 10.0 | 5.3 | 0.32 | 0.24 |
| **1,100 lb. Mature Weight** | | | | | | | | | |
| 3 | 250 | 2.50 | 10.0 | 4.0 | 1250 | 19.0 | 14.1 | 0.69 | 0.44 |
| 6 | 500 | 1.75 | 12.5 | 2.5 | 1250 | 13.4 | 9.6 | 0.82 | 0.51 |
| 12 | 725 | 1.25 | 13.5 | 1.9 | 1250 | 12.3 | 7.7 | 0.43 | 0.28 |
| 18 | 900 | .75 | 14.0 | 1.6 | 1250 | 11.3 | 6.7 | 0.37 | 0.26 |
| 42 | 1,100 | .00 | 13.0 | 1.2 | 1250 | 10.0 | 5.3 | 0.34 | 0.25 |
| **1,325 lb. Mature Weight** | | | | | | | | | |
| 3 | 300 | 2.75 | 11.5 | 3.8 | 1250 | 18.6 | 13.7 | 1.01 | 0.63 |
| 6 | 600 | 2.00 | 14.0 | 2.3 | 1250 | 13.9 | 9.2 | 0.81 | 0.51 |
| 12 | 850 | 1.25 | 15.0 | 1.8 | 1250 | 12.2 | 7.6 | 0.48 | 0.30 |
| 18 | 1,050 | .75 | 15.5 | 1.5 | 1250 | 11.1 | 6.6 | 0.45 | 0.28 |
| 42 | 1,325 | .00 | 15.0 | 1.1 | 1250 | 10.0 | 5.3 | 0.35 | 0.26 |

* Data derived from Nutrient Requirements of Horses, National Research Council, 1973
** Assume 1250 Calories of digestible energy per lb. of 100% dry feed

# 3

# Quantitative Nutrient Requirements

Once the horseman has gained an understanding of the basic functions of the different nutrient substances, it is vital that he develop a knowledge of their quantitative requirements. Although the exact requirements for some nutrients have not yet been determined for horses, there are guidelines for ascertaining the amounts in most cases. Knowledge of quantitative nutrient requirements serves a dual purpose. It provides for a sound, well-balanced ration, and it allows for economical use of feeds.

## Protein Requirements

The amount of protein required by the horse depends on the stresses to which its body is subjected. Rapid growth, reproduction, and lactation will greatly increase the percentage of protein in feed required. There is a decrease in protein needs inversely proportional to the age of the horse, since growth is most rapid immediately after foaling, and gradually slows until maturity is reached.

Assuming that a high quality protein is fed, and all essential amino acids are included, certain protein requirements can be quantitatively determined. Since protein is considered by some researchers to be the nutrient most often deficient in the ration of horses, special attention should be paid to these requirements. (1)

Recent research indicates that foals may require as much as eighteen to twenty percent protein in the ration. (2) This is logical, since the body of the foal contains about twenty percent protein. Mare's milk contains

Eight lengths separated Riva Ridge from the rest of the pack, as he carried the Meadow Stable's colors to victory in the 1972 Belmont Stakes, winning two of the three Triple Crown races for that year.

23

approximately nineteen percent protein on a dry weight basis, and it is about ninety-eight percent digestible as compared to between seventy and eighty-five percent digestibility for other feeds. (3)

With increasing age, the requirements for protein decrease. A minimum of thirteen percent is required for the yearling, with sixteen percent being more desirable in a high energy ration. The two year old should have fourteen percent protein for maximum growth, and twelve percent protein should be considered to be a maintenance amount for mature horses. In no case, however, should the percentage of protein fall below ten percent, even for the mature horse which is relatively idle. (4)

It is recommended that these maintenance amounts be increased by about one-fourth for the stallion during breeding season, and for the mare during the last sixty to ninety days of gestation. A normal maintenance ration may be fed during the earlier stages of pregnancy, since fetal growth is slow during this time, and the mare's body can adequately provide nutrients without undue strain. During lactation, the protein requirement essentially doubles from the maintenance amounts, since the mare must meet not only her own protein needs, but the higher percentage requirements of the growing foal. Prolonged heavy work and special stresses, such as racing, may increase protein needs. However, this increase is small and can usually be met by increasing the amounts of feed to meet energy needs in mature horses. Young horses in training must be fed adequate protein to meet growth requirements. It should be noted that the protein requirements per pound of body weight are slightly greater for a larger breed and build of horse than for a smaller horse of the same physiological age. Again, this increased need can usually be met by increasing feed amounts rather than protein percentage. In every case, however, the minimum requirements as given, should be carefully used as a guide, and the final adjustments must depend on the animal's appearance and condition.

# Fat Requirements

No exact requirement for fats in the diet of horses has been set. It is recognized that some fat is essential as a source of linoleic acid, to provide energy, and as a carrier of the fat-soluble vitamins in feeds, including vitamins A, D, E, and K. There is some fat synthesis in the intestines by bacterial action, but exactly how much is not known. As a general rule, however, the amount of fats and fat-like substances contained in most quality feeding programs is adequate.

# Carbohydrate Requirements

In considering the amount of carbohydrates necessary for health and activity in the horse, there are two factors which must be measured separately. These are the basic requirement for energy, and the need for some roughage in the diet of the yearling and older horse. The amount of carbohydrate in a feed is commonly measured in two ways which correspond to these needs. The part of the carbohydrate called nitrogen-free extract is the more digestible part, which includes the sugars and starches. The remainder of the carbohydrate is fiber, and is mainly the cellulose portion of the feed.

The arrangement of the horse's digestive tract limits the amount of fiber he can utilize. While no maximum fiber requirements have yet been determined, there are guidelines which can be followed. The suckling or weanling should have a diet which is very low in fiber; not more than about six percent. (5) For growing horses, this can be increased to twenty percent of the ration, with a maximum of one percent of body weight. Mature horses that are not under heavy stress can receive as much as one and one-half percent of body weight per day in fiber. This amount should be reduced for horses under heavy work, or in race training. Feeding an excess of low-quality roughage which is very high in fiber (fifty to seventy-five percent) can cause distension of the digestive tract.

The amount of nitrogen-free extract also has not been quantitatively determined. It depends largely on the age and activity of the horse, since it is essentially an energy supply. It also varies with the amounts of protein and fats in the diet. Mature, idle horses may actually have very low requirements for nitrogen-free extract. However, the requirements for energy are much higher in the growing horse and the horse under stress, and more carbohydrates should be included in the rations for these animals. Under normal circumstances, if the horse is receiving enough total energy from the ration, the amount of nitrogen-free extract will usually be sufficient. This topic will be discussed more fully in Chapter Seven.

# Balancing the Ration

The first concern in balancing a ration is usually its protein content. First, the total amount of feed is calculated by weight. For example, this might be ten pounds of hay and ten pounds of a concentrate mix, for a total of twenty pounds. Next, the percentage of protein desired is multiplied by this total weight to get a weight value for protein. If the correct protein content was fifteen percent, this would give a protein weight of three pounds. Third, the protein percentages of the different components in the ration are multiplied by the component amounts and then added together, to get the actual amount of protein in the ration. If the concentrate mix contains twelve percent protein, this would yield 1.2 pounds, and if the hay being fed was an alfalfa-timothy mix containing 7.9 percent, it would yield .79 pounds for a total of 1.99 pounds of protein. This gives a deficiency of 1.01 pounds. To balance the ration, high quality soybean meal, with a protein content of 42 percent, might be substituted for a part of the concentrate ration. Since the soybean meal contains .42 pounds of protein per pound of meal, and the concentrate mix contains .12 pounds of protein per pound, every pound of soybean meal substituted for a pound of the concentrate ration would increase the protein content of the ration by .3 pounds. To increase the protein amount by one pound, three and one-third pounds of soybean meal should be substituted for the concentrate ration. This would yield a ration composed of six and two-thirds pounds of the original concentrate ration, three and one-third pounds of soybean meal, and ten pounds of alfalfa-timothy hay. The net protein content would be three pounds, or fifteen percent. This ration is only a hypothetical one and not a suggestion. But if the ingredients were of good quality and all other nutrients were present in sufficient amounts, it would then be considered to be balanced for the purposes of our demonstration.

## Summary

A knowledge of quantitative nutrient requirements is essential in providing an economical, well-balanced ration. Protein is the nutrient most likely to be deficient, and the protein requirements should be carefully followed. Percentage protein requirements are higher during growth, reproduction, and lactation. Fat requirements have not been quantitatively determined, but some fat is necessary in the diet. Most diets contain adequate amounts, however. Carbohydrate in the diet provides energy and fiber. Fiber requirements increase with age, and are guided by maximum amounts rather than minimums. Nitrogen-free extract should be sufficient to meet energy needs. Once the quantitative requirements have been determined, the ration should be balanced to make sure that all nutrients are present in the correct amounts.

# REFERENCES CITED

1. Bullard, T. L., D.V.M., "Nutrition — Some Basic Thoughts on Horse Feeding," Paper presented to Southwestern Planning Conference for Livestockmen, Waco, Texas, March 1973.
2. Bullard, T. L., D.V.M., **Op. Cit.**
3. The Borden Company, **Guide to the Care and Feeding of Orphan and Early Weaned Foals.** Borden Chemical Division, Norfolk, Virginia, (1972)
4. Potter, Gary D., Ph.D., "Horse Feeding Management," Paper presented at Texas Agricultural Extension Service Research Center, Renner, Texas, May 1973
5. Rossdale, Peter D., M.A., F.R.C.V.S., **The Horse.** The California Thoroughbred Breeders Association, California, (1972)

# QUANTITATIVE NUTRIENT REQUIREMENTS
## OF
## MATURE HORSES, PREGNANT MARES, AND LACTATING MARES *

(Daily Nutrients per Animal)

| BODY WEIGHT | DAILY FEED ** | DIGESTIBLE ENERGY | PROTEIN | DIGESTIBLE PROTEIN | PROVITAMIN A (Carotene) *** | CALCIUM | PHOSPHORUS |
|---|---|---|---|---|---|---|---|
| (lbs.) | (lbs.) | (Calories) | (grams) | (grams) | (milligrams) | (grams) | (grams) |

Mature Horses at Rest (maintenance):

| BODY WEIGHT | DAILY FEED ** | DIGESTIBLE ENERGY | PROTEIN | DIGESTIBLE PROTEIN | PROVITAMIN A (Carotene) *** | CALCIUM | PHOSPHORUS |
|---|---|---|---|---|---|---|---|
| 450 | 6.5 | 8,240 | 300 | 160 | 12.5 | 8.0 | 6.0 |
| 900 | 11.0 | 13,860 | 505 | 268 | 25.0 | 16.0 | 12.0 |
| 1,100 | 13.0 | 16,390 | 597 | 317 | 31.3 | 20.0 | 15.0 |
| 1,325 | 15.0 | 18,790 | 684 | 364 | 37.5 | 24.0 | 18.0 |

Mature Horses at Light Work (2 hr/day)

| | | | | | | | |
|---|---|---|---|---|---|---|---|
| 450 | 8.5 | 10,440 | 383 | 202 | 12.5 | 8.0 | 6.0 |
| 900 | 15.0 | 18,360 | 672 | 355 | 25.0 | 16.0 | 12.0 |
| 1,100 | 17.5 | 21,890 | 803 | 424 | 31.3 | 20.0 | 15.0 |
| 1,325 | 20.5 | 25,390 | 930 | 491 | 37.5 | 24.0 | 18.0 |

Mature Horses at Medium Work (2 hr/day)

| | | | | | | | |
|---|---|---|---|---|---|---|---|
| 450 | 10.5 | 13,160 | 483 | 255 | 12.5 | 9.2 | 7.0 |
| 900 | 19.0 | 23,800 | 871 | 460 | 25.0 | 17.2 | 13.0 |
| 1,100 | 23.0 | 28,690 | 1,047 | 553 | 31.3 | 21.2 | 16.0 |
| 1,325 | 27.0 | 33,550 | 1,229 | 649 | 37.5 | 25.2 | 19.0 |

Mares, Last 90 Days of Pregnancy

| | | | | | | | |
|---|---|---|---|---|---|---|---|
| 450 | 7.0 | 8,700 | 364 | 216 | 25.0 | 10.4 | 8.0 |
| 900 | 12.0 | 14,880 | 613 | 375 | 50.0 | 19.5 | 15.0 |
| 1,100 | 14.0 | 17,350 | 725 | 434 | 62.5 | 24.0 | 18.0 |
| 1,325 | 16.0 | 19,950 | 837 | 502 | 75.0 | 28.0 | 21.0 |

Mares, Peak of Lactation

| | | | | | | | |
|---|---|---|---|---|---|---|---|
| 450 | 12.5 | 15,240 | 750 | 480 | 25.0 | 34.0 | 23.4 |
| 900 | 19.5 | 24,390 | 1,181 | 748 | 50.0 | 42.0 | 35.6 |
| 1,100 | 22.0 | 27,620 | 1,317 | 829 | 62.5 | 47.0 | 38.6 |
| 1,325 | 24.0 | 30,020 | 1,404 | 876 | 75.0 | 51.0 | 39.0 |

* Data derived from _Nutrient Requirements of Horses_, National Research Council, 1973
** Assume 1250 Calories of digestible energy per lb. of 100% dry feed
*** One mg of carotene equals 400 IU of vitamin A

# QUANTITATIVE NUTRIENT REQUIREMENTS
## OF
## GROWING HORSES *

(Daily Nutrients per Animal)

| AGE | BODY WEIGHT | DAILY GAIN | DAILY FEED ** | DIG. ENERGY | PROTEIN | DIG. PROTEIN | PRO-VITAMIN A (Carotene)*** | CALCIUM | PHOS-PHORUS |
|------|------|------|------|------|------|------|------|------|------|
| (mos.) | (lbs.) | (lbs.) | (lbs.) | (Calo-ries) | (grams) | (grams) | (milli-grams) | (grams) | (grams) |
| **450 lb. Mature Weight** | | | | | | | | | |
| 3 | 100 | 1.50 | 6.5 | 7,400 | 526 | 383 | 5.0 | 17.4 | 10.9 |
| 6 | 200 | 1.00 | 7.0 | 8,530 | 462 | 315 | 9.0 | 16.6 | 10.4 |
| 12 | 300 | .50 | 6.5 | 7,950 | 338 | 206 | 13.5 | 12.0 | 7.5 |
| 18 | 350 | .25 | 6.5 | 8,080 | 314 | 181 | 16.5 | 10.4 | 6.5 |
| 42 | 450 | .00 | 6.5 | 8,240 | 300 | 160 | 12.5 | 8.0 | 6.0 |
| **900 lb. Mature Weight** | | | | | | | | | |
| 3 | 200 | 2.25 | 8.5 | 10,440 | 741 | 553 | 8.5 | 26.1 | 16.4 |
| 6 | 400 | 1.50 | 10.0 | 12,410 | 640 | 430 | 17.0 | 35.0 | 21.9 |
| 12 | 550 | 1.00 | 11.0 | 13,630 | 600 | 370 | 26.0 | 22.0 | 14.8 |
| 18 | 725 | .50 | 11.5 | 14,100 | 575 | 339 | 35.5 | 19.0 | 13.8 |
| 42 | 900 | .00 | 11.0 | 13,860 | 505 | 268 | 25.0 | 16.0 | 12.0 |
| **1,100 lb. Mature Weight** | | | | | | | | | |
| 3 | 250 | 2.50 | 10.0 | 12,070 | 834 | 618 | 11.0 | 30.5 | 19.1 |
| 6 | 500 | 1.75 | 12.5 | 15,400 | 800 | 536 | 22.5 | 46.0 | 28.7 |
| 12 | 725 | 1.25 | 13.5 | 16,810 | 750 | 472 | 27.5 | 26.0 | 17.4 |
| 18 | 900 | .75 | 14.0 | 17,160 | 700 | 418 | 40.0 | 23.0 | 16.1 |
| 42 | 1,100 | .00 | 13.0 | 16,390 | 597 | 317 | 31.2 | 20.0 | 15.0 |
| **1,325 lb. Mature Weight** | | | | | | | | | |
| 3 | 300 | 2.75 | 11.5 | 14,150 | 958 | 705 | 14.0 | 52.0 | 32.2 |
| 6 | 600 | 2.00 | 14.0 | 17,210 | 870 | 582 | 26.5 | 51.2 | 32.0 |
| 12 | 850 | 1.25 | 15.0 | 18,860 | 837 | 524 | 15.4 | 32.9 | 20.6 |
| 18 | 1,050 | .75 | 15.5 | 19,200 | 775 | 458 | 48.0 | 31.3 | 19.6 |
| 42 | 1,325 | .00 | 15.0 | 18,790 | 684 | 364 | 37.5 | 24.0 | 18.0 |

* *Data derived from Nutrient Requirements of Horses, National Research Council, 1973*
** *Assume 1250 Calories of digestible energy per lb. of 100% dry feed.*
*** *One mg of Carotene equals 400 IU of vitamin A*

# 4

# Water

Water makes up two-thirds of the weight of an adult horse. (1) In a growing horse, where water deposits in the tissues have not yet been replaced by fat, the proportion of water is even higher. Without water, the horse would be unable to see or hear, since both senses depend on fluid-filled membranes. Without water, nutrients could not be transported to the cells, and waste could not be removed. The evaporation of water through the skin in the form of perspiration is the major means an animal has for regulating its body temperature. Water is the primary component of all the body fluids. If completely deprived of water, the horse could live only a few days.

Fortunately, while water is vital in importance, it is also plentiful and inexpensive. There is no reason why the need for a pure, fresh, constant water supply cannot easily be met.

## Normal Water Requirements

Exact water requirements depend on the age, weight, and activity of the animal. As a general rule of thumb, however, the horse should drink its weight in water every two weeks, in addition to the water contained in feeds. With a standard weight for water of eight pounds per gallon, this is about twelve gallons per day for the average adult horse under light work. (2) While horses may on occasion drink as little as six gallons per day without harm, at least twelve gallons should be available. Special stresses will increase this need, however, and careful attention should be paid. During lactation, for example, additional water must be provided to allow for the water content in the milk (about eighty-seven percent of milk volume). Hot weather and heavy work both increase water require-

*Equine Research Publications Staff Photo*

**A too-shallow watering spot. Filth and disease are ever-present hazards here.**

ments because they place stresses on the body's cooling system, requiring more water for evaporation in the form of perspiration. Therefore, the twelve gallon figure should be considered a minimum, and the horse in good health should always receive as much water as it will drink. The obvious exception to this rule is in the case of an overheated, thirsty horse. Water intake in this instance should be carefully regulated to ensure that too much water is not consumed too quickly. Small measured amounts should be given the horse at about three to five minute intervals until he has completely "cooled out," and is no longer thirsty.

Ideally, water should be constantly available so that the horse may drink frequent small amounts. An easy way of providing it is with automatic self-filling water troughs. These devices ensure that the water level is constant and water is fresh. In cold climates, they should contain a temperature regulating mechanism to prevent freezing.

When automatic water troughs are not possible, horses should be watered as often as is necessary. The minimum water intake should always be provided no matter what method is used. There may be cases in which it is desirable to measure the amount of water consumed by each horse on a daily basis. This is particularly true in the case of horses which are sick, or which may be off their water while traveling or racing. Measured amounts can be provided individually, but water should still be changed at least twice a day.

All water troughs, whether manual or automatic, should be frequently cleaned and disinfected. Horses should never have to drink water that is dirty or contains foreign material. Even stale water can cause a reduction in water consumption below safe levels, and water which is dirty rapidly becomes a carrier of disease. Disease can also be spread rapidly when several horses drink from the same trough. If a horse becomes ill, it should immediately be isolated from the trough, and the trough should be disinfected and cleaned.

## Dehydration

Dehydration is an abnormal depletion of body fluids. It results when water intake is insufficient for maintenance, and may be caused by several different factors. These include limited water supply, contaminated or stale water, and illness. Normally, about three percent of the body weight in fluid must be lost before dehydration becomes visible. (3) Symptoms include drying and tightening of the skin, loss of weight, and drying of mucous membranes and eyes. The urine becomes concentrated, and is reduced in amount. If the process is not checked, death will result. A loss of twenty percent of the body weight in fluid is normally fatal. (4)

Simple dehydration should be treated by replacement of the lost water. Ample water should be provided, and the horse should be carefully watched to ensure that it is drinking. If not, water may be administered by stomach tube, by a veterinarian. In more severe cases, and when dehydration is complicated by a mineral or electrolyte imbalance (electrolytes are free mineral ions carried in the body fluids), then veterinary care will definitely be required. This may include intravenous fluid replacement and injection therapy.

## Overhydration

Overhydration, an excess of water in the body, is not common in horses. It may result from excessive fluid intake or from water retention. Excessive fluid intake is usually caused through forced administration of water (by stomach tube or intravenously), and not by thirst or increased water consumption. Water retention is characterized by swelling in the legs and weight gain. When it is localized, it is usually due to trauma or injury of the swollen area. When it is generalized, however, it is frequently a sign of serious illness.

## Water Excretion and Digestion

Water is normally the only nutrient fed to horses in its pure form. It does not have to be simplified or broken down in order to be used by the body. It passes almost directly from the stomach into the cecum, and it is absorbed in the intestines. If water is withheld from a thirsty horse until after it has eaten, partially digested food can sometimes be forced through the stomach too rapidly, with the possibility of colic. (5) Therefore, it is better to allow some water before feeding as well as after.

Water is excreted from the body in the urine, feces, as water vapor from the lungs, and as perspiration through the skin. In growing animals, water is also retained as a constituent of new tissue. In the mature horse, however, average water intake and average water excretion will be approximately the same, so that total body fluid volume will remain constant. It must be remembered that there is some water contained in feeds, so this additional fluid must be excreted also.

## Water and Mineral Intake

After reaching the earth's surface in the form of rain, water begins to dissolve minerals in the soil, and to carry them in solution. The more minerals that are contained in the water, the harder it becomes. Soft water contains fewer minerals. The hardness of the water in a particular area depends on the mineral content of the soil through which the water is filtered. County Agricultural Agents can provide information on the

*Equine Research Publications Staff Photo*
**THIRSTY?**
**If you wouldn't want to drink it . . . don't ask your horse to!**

degree of hardness of the water in an area and its mineral content.

Although water hardness may affect the palatability of a water supply, it does not affect its use as a drinking source. Horses may be safely given any water which has been tested and found to be pure and safe, regardless of its hardness. However, because there is a difference in palatability, horses which are traveling or which have been moved to another location may refuse water at first. It is better to accustom them to a new water supply gradually if at all possible by mixing water from old and new sources. If this is not possible, water intake should be carefully watched to make sure that there are no signs of dehydration.

When there is a significant amount of calcium in water from a limestone source, it should be considered as a part of the total mineral intake. However, many mineral salts are relatively insoluble, and pass through the body without being absorbed. Even in hard water, the amount of minerals ingested from the water is not likely to be substantial.

There are two major exceptions, where minerals can be highly significant. Salty water, containing a large amount of sodium chloride is unsuitable for horses. It changes the electrolyte balance and intracellular pressure in the body, producing a form of dehydration, and it places a strain on the kidneys. A high fluoride content in water is also harmful to horses. This is discussed fully in Chapter Six.

## Summary

Water is vital to the horse's health. Horses should have frequent or unlimited access to a pure, clean, fresh water source. An adult horse may drink as much as twelve gallons per day under normal circumstances, and should always be provided at least this much. The self-filling water trough is an excellent method to ensure that the water supply is unlimited. Water troughs should be frequently cleaned and disinfected.

If insufficient water is ingested, dehydration can result. Excessive water intake is unlikely, and overhydration is usually the result of disease.

In the healthy horse, water intake, including the water content of feeds, and water excretion, through urine, feces, perspiration, and exhalation, should remain approximately the same. Horses should have access to water before eating as well as after.

The mineral content of water may affect its flavor, but rarely has a substantial effect on total mineral intake. Salty water or highly fluoridated water should be avoided.

**This pretty little stream was the major water supply for a large breeding farm. Laboratory testing in 1972 however, showed it to be too polluted for further use.**

# REFERENCES CITED

1. Hafez, E. S. E., and Dyer, I. A., **Animal Growth and Nutrition.** Lea and Febiger, Philadelphia, (1969)
2. Catcott, E. J., D.V.M., Ph.D., and Smithcors, J. F., D.V.M., Ph.D., Editors, **Equine Medicine and Surgery.** American Veterinary Publications, Inc., Wheaton, Illinois, (1972)
3. Catcott, E. J., and Smithcors, J. F., **Op. Cit.**
4. Wilson, Eva D., Fisher, Katherine H., and Fuqua, Mary E., **Principles of Nutrition.** John Wiley and Sons, Inc., New York, (1965)
5. Simons, Hoyt, **Horseman's Veterinary Guide.** The Western Horseman, Colorado Springs, Colorado, (1963)

# 5

# Vitamins

The role of vitamins in the diet is very complex, and, as yet, is not completely understood. Among other functions, vitamins are thought to have a catalytic effect on metabolism. That is, their presence is required for various body functions to take place. An example of this is choline, which is required in order for nerve impulses to be properly transmitted along the nervous system. (1) Vitamins are also essential components of different body fluids. Some vitamins can be synthesized in the intestines in sufficient amounts, while others must be present in the diet. While only minute amounts of each vitamin are required for proper body function, their absence will cause definite side effects or illnesses once reserves are depleted and a deficiency becomes established.

The vitamins can be divided into two groups. The fat-soluble vitamins, including vitamins A, D, E, and K are defined as those vitamins which will dissolve in fat or fat solvents. They can be stored in the body for later use, either in the liver or in the fat cells, so that a deficiency will not occur immediately if they are not present in the diet. Because they are stored, however, it is possible to build up excessive amounts, which also will cause abnormal symptoms. The water-soluble vitamins will dissolve in water, and cannot be stored. They must be ingested or manufactured in sufficient quantities to meet daily needs, and there is no reserve supply. Excess amounts are excreted in the urine. This group includes vitamin C and the B-complex vitamins.

The first vitamin to be clearly recognized was vitamin A, in 1913. (2) The last of the known vitamins to be discovered was vitamin $B_{12}$ (cobalamin), in 1948. In the intervening years, thirteen others were discovered. They are, in order of identification, vitamin D, thiamine ($B_1$), vitamin E,

**Bold Ruler [right], sire of the illustrious Secretariat, was quite an outstanding race horse in his own respect. He retired with earnings of over $760,000.00 and copped "Horse of the Year" honors in the 1957 Thoroughbred polls.**

inositol, choline, riboflavin ($B_2$), vitamin C (ascorbic acid), pantothenic acid, pyridoxine ($B_6$), vitamin K, biotin, niacin, and folacin. (3) Thiamine, $B_{12}$, inositol, choline, riboflavin, pantothenic acid, pyridoxine, biotin, niacin, and folacin are what is known as the B-complex group. They were formerly thought to be different forms of the same type of water-soluble vitamin, called vitamin B, but it is now known that they have independent functions.

Vitamin amounts in feeds may be measured in three ways. The amounts may be listed in either I.U. (International Units) or U.S.P. Units (United States Pharmacopeia Units), which are equal in strength. One of these units is the amount required to produce a measured reaction in a test animal, and has been standardized for each vitamin. Vitamins may also be measured in milligrams (mg.), which is a measure of weight rather than of effect.

The water-soluble vitamins may be found in their true form in plants, and require no conversion by the horse's body. The fat-soluble vitamins, however, have what are known as precursors, or provitamins. (4) These are related substances which do not have vitamin action, but which are acted upon by the horse's body to yield the true vitamins. An example of these precursors is carotene, a pigment found in hay. Carotene has no metabolic effect, but within the horse's body it is converted into vitamin A, which is a true vitamin.

## Vitamin A

Vitamin A is soluble in fat. Its primary source is its precursor, carotene, the yellow pigment found in green, growing plants and good quality hay. The yellow color of the carotene is masked by the bright green chlorophyll, but a healthy green color indicates high carotene levels. Hay that appears faded or weathered has probably lost most of its carotene content. Carotene is converted into vitamin A in the intestines, and is absorbed into the body through the intestinal mucosa. Surplus amounts are stored in the liver, up to as much as a six-month's supply. (5)

Vitamin A is necessary for healthy skin, hair, and hooves, and proper eye function. It also may have an effect on the blood levels of vitamin C, so that if there is an A deficiency, there may be a C deficiency also. (6) Vitamin A deficiency can be recognized by night blindness, infertility, poor hoof growth, digestive disturbances, and respiratory illnesses. An exact maintenance requirement has not yet been determined, but is believed to be approximately 12,500 International Units per day for the mature horse weighing about one thousand pounds at light work. Requirements are believed to increase during the later stages of gestation, and under periods of stress, such as heavy work or racing, but this

## CELEBRITY QUIZ

Nippy Bars in the winner's circle after winning the first running of the Rainbow Derby at Ruidoso Downs, New Mexico, in 1965. Owner Hugh Huntley is accepting the trophy, trainer Newt Keck is holding Nippy Bars, the jockey is Curtis Perner. Do you recognize the two famous horsemen to the right of Perner?

has not yet been fully documented.

The vitamin A requirements can normally be met by feeding good quality, bright green hay or allowing access to adequate pasture. Alfalfa is an especially good source. However, carotene is quickly lost from hay if it is not properly cured and stored. Sun and rain may deplete ninety percent of the carotene in hay over a year's time if it is not protected from these elements. Vitamin A added to feeds and supplements in the true vitamin state is also destroyed by air, light, and heat, so careful storage of feed is essential to maintain adequate vitamin A levels. Therefore, if hay is not of good quality, if feed has aged or is not safely stored, or at times of the year when pasture is of low quality, it may be desirable to add a vitamin A supplement to the ration. This is especially true if a deficiency has been noted. Supplementation should also be provided during late pregnancy and for horses in heavy training, while racing, and under hard work. However, since the vitamin is stored, it is recommended that the amount of vitamin A added in supplements be no more than the minimum daily requirement (about 12,500 Units), except when recommended by a veterinarian. While vitamin A excesses are unlikely, they are possible, and may produce symptoms similar to those of a deficiency.

## The B-Complex Vitamins

The B-complex vitamins, as previously discussed, are a group of ten water-soluble vitamins that were previously thought to be members of the same group. It is now known that they have separate functions in the body of the horse. These vitamins are normally synthesized by bacteria in the intestines of the horse in amounts which are adequate to meet maintenance needs.

Thiamine, formerly called vitamin $B_1$, is believed to function as a part of the enzyme which releases energy during carbohydrate metabolism. It also regulates some of the functions of the nervous system. Thiamine occurs in the greatest quantities in the cereal grains. A thiamine deficiency may cause nervousness or loss of appetite in the horse. Thiamine is destroyed by heat and cooking, therefore heat-processing of concentrates will significantly reduce the amounts of this vitamin contained in the feed. (7)

Niacin, formerly called nicotinic acid, is essential in cellular respiration and metabolism. It is believed to be synthesized from the amino acid tryptophan within the cells. Corn does not contain adequate amounts of tryptophan, so a diet in which corn is the primary concentrate and which has no protein supplements added may produce a niacin deficiency. There are no specific symptoms, but growth is reduced and appetite may be poor.

Riboflavin, like thiamine, is essential for proper energy release and nervous system function. It is synthesized in the lower portion of the small intestine of the horse by bacteria. It has been suggested that there is a link between riboflavin and periodic ophthalmia (inflammation of the conjunctiva or eyeball). (8) When riboflavin supplements are given to horses, the incidence of periodic ophthalmia is greatly reduced, indicating that a lack of this vitamin may be a causative factor in the disease. However, riboflavin will not cure periodic ophthalmia, so it cannot be considered to be the only factor involved. Riboflavin, formerly called vitamin $B_2$, is a very stable vitamin, and is highly resistant to destruction by heat and air. Supplementation at the rate of twenty mg. per day for each animal seems to be an adequate level for prevention of deficiencies. (9)

Pyridoxine was originally called vitamin $B_6$. It is necessary for protein and fat metabolism. Pyridoxine is abundant in the whole grains, and it is also synthesized in the lower digestive tract, so it is therefore highly unlikely that a deficiency would be present in the horse.

Folacin, formerly called folic acid, is actually a group of related substances of which folacin is the active form, and the others are derivatives. Folacin is necessary for cell metabolism and normal blood formation. A folacin deficiency may be related to some types of anemia. Folacin can be synthesized in the intestinal tract, and is rarely deficient. Supplementation at the rate of 2.5 mg. per day is not harmful, and will normally prevent folacin deficiency. (11)

Biotin, choline, and inositol are also necessary for proper metabolism, and may function as coenzymes, which means that they combine with other substances in the body to form the active parts of certain enzymes. Their exact functions have not yet been determined. All are produced in large amounts in the body, and deficiencies are not likely to occur. However, biotin deficiencies have been experimentally produced, and may cause loss of hair and loss of appetite. Choline and inositol are the two vitamins for which quantitative requirements are the greatest as far as is currently known. Intestinal synthesis is usually sufficient to maintain these high levels without added supplementation, however.

Vitamin $B_{12}$ is also called cobalamin. It is the only vitamin which contains a metal as part of its normal chemical structure. This metal is cobalt, and adequate cobalt intake is necessary for synthesis of vitamin $B_{12}$. Its importance in the body is its role in the prevention of anemia. It functions in cell metabolism, and seems to be vital for the production of red blood cells. The requirements for cobalamin are small, and have not been exactly determined, but are usually met by feeding high quality feeds and allowing access to good pasture. Horses which are anemic may benefit from low-level supplementation.

Exact requirements for most of the B-complex vitamins have not yet been quantitatively determined, except where doses are prescribed for the treatment of specific deficiencies. The vitamins are, as mentioned, synthesized within the body of the horse by bacterial action, and are also present in many feeds, especially the cereal grains. Most are especially sensitive to heat, and nearly all may be destroyed by strong light. It should therefore be noted that cooking or processing feeds with heat will greatly reduce the amount of B-vitamins present, unless additional amounts are added after processing. Vitamin supplementation with the B-complex vitamins is not harmful, and may be especially helpful in the cases of horses with poor appetites, slow growth patterns, loss of appetite, and nervous dispositions. Supplementation should definitely be considered for race horses, mares in late gestation, and horses under heavy work or rigorous show schedules, or whenever feeds are not of top quality. Good supplements are brewer's yeast, dried distillers solubles, and fish oil meals. Brewer's yeast is particularly valuable, containing riboflavin, niacin, pantothenic acid, and choline in large amounts, as well as traces of the other B-vitamins. It is also high in protein. (12) A word of caution: It is best to use only one supplement or mix, of high quality to avoid over-supplementation or imbalances, and this supplement should be carefully fed according to directions.

## Vitamin C

Vitamin C, also called ascorbic acid, is a water-soluble vitamin and is synthesized in large amounts by the horse. Most growing plants also contain this vitamin. In the normal animal it does not require supplementation. It may prove of value in cases of infertility, however. Although excess vitamin C is destroyed in the digestive tract, the feeding of high levels of vitamin C supplement (1,000 mg. per day) seem to improve the breeding performance of mares and stallions. (13) It is not yet known why this is true, and research to date has not been conclusive. Within the body, vitamin C is apparently required for the production of certain essential amino acids. It is also necessary for the production of collagen, an insoluble, fibrous protein which is required for cell bonds. It appears to be important in the proper healing of cuts and wounds. Except for the possible (and as yet unproven) link with infertility, however, horses are able to synthesize sufficient amounts of vitamin C within the body, and supplementation is unnecessary.

## Vitamin D

Vitamin D is soluble in fat. Its primary function in the body appears to

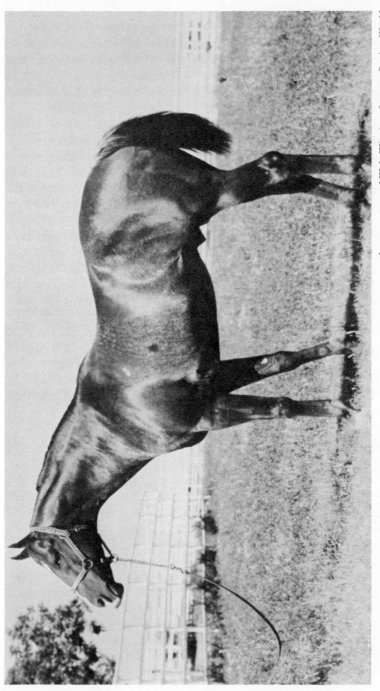

Go Man Go, considered by many experts as the greatest running and siring Quarter Horse of all times, proves the top condition a stallion can maintain, even at the advanced age of 20! Go Man Go stands at Buena Suerte Ranch, Roswell, New Mexico.

be promoting the proper absorption, transportation, and metabolism of calcium. The two major sources of vitamin D for the horse are sun-cured hay, and sunlight. The action of the ultra-violet rays in the sunlight act on a fat-related substance in the animal's body, and convert it into true vitamin D. Horses which are allowed reasonable exposure to sunlight each day, will normally manufacture sufficient amounts of the vitamin for maintenance. An exact requirement of daily sunlight exposure has never been clearly established. However, a fairly safe rule of thumb would probably include thirty minutes to one hour of sunlight per day.

The action of the sunlight on hay in the curing stage, will also synthesize vitamin D, and this source is also important. The vitamin is most important for the growing animal, when bone development is most rapid. Excess amounts of vitamin D are stored in the body, primarily in the liver.

No exact determination of requirements for vitamin D has ever been made for the horse. (14) Symptoms in the growing foal which are similar to human rickets have been tentatively linked to vitamin D deficiency, but an imbalance of the calcium-phosphorus ratio is also considered a possibility. Further research is needed to clarify this point. The main problem to date is hypervitaminosis, or excessive amounts of the vitamin. Too much vitamin D will cause improper calcium mobilization, and calcium may be deposited in the soft tissues. The result will be loss of proper joint function, hardening of soft tissues, and an enlargement of the skull and jaw. Therefore, vitamin D supplementation should be approached with caution, and supplements should only be fed according to directions.

## Vitamin E

Vitamin E is a fat-soluble vitamin. It has only recently begun to be considered as essential in the diet of the horse, and its effects are still controversial. The primary sources of vitamin E are wheat germ and wheat germ oil, good quality hay and forage, and the cereal grains.

Little is known about the actual function of vitamin E in the body. It has been associated with a number of processes, including muscle development, oxygen transportation in the blood stream, proper development of erythrocytes (red blood cells), and fertility. Vitamin E deficiency can cause infertility, myositis, muscular dystrophy of foals, degeneration of muscle tissue, and it may be a factor in azoturia. Myositis is considered by many to be a mild form of azoturia, and both diseases involve rapid respiration, profuse sweating, and muscle rigidity. (15)

Vitamin E is made of several substances called tocopherols, which are alcohol compounds. The name tocopherol means child-birth conferring alcohol, because the first use of vitamin E was in relieving infertility. The most common form is alpha tocopherol. It is normally adequate for maintenance in the ration, but there are many substances which may also be present that act as tocopherol antagonists. That is, they either destroy or prevent the utilization of the vitamin E in feeds. These substances include unsaturated fatty acids and other compounds found in weed seeds, legumes, and cottonseed meal. For this reason, vitamin E supplementation is believed to be beneficial, and probably should be considered essential for horses involved in racing or breeding.

Large doses of vitamin E, from 1,000 to 2,000 International Units daily, have been shown to greatly improve breeding performance, and also appear to have a significant effect on racing performance. The Darlington-Chassels report, published in 1956, 1958, and 1960, gives the results of controlled administration of vitamin E in large doses to race horses. There was a significant increase in speed, stamina, and number of wins. While further research is needed to conclusively establish a relationship, vitamin E must be considered a probable aid to racing performance. (16) Foal survival rate appears to be increased to some degree if mares receive vitamin E supplementation during late gestation. Also, the intake of vitamin E has a sparing action on vitamin A. That is, if vitamin E levels in the body are adequate, then vitamin A is used more efficiently and less of it is required.

Vitamin E may be added in commercial supplements, since it is quickly lost from feeds during storage. Almost all research on this vitamin to the present date shows that it may be extremely beneficial to the horse when fed in supplementary doses, at the level of about 1,000 I.U. per day.


# Vitamin K

Vitamin K is soluble in fat. Its primary function is to promote normal blood coagulation and prevent hemorrhaging. Horses obtain a precursor of vitamin K from green leafy plants, and synthesize the true vitamin from bacteria in the intestinal tract. Normal horses will synthesize adequate amounts of the vitamin, but horses which have been fed antibiotic agents that would destroy intestinal bacteria may need vitamin K supplementation. It is now known that there is a factor in moldy hay and in some clover pastures that destroys vitamin K in the body. Care should be taken that hay is fresh and pasture is good in order to maintain normal vitamin K levels. In cases where hay or pasture are poor, supplementation may again be beneficial. This is especially true at foaling, when postparturient hemorrhage is likely if the blood does not clot properly.

## Supplementation of Vitamins in Feed

Commercial vitamin supplements are available in a wide range of varieties and potencies. They may be given orally in feed, and injectable supplements are also available. It is recommended that injectable supplements be avoided, except when they are administered by a veterinarian in cases of deficiency or disease. Used routinely, they may be hazardous. Orally administered supplements should be carefully evaluated before using. The vitamin content of the feed ration should be determined, and areas where supplementation would be beneficial should be outlined. The assistance of a veterinarian, professional equine nutritionist, or a County Agent is valuable for this purpose. After determination of needs, a commercial supplement from a reputable manufacturer should be selected. It should contain only those vitamins considered to be necessary for a particular horse, **and should not contain amounts which greatly exceed the minimum daily requirements of vitamins which can produce excesses.** The use of several different supplements should be avoided in most cases. It is best to choose one supplement or mix, that closely approximate the animal's needs, and then use only that supplement until the results of its use can be evaluated. Directions for use should always be carefully followed.

## Summary

Vitamins are essential to the metabolic processes of the horse. They may be divided into two groups: those which are soluble in fat, and those which are soluble in water. The fat-soluble vitamins include A, D, E, and K. Those which are water-soluble are vitamin C, and the B-complex vitamins, including thiamine, niacin, riboflavin, pyridoxine, pantothenic acid, biotin, choline, folacin, inositol, and vitamin $B_{12}$. Most vitamins are either produced in adequate amounts in the body, or will be found in the normal ration, but special stresses increase the need for vitamins. Supplementation can then be valuable. Commercial vitamin supplements should be carefully chosen and used in moderation. Injectable supplements are recommended only in extreme cases, and should be administered by a veterinarian.

# REFERENCES CITED

1. Weikel, Bill, Editor, **Know Practical Horse Feeding.** The Farnam Horse Library, Omaha, Nebraska, (1971)
2. Guthrie, Helen Andrews, **Introductory Nutrition.** The C. V. Mosby Company, Saint Louis, (1971)
3. Guthrie, Helen Andrews, **Op. Cit.**
4. Guthrie, Helen Andrews, **Op. Cit.**
5. Seiden, Dr. Rudolph, **The Handbook Of Feedstuffs.** Springer Publishing Company, Inc., New York (1957)
6. Cunha, T. J., Ph.D. "Vitamins and Minerals for Horses," **Feedstuffs.** Vol. 38 (33): 62-66, (1966)
7. Guthrie, Helen Andrews, **Op. Cit.**
8. Siegmund, O. H. Editor, **The Merck Veterinary Manual.** Merck and Company, Inc., Rahway, New Jersey, (1967)
9. National Research Council, **Nutrient Requirements of Horses.** National Academy of Sciences — National Research Council, Washington, D.C., (1973)
10. Guthrie, Helen Andrews, **Op. Cit.**
11. Ensminger, M. E., Ph.D., **Horses and Horsemanship.** Interstate Printers and Publishers, Inc., Danville, Illinois, (1969)
12. Morrison, Frank B., **Feeds and Feeding, Abridged, Ninth Edition.** The Morrison Publishing Company, Claremont, Ontario, Canada, (1958)
13. Cunha, T. J., Ph.D., **Op. Cit.**
14. Bullard, T. L., D.V.M., "Nutrition — Some Basic Thoughts on Horse Feeding," Paper presented to Southwestern Planning Conference for Livestockmen, Waco, Texas, March 1973
15. Bailey, Herbert, **Vitamin E: Your Key to a Healthy Heart.** Arc Books, Inc., New York, (1970)

# 6

# Minerals

Minerals are inorganic compounds which are found throughout the body. They serve two major functions within the body: they are components and building materials of body tissues, and they are catalytic compounds that help to trigger reactions within the body. Exact mineral requirements for the horse are still being determined, but at the present time there are at least sixteen minerals which are considered essential and which occur normally in body tissues. (1) Some of these are present in very small amounts, and needs are sufficiently met by the normal diet. Others are required at higher levels, and must be supplemented. Some of these minerals work in combination with other minerals or with vitamins, while others have a completely independent action.

The mineral intake of the horse is greatly determined by the water and soil content of the area in which the animal is raised, and the geographic location in which his feed is grown. Another important factor in mineral intake is the proportion of hay to grain. The third major consideration is quality of feed. Feed which is aged, weathered, or improperly harvested or cured will tend to be lower in mineral content. Pasture which is poorly fertilized, or that which is not well-maintained or weeded may either lack necessary minerals, or it may have toxic levels of others. Disease and weakness in the horse can be caused by either excesses or deficiencies of certain minerals.

## Salt

Salt is the mineral substance most often added to the ration of the horse. It provides equal parts of sodium and chloride. These minerals help to regulate the fluid balance within the body, and they also affect

Swaps, a 1952 Thoroughbred stallion, is shown setting the world's record for 1 mile and 70 yards, while campaigning for Mr. Rex C. Ellsworth of California. Swaps was bred and raised on Mr. Ellsworth's ranch under the strictest of feeding programs, highlighted by the ranch's own feed processing mill.

fluid intake by creating thirst. In many cases, salt may be the means by which iodine and trace minerals are added to the diet.

Salt may be fed either in block form or loose. It may be either iodized, plain, or trace-mineralized, and it may be fed free-choice or added to the ration in measured amounts. Most horses regulate their salt intake according to their body needs, and should have salt available at all times. It is best not to supply the entire amount of salt in block form unless the climate is wet and the salt crumbles easily. Otherwise, it is too difficult for the horse to consume its full salt requirement. Block salt is useful for supplementary feeding in pastures, however, if loose salt is given in the stall or in the ration.

Salt should be iodized in areas where the soil is deficient in iodine. This so-called "goiter belt" includes the states of California, Colorado, Illinois, Indiana, Iowa, Michigan, Montana, Nebraska, Nevada, New York, North Dakota, Ohio, Oregon, South Dakota, Utah, Washington, and Wisconsin. (2) In other areas of the country, iodized salt is not usually necessary.

The mature horse should be supplied with at least sixty grams of salt per day. There are several methods of accomplishing this. Probably the most satisfactory is to mix a low level of salt in with the ration, about one-half of one percent of the total amount of feed. Then, supplementary salt should be provided free-choice. It is not advisable to supply salt only in the ration, as salt needs of individual horses may be different, and will certainly vary with changes in weather and activity. Supplementary salt may be made available in loose form in a box in the stall, or in boxes or blocks in the pasture. These boxes should be protected from the wind and weather. Ideally, both plain and trace-mineralized salt should be provided, since some horses do not find mineralized salt palatable, and will not consume enough of it. However, if mineralized salt is to be used, either the mineralized salt alone or a mixture of two parts plain to one part mineralized will also be satisfactory. Salt boxes should always be kept clean and well filled.

Salt helps the horse to regulate the cooling mechanism of the body, and it is critical that an adequate amount be supplied in warm weather. The amount of salt excreted from the body is in direct proportion to the amount of water excreted, and when large amounts of water are consumed and excreted in hot weather, extra salt must be consumed to maintain the salt concentration at normal levels within the body. (3) Even where heat is not a significant factor, a salt deficiency will cause changes in the appetite or abnormal appetite, insufficient water intake, rough hair coat, and a poor appearance. If recommended supplementation is not exceeded, salt excess is unlikely unless the animal is either deprived of sufficient water, or is supplied with salt in unlimited

*photo courtesy of Quarter Racing Record*

**Mr. Jet Moore, a 1969 son of Jet Deck - Dyna Van by Vandy was named "World Champion Quarter Running Horse" in 1972 by the American Quarter Horse Association at its annual convention. He is pictured here with his owners, Mr. Robert Moore (right) and Mr. Melvin Hatley, both of Oklahoma.**

amounts after being deprived of salt for a long period of time. If this condition does occur, it will cause fluid imbalance within the cells, and may induce fatal poisoning.

## Calcium, Phosphorus, and the Calcium-Phosphorus Ratio

Calcium and phosphorus intake in the horse should be considered as a single subject, since these two minerals affect each other. Calcium and phosphorus are most important in bone growth, development, and repair. If the two minerals are fed in improper proportions, however, serious disturbances may result. Recent scientific research has placed the desired ratio of calcium to phosphorus in the feed from 1.1 to 1 up to 1.5 to 1. (4), (5) In the body, the ratio is 2 to 1, because phosphorus is not completely utilized. The mature horse can accommodate for slight differences in the ratio, which is why a fixed figure cannot be given. Also, the use of phosphorus depends on the source from which it is derived. In the diet of the mature, idle horse, calcium should comprise about .35 per cent, and phosphorus about .25 percent. Both minerals should be increased proportionately for animals involved in racing, broodmares, and growing foals.

When determining the calcium-phosphorus ratio in formulating a ration, it should be remembered that hays tend to be high in calcium, while the cereal grains are good sources of phosphorus. Bran contains very large amounts of phosphorus in proportion to other feeds. Calcium is the mineral most likely to be deficient when horses are fed poor quality hay, or a diet which is high in concentrates and contains a proportionately small amount of hay. If the diet is well-balanced, however, the calcium-phosphorus ratio can be maintained at safe levels with ease.

Vitamin D works closely with calcium and phosphorus in the body. For this reason, a sufficient vitamin D intake will ensure a more efficient usage of calcium and phosphorus, while if vitamin D levels are low, calcium and phosphorus may need to be increased in the diet. However, excessive amounts of vitamin D will result in improper metabolism of calcium and phosphorus, and this should also be regulated carefully.

The primary diseases caused by calcium-phosphorus imbalances or insufficiencies are bone disorders. Osteomalacia, (a disease characterized by softening of the bones), and osteoporosis, (an absorption of bone, resulting in abnormally porous tissue), in adult horses are due to insufficient calcium in relation to phosphorus. An imbalance in the phosphorus intake may cause parathyroid disorders. A disease in foals which is similar to human rickets, where bone development is improper, has been linked to a calcium-phosphorus imbalance, although this has not yet been

photo courtesy of Fruen Milling Co.

Any strenuous performance event will reveal nutritional inadequacies, but jumping events are probably one of the more taxing events on the legs of horses. Proper calcium and phosphorus intake, and the proper calcium/phosphorus ratio are critical factors in the diet of the jumper.

proven.

Since the calcium-phosphorus ratio is so important, it is best to have soil and feed analyzed before supplementing. Both the total amount of calcium and phosphorus in the ration should be measured, and also the proportion of calcium to phosphorus. If it is below 1.1 to 1, calcium sources should be added to the diet. If it is higher than 1.5 to 1, either phosphorus sources should be added, or pastures should be enriched with a high-phosphate fertilizer. Since commercial feeds are labeled with the amounts of calcium and phosphorus they contain, determination of the dietary levels is not difficult. Good supplementary sources of calcium are ground limestone, calcium phosphate, and dicalcium phosphate. Steamed bone meal is a good source of calcium and phosphorus, but many horses may find it unpalatable. If it is used, therefore, it should be added to the ration gradually. County Agricultural Agents can supply information on local sources of both minerals, and information on which are most likely to be insufficient or excessive in a particular geographic area.

# Iodine

No exact level of iodine requirement has been set for horses, but the National Research Council estimates that rations containing 0.1 parts per million of iodine are satisfactory for the mature horse. This requirement may be slightly increased with pregnancy. In most parts of the country, this requirement is adequately met by the normal diet. In the "goiter belt", previously described, however, supplementation with potassium iodide in the feed or the use of iodized salt may be necessary to meet maintenance requirements.

Iodine is necessary for proper thyroid function. Insufficient intake may be recognized by poor growth, and a high foal death rate. Excessive amounts of iodine, more than forty milligrams per day, are dangerous to the health of the horse. (6) Either excesses or insufficiencies may result in enlargement of the thyroid gland, called goiter, and this condition can be fatal if not treated.

# Magnesium

Magnesium is required by horses in small amounts. It is normally adequate in rations where forage is good. If hay is of poor quality and there is no access to pasture, magnesium intake may be insufficient, and hypomagnesemia may develop. Its symptoms include muscle incoordination and nervousness. Magnesium contained in trace-mineralized salt, in the form of magnesium oxide or magnesium limestone, is usually sufficient to prevent this disorder.

# Potassium

Potassium is necessary to maintain the proper acid-alkali balance within the cells. The amount of potassium contained in the ordinary diet is usually adequate, and no exact requirement has yet been determined. However, potassium can be rapidly lost from the body where fluid excretion is abnormally high. This might occur in cases of severe intestinal disturbance, such as diarrhea or kidney disorder. Potassium deficit in the healthy horse is highly unlikely. However, in cases of serious illness serum potassium levels should be monitored by frequent blood testing, and supplemental potassium should be provided if necessary on veterinary recommendation. Permanent disorder of the heart or kidneys may result if potassium supplies in the body become depleted and are not restored.

# Cobalt

The cobalt requirements of the mature horse are extremely low. However, a minimum amount of cobalt in the diet is necessary for synthesis of vitamin $B_{12}$. This process is explained more fully in Chapter Five. This maintenance requirement is easily met by the normal diet of the horse.

# Sulfur

No sulfur requirement has been determined for the horse. At the present time, sulfur is not considered to be essential in the diet.

# Copper

The horse needs only trace amounts of copper in the diet. A level of five to eight parts per million is considered adequate by the National Research Council. (7) This would normally occur in most rations. Copper is necessary for healthy blood formation. If serum copper levels are low at foaling, hemorrhaging may occur in the mare. (8) This deficiency, however, is unlikely.

# Iron

The requirement for iron in the diet is low. An estimate places it currently at about forty parts per million in the ration. (9) Iron is necessary for healthy blood formation, and a deficiency is quickly revealed by a blood analysis. Iron intake is sufficient in the normal diet.

# Manganese

The horse requires small amounts of manganese, but no exact determination has been made. Most hay is high in manganese, and the requirements are easily met.

## Fluorine

While no minimum requirements for fluorine have been set, it has been shown that excessive amounts of fluorine are toxic. In areas where the fluoride content of the water is high, or where hay with a high fluorine content is fed, care should be taken that the total fluorine intake does not exceed fifty parts per million in the ration, or about 1 milligram per kilogram of body weight. (10) If a high fluorine content hay is used, it should be mixed with low-fluoride hay to lower the total intake. Excessive fluorine intake can cause irreversible damage to the teeth.

## Zinc

Although no exact zinc requirement has been determined, it is an essential element in the diet. Insufficient zinc intake may cause stunted growth in foals. A level of twelve parts per million in the diet can be considered sufficient, and this is easily met unless the horse is confined to a small area with little access to pasture and a poor quality diet. (11) If zinc deficiency symptoms develop, or if the diet is poor in quality, the amounts of zinc contained in trace-mineralized salt should be adequate to balance the diet.

## Selenium

Selenium has recently been shown to be an essential mineral in the diet of the horse. It is present in adequate amounts in the normal diet however. Selenium appears to have a relationship with vitamin E. Although the exact nature of this relationship is not known, it is probable that selenium has a sparing action on vitamin E. That is, if selenium is present in sufficient amounts in the diet, vitamin E is used more efficiently and smaller doses of the vitamin will have the same effect as larger doses without selenium. Further research is needed to document this, however.

If ingested in large amounts, selenium toxicity does occur in horses. This is most likely to occur in alkaline or desert climates, where the selenium levels in forage are extremely high. This disease can be fatal in horses, and where selenium levels are high, horses should be moved from pasture and fed a carefully controlled diet. Hay should not be locally grown in these areas. Symptoms of selenium excess include loss of hair, and the development of a ring around the hoof.

# Ensuring Proper Mineral Balance in the Diet

In the normal diet, when the hay and grain rations are of high quality and are fed in proper proportion, the addition of trace-mineralized salt should be sufficient for most horses. There are also many commercial mineral mixes available, and many establishments formulate their own mixtures. Before supplementing, it is wise to test soil and feed. Mineral content of the soil varies greatly from one region of the country to the next, and has a direct bearing on the total mineral intake of the horse. Where minerals are lacking, proper fertilization of pasture can supply many of the needed elements. Commercial mineral supplements may be either those designed to supply primarily calcium and phosphorus, or they may contain only trace minerals. In either case, these supplements should be used with the advice of a professional nutritionist, County Agricultural Agent, or veterinarian, and these supplements should be bought only from reputable feed dealers. Minerals which are deficient in the diet vary greatly in different parts of the country, so no one mixture can be recommended. The area and the total ration must be considered, and the specific weaknesses and deficiencies isolated. Then a mixture may be purchased or prepared which will satisfy these exact needs, containing the proper minerals in the correct proportions. Once this mixture has been determined, it may be mixed with salt or fed plain. The important factor is providing the minerals in correct proportion, so that it is not necessary for the horse to consume excessive amounts of one mineral in order to obtain sufficient amounts of another.

## Summary

Minerals are inorganic compounds necessary for proper body growth and function. Salt, calcium and phosphorus are the mineral elements most commonly added to the ration. Either plain salt or trace-mineralized salt can be used, depending on the needs of a given feeding program for trace minerals. Iodine may be added to the salt in areas where it is deficient. The calcium-phosphorus ratio should be maintained at from 1.1 to 1 up to 1.5 to 1, and this should be carefully regulated. Other minerals utilized by the horse should be present in a good trace-mineral mixture, and these include iodine, magnesium, potassium, cobalt, sulfur, copper, iron, manganese, fluorine, zinc, and selenium. Mineral supplementation other than the use of trace-mineralized salt or fertilization of pastures should be done carefully, and only on the advice of a competent professional.

# REFERENCES CITED

1. National Research Council, **Nutrient Requirements of Horses.** National Academy of Sciences — National Research Council, Washington, D.C., 1973
2. Donahue, Roy L., Shickluna, John C., and Robertson, Lynn S., **Soils: An Introduction to Soils and Plant Growth.** Prentice-Hall, Inc., Englewood Cliffs, New Jersey, (1971)
3. Wilson, Eva D., Fisher, Katherine H., and Fuqua, Mary E., **Principles of Nutrition.** John Wiley and Sons, Inc., New York (1965)
4. Teeter, S. M., D.V.M., Stillions, Merle C., Ph.D., and Nelson, W. E., Ph.D., "Calcium and Phosphorus Requirements" **Journal of the American Veterinary Medical Association,** Vol. 151 (12): 1625-1628, (1967)
5. National Research Council, **Op. Cit.**
6. National Research Council, **Op. Cit.**
7. National Research Council, **Op. Cit.**
8. Catcott, E. J., D.V.M., Ph.D., and Smithcors, J. F., D.V.M., Ph.D., Editors, **Progress in Equine Practice, Volume Two.** American Veterinary Publications, Inc., Wheaton, Illinois, (1970)
9. National Research Council, **Op. Cit.**
10. National Research Council, **Op. Cit.**
11. Morris Animal Foundation, "Zinc Requirements of the Horse," Paper, Morris Animal Foundation, Denver, Colorado, March 1972

## MINERAL CONTENT OF POPULAR HORSE FEEDS AND FORAGES *

| FEED/or FORAGE | DRY MATTER (%) | FIGURED ON A DRY BASIS (moisture free) | | | | | | | | | | |
|---|---|---|---|---|---|---|---|---|---|---|---|---|
| | | CALCIUM (%) | COBALT mg/kg | COPPER mg/kg | IRON (%) | MAG-NESIUM (%) | MANGA-NESE mg/kg | PHOSPHORUS (%) | POTAS-SIUM (%) | SODIUM (%) | SULFUR (%) | ZINC mg/kg |
| **ALFALFA** | | | | | | | | | | | | |
| hay, s-c, early bloom ** | 90.0 | 1.25 | .090 | 13.4 | .020 | .30 | 31.5 | .23 | 2.08 | .15 | .30 | --- |
| hay, s-c, mid-bloom | 89.2 | 1.35 | --- | 15.4 | .010 | .35 | 16.5 | .22 | 1.46 | .15 | .30 | --- |
| hay, s-c, full bloom | 87.7 | 1.28 | .124 | 13.4 | .020 | .35 | 33.7 | .20 | 2.55 | --- | --- | --- |
| hay, s-c, mature | 91.2 | .71 | --- | --- | --- | .36 | --- | .16 | 2.39 | --- | --- | --- |
| pasture, fresh, pre-bloom | 21.1 | 2.30 | --- | --- | --- | .03 | 27.7 | .31 | 1.92 | .20 | .60 | --- |
| pasture, fresh, full bloom | 25.3 | 1.53 | --- | --- | .040 | .27 | --- | .27 | 2.13 | .15 | .31 | 14.1 |
| **BARLEY** | | | | | | | | | | | | |
| grain, (overall avg.) | 89.0 | .09 | .100 | 8.6 | .006 | .14 | 18.3 | .47 | .63 | .02 | .17 | 17.2 |
| **BERMUDAGRASS** | | | | | | | | | | | | |
| pasture, fresh, (ov'all avg.) | 36.7 | .53 | .070 | 5.7 | .110 | .23 | 100.1 | .22 | 1.63 | .44 | --- | --- |
| **BERMUDAGRASS, COASTAL** | | | | | | | | | | | | |
| hay, s-c, (overall avg.) | 91.5 | .46 | --- | --- | --- | .17 | --- | .18 | 1.77 | --- | --- | --- |
| **BLUEGRASS, KENTUCKY** | | | | | | | | | | | | |
| pasture, fresh, immature | 30.5 | .56 | --- | 14.1 | .030 | .18 | 80.3 | .47 | 2.28 | --- | .66 | 170.4 |
| pasture, fresh, milk-stage | 35.0 | .19 | --- | 13.9 | .017 | .23 | 80.3 | .27 | 1.95 | .23 | .66 | 170.4 |
| hay, s-c, (overall avg.) | 88.9 | .45 | --- | 9.9 | .028 | .21 | 85.6 | .30 | 1.87 | .11 | .13 | --- |
| **BLUESTEM** | | | | | | | | | | | | |
| pasture, fresh, immature | 31.6 | .63 | --- | 36.8 | .070 | --- | 83.3 | .17 | 1.35 | --- | --- | --- |
| pasture, fresh, mature | 71.3 | .40 | --- | 16.1 | .060 | .06 | 36.8 | .11 | .51 | --- | --- | --- |
| **BROME, CHEATGRASS** | | | | | | | | | | | | |
| pasture, fresh, immature | 21.0 | .64 | --- | --- | --- | --- | --- | .28 | 1.60 | --- | --- | --- |
| pasture, fresh, dough-stage | 30.0 | .38 | --- | --- | --- | --- | --- | .27 | ---- | --- | --- | --- |

* Data derived from <u>Nutrient Requirements of Horses</u>, National Research
Council, 1973, and <u>Atlas of Nutritional Data on United States and
Canadian Feeds</u>, National Academy of Sciences, 1971

** s-c is abbreviation for suncured

# MINERAL CONTENT OF POPULAR HORSE FEEDS AND FORAGES (CONTINUED)

| FEED/or FORAGE | DRY MATTER (%) | CALCIUM (%) | COBALT mg/kg | COPPER mg/kg | IRON (%) | MAG-NESIUM (%) | MANGA-NESE mg/kg | PHOSPHORUS (%) | POTAS-SIUM (%) | SODIUM (%) | SULFUR (%) | ZINC mg/kg |
|---|---|---|---|---|---|---|---|---|---|---|---|---|
| | | | | | *FIGURED ON A DRY BASIS (moisture free)* | | | | | | | |
| BROME, SMOOTH | | | | | | | | | | | | |
| hay, s-c, mid-bloom | 89.7 | .40 | ---- | 8.6 | .012 | .22 | 58.0 | .20 | 2.52 | .63 | .19 | ---- |
| hay, s-c, mature | 92.8 | .43 | .130 | 6.8 | .010 | .19 | 105.8 | .22 | 2.76 | ---- | --- | ---- |
| CLOVER, ALSIKE | | | | | | | | | | | | |
| hay, s-c, (overall avg.) | 87.9 | 1.31 | ---- | 6.0 | .030 | .45 | 69.0 | .25 | 1.70 | .46 | .21 | ---- |
| pasture, fresh, (ov'all avg.) | 22.5 | 1.36 | ---- | 6.0 | .043 | .32 | 117.1 | .29 | 2.70 | .45 | .22 | 60.2 |
| CLOVER, CRIMSON | | | | | | | | | | | | |
| hay, s-c, (overall avg.) | 87.4 | 1.42 | ---- | ---- | .070 | .27 | 171.3 | .18 | 1.54 | .39 | .28 | ---- |
| pasture, fresh, (ov'all avg.) | 17.7 | 1.62 | ---- | ---- | .070 | .41 | 290.6 | .35 | 2.41 | .40 | .28 | ---- |
| CLOVER, LADINO | | | | | | | | | | | | |
| hay, s-c, pre-bloom | 88.4 | 1.73 | ---- | 8.7 | .018 | .52 | 181.1 | .33 | 2.45 | --- | .21 | ---- |
| pasture, fresh, (ov'all avg.) | 18.0 | 1.27 | ---- | ---- | .036 | .48 | 71.7 | .42 | 1.87 | .12 | .12 | ---- |
| CLOVER, RED | | | | | | | | | | | | |
| hay, s-c, (overall avg.) | 90.1 | 1.45 | ---- | 10.7 | .011 | .52 | 76.9 | .23 | 2.67 | .20 | .16 | ---- |
| pasture, fresh, (ov'all avg.) | 22.7 | 1.80 | .141 | 9.0 | .033 | .43 | 123.3 | .26 | 2.46 | .20 | .17 | ---- |
| CORN | | | | | | | | | | | | |
| ground ears | 87.0 | .05 | .300 | 8.8 | .008 | .17 | 15.0 | .31 | .61 | --- | --- | ---- |
| #2 Dent Yellow mn. wt. 54 lbs. per bushel | 89.0 | .02 | .020 | ---- | ---- | ---- | ---- | ---- | ---- | --- | --- | ---- |
| COTTONSEED MEAL | | | | | | | | | | | | |
| solv-extd, 41% protein | 91.5 | .17 | .164 | 21.3 | .033 | .61 | 23.5 | 1.31 | 1.53 | .04 | .23 | 66.0 |
| FESCUE, MEADOW | | | | | | | | | | | | |
| hay, s-c, (overall avg.) | 88.5 | .50 | ---- | ---- | ---- | .50 | 24.5 | .36 | 1.87 | --- | --- | ---- |
| pasture, fresh, (ov'all avg.) | 27.6 | .51 | .135 | 4.0 | ---- | .37 | ---- | .38 | 2.00 | --- | --- | ---- |
| JOHNSONGRASS (Sorghum Johnsongrass) | | | | | | | | | | | | |
| hay, s-c, (overall avg.) | 90.6 | .89 | ---- | ---- | .058 | .35 | ---- | .30 | 1.35 | --- | --- | ---- |

| Feed | | | | | | | | | | | |
|---|---|---|---|---|---|---|---|---|---|---|---|
| JOHNSONGRASS (continued) pasture, fresh, (ov'all avg.) | 24.8 | .91 | --- | --- | --- | .25 | --- | .26 | 3.12 | --- | --- | --- |
| LESPEDEZA hay, s-c, full bloom | 93.2 | 1.04 | --- | --- | .030 | .24 | 151.5 | .23 | 1.03 | --- | --- | --- |
| LINSEED MEAL mech-extd | 91.0 | .48 | .500 | 29.0 | .019 | .64 | 43.3 | .98 | 1.36 | .12 | .43 | --- |
| MILO (Sorghum Milo) grain, (overall avg.) | 89.0 | .04 | .100 | 15.8 | .005 | .22 | 14.5 | .33 | .39 | .01 | --- | --- |
| OATS hay, s-c, (overall avg.) | 88.2 | .26 | .070 | 4.4 | .050 | .29 | 74.7 | .24 | .97 | .17 | --- | --- |
| OATS grain, (overall avg.) | 89.0 | .11 | .064 | 9.3 | .008 | .18 | 48.6 | .37 | .48 | .08 | .23 | --- |
| ORCHARDGRASS hay, s-c, (overall avg.) | 88.3 | .45 | .020 | 13.7 | .010 | .22 | 249.6 | .22 | 2.10 | --- | .26 | 18.1 |
| ORCHARDGRASS pasture, fresh, immature | 23.8 | .58 | --- | --- | .020 | .31 | 134.3 | .55 | 3.38 | .04 | .21 | --- |
| PRAIRIE HAY hay, s-c, (overall avg.) | 91.0 | .35 | --- | --- | .009 | .24 | --- | .14 | 1.08 | --- | --- | --- |
| RYE grain, (overall avg.) | 88.2 | .08 | --- | 8.6 | .007 | .13 | 83.3 | .39 | .52 | .02 | .17 | 34.4 |
| SOYBEAN MEAL solv-extd | 89.0 | .36 | .100 | 40.8 | .013 | .30 | 30.9 | .75 | 2.21 | .38 | .48 | --- |
| TIMOTHY hay, s-c, mid-bloom | 88.4 | .41 | .082 | --- | --- | .20 | 45.0 | .19 | 2.42 | --- | .18 | --- |
| WHEAT bran, dry milled | 89.0 | .16 | .044 | 13.8 | .019 | .62 | 130.0 | 1.32 | 1.39 | .07 | .25 | --- |
| WHEAT grain, (overall avg.) | 89.0 | .09 | --- | 9.1 | .007 | .16 | 49.0 | .41 | .58 | .10 | .22 | --- |
| WHEAT middlings | 89.0 | .09 | --- | 4.9 | .007 | .33 | 42.3 | .58 | .67 | .74 | --- | --- |
| WHEATGRASS, CRESTED pasture, fresh, immature | 30.8 | .46 | --- | --- | --- | .28 | --- | .35 | --- | --- | --- | --- |
| YEAST, BREWERS dehy/grnd/mn. 40% protein | 93.0 | .14 | .200 | 35.5 | .010 | .25 | 6.1 | 1.54 | 1.85 | .08 | --- | 41.6 |

# 7

# Energy and Energy Measurement

The major consideration in planning the total ration for a horse is the amount of energy the horse requires, and the most effective and efficient method of providing that energy. Energy is supplied most readily through carbohydrates, and secondarily, from fats. Excess protein in the diet that is not used for muscle development is also converted into energy. The total amount of energy required is affected by the size of the horse and the amount of daily exercise, productivity, or work performed.

## Energy

Energy may be commonly defined as the capacity to do work. (1) It is the "fire of life" or fuel for the body systems. The use of energy is most commonly expressed through physical activity, growth, milk production, and repair of body tissues. A deficiency of energy intake will therefore be manifested by dulled physical activity, general weakness, insufficient lactation, or slow growth. Conversely, if energy intake is substantially greater than energy requirement, much of the ingested energy is stored in the body as fat, and weight gain can become a problem.

Energy requirements have been quantitatively determined by the National Research Council for horses of different sizes and activity levels. The maintenance energy level is considered to be that at which a mature animal, not pregnant, lactating, or working, will maintain normal weight under average climate conditions. Energy requirements will be increased by pregnancy, lactation, growth, or heavy work. In addition, markedly lowered atmospheric temperature will increase energy needs, while the requirement for energy will be somewhat decreased by very hot weather. This is because energy is utilized in maintaining body temperature. If the weather is hot, smaller amounts of body heat are needed to keep body temperature normal. If the weather is very cold, however, energy in the form of heat must be used to raise the animal's body temperature.

It is important to realize that the critical figure in planning a balanced ration is **usable energy** in feed, rather than total energy content. A feed which is high in total energy content may be difficult to digest, thereby releasing only a portion of its energy content for actual use by the animal. There are several ways in which the amount of usable energy in feed may be estimated.

## The Total Digestible Nutrient System (TDN)

The oldest method for measuring the energy value of a feed is the Total Digestible Nutrient System, commonly referred to as TDN. Until recently, this method was most acceptable. However, the National Research Council has recently begun adopting the measurement of energy in calories as the preferred method. To determine the TDN value of a feed, the different nutrient components of the feed are rated according to how digestible they are, and are given a numerical value indicating the percentage of the nutrients in the feed which are actually utilized by the horse. For example, the protein in oats is considered to be seventy-eight percent digestible. In other words, seventy-eight percent of the total protein in the oats is actually assimilated by the horse, while the remaining twenty-two percent is excreted. (2) To determine the TDN value of a feed, numerical coefficients of digestibility are applied to each of the nutrients contained in the feed. The TDN value is the sum of the digestible crude protein, plus the digestible carbohydrates, plus 2.25 times the digestible crude fat. (3) The digestible fat is multiplied by 2.25 because it is considered to have approximately 2.25 times the energy value of carbohydrates in animal feeding. To obtain the figures necessary to compute TDN, a lengthy and elaborate chart showing the digestibility of feeds, such as the Morrison Feeding Standards is necessary. The total amount of protein in the feed, which is expressed as a percentage, is multiplied by the coefficient of digestibility of the protein of that particular feed to give the percentage of digestible protein. For example, oats, containing about 12 percent protein, have a protein digestibility coefficient of 78%, as previously explained. Multiplying these two figures

*photo courtesy of Meadow Lands Farm*

**A good feeding program helped Meadow Helene win many races for her owners.**

together gives 9.4%, which would be the amount of **digestible** protein in the feed, less than the **total** amount of protein. The same calculation is made for the carbohydrate and fat in the feed, and the derived percentage for fat is multiplied by 2.25. The resulting percentages, or the amount of digestible protein, digestible carbohydrate, and digestible fat are then added together. This gives the total percentage of digestible nutrients in the feed. In the example of oats, if the values were correctly calculated, the percentage of total digestible nutrients would be 70.1 percent. By computing TDN values for different feeds and then comparing them, it is possible to see which feeds are highest and lowest in energy, and which feeds would provide the most usable energy for the least possible cost. Also, a high energy feed can be mixed with a lower energy feed to balance a ration and prevent it from being too high in energy content, causing weight gain and the possibility of colic, or too low in energy, and insufficient to support the needs of the animal.

## Caloric Measurement of Energy Values

More recently, the National Research Council has begun describing feed energy values in terms of calorie content, rather than Total Digestible Nutrients. A calorie is the amount of heat required to raise the temperature of one gram of water one degree Centigrade. (4) A large calorie, written **Calorie** or kilocalorie, is equal to one thousand calories. Since energy is released in the form of heat, it is easy to see why it is measured in terms of heat. If the feed is burned under test conditions in a special container called a calorimeter, where the feed is enclosed in a sealed container immersed in a measured amount of water, the total amount of heat given off can be measured. In turn, animals are tested in closed chambers after consumption of a measured amount of a feed with a known caloric content, and the amount of energy given off by the body can be measured. This energy is produced in four main forms: in the urine and other nitrogenous wastes, in the feces, in the bacterial fermentation process in the intestines (released as methane gas), and in body heat lost through energy used in consuming and digesting the feed. If this waste energy is subtracted from the total energy measured in the calorimeter, the remaining amount is called the Net Energy Value of the feed. This Net Energy Value is described in calories for a specific quantity of feed. It is possible to quantitatively measure the caloric requirements of an individual animal under specific work conditions. Then, the energy content of the ration may be balanced by adding the total caloric content of the feeds in the ration, and substituting higher or lower calorie feeds as necessary. Feeding too many calories per day would produce an energy surplus and excess fat, and feeding too few calories per day would cause an energy shortage.

Another term used for describing the total energy value of a feed is its Metabolizable Energy Value. (5) Also measured in calories, this differs from the Net Energy Value only in that the amount of body heat produced during feed consumption is not subtracted, because this is considered to be part of the animal's normal requirement for body heat production. Since this heat lost in digestion cannot be used for actual work, the Metabolizable Energy Value is actually usable only for describing the amount of energy available in a feed for metabolic processes at the tissue level.

Digestible Energy is the descriptive value most commonly used in describing animal feeds. It consists of the total energy in the feed with only the amount of energy lost in the feces subtracted. (6) In other words, it is the Net Energy Value without the subtraction of energy produced by digestion, urine and nitrogenous wastes, and products of fermentation. The only energy subtracted is that of the undigested feed, and the other energy losses are considered to be a normal metabolic requirement.

## Reasons for Quantifying the Energy Value of Feeds

Generally speaking, the practiced horseman can tell by observation whether or not a particular animal is receiving sufficient energy from a ration. Also, exact energy measurement is time consuming and requires either elaborate equipment or detailed charts. Why, then, is energy measurement desirable? Economy is an important part of good feeding management. While the horseman desiring optimum performance from his horses would be well advised to never skimp on quality to save money, it is nevertheless desirable to feed the optimum quality feed for a reasonable amount of money. When formulating a ration, it is wise to avoid future complications, over-rich feeds, and to use the best available sources of energy in balancing the diet. Sometimes a high-energy feed of low cost can be substituted with equal or better effect for a higher cost feed on a cost per unit of digestible energy basis. Also, it is desirable to know which feeds are the best energy sources in addition to their other nutrient value. A ration for a highly productive horse or a hard working horse must contain sufficient digestible energy in the quantity of feed that the horse can comfortably consume in a day.

## Summary

Energy is necessary to maintain body tissues, provide body heat, and to allow growth, reproduction, lactation, and work capacity. By quantitatively measuring the amount of energy in a feed, it is possible to balance a ration which provides the proper amount of energy for a given need. There are two main systems for measuring feed energy. These are the Total Digestible Nutrients method, which gives the percentage of energy contained in a feed, and the caloric systems of measurement. While adequate satisfaction of energy requirements for a given horse can usually be determined by monitoring body weight and condition, energy measurement provides for scientific optimization of ration contents by availability, quality, and cost of feeds, and allows consideration of the limitations of digestive physiology in the horse.

## REFERENCES CITED

1. Crampton, E. W., and Harris, L. E., **Applied Animal Nutrition.** W. H. Freeman and Company, San Francisco, (1969)
2. Morrison, Frank B., **Feeds and Feeding, Abridged, Ninth Edition.** The Morrison Publishing Company, Claremont, Ontario, Canada, (1958)
3. Morrison, Frank B., **Op. Cit.**
4. Guthrie, Helen Andrews, **Introductory Nutrition.** The C. V. Mosby Company, Saint Louis, (1971)
5. Morrison, Frank B., **Op. Cit.**
6. Crampton, E. W., and Harris, L. E., **Op. Cit.**

# 8

# Grains:
# Oats and Corn

Of the many different varieties of grain fed to horses, oats and corn
are by far the most common. This is due not only to availability and costs,
but to other factors as well.

## Advantages of Feeding Oats

Oats are the most commonly fed grain for horses in the United States
today, and they form the basis for many feeding programs. Why is this
true? First, oats are highly palatable. They appeal to almost all horses
without exception. Normally, the only cases in which oats are refused is
when they are of poor quality and should not have been fed in the first
place. Oats are highly digestible also. They contain about seventy percent or more of Total Digestible Nutrients. (1) The protein content is
approximately twelve percent. This compares favorably with other
grains. If they are cut at the proper stage, when they are plump, heavy,
and fully ripe, oats have fairly good keeping qualities if they are still in
whole form and have not been crushed. Oats contain a moderate amount
of fiber, about twelve percent, so they are not overly rich and are safe to
feed horses. This is probably the biggest reason for their popularity with
horsemen. Finally, the price of oats, when compared to the quantity and
quality of nutrients they contain and the other grains that might be substituted is usually reasonable.

## Judging the Quality of Oats

The best oats are plump, heavy, clean, ripe, and have a low proportion

*Equine Research Publications Staff Photo*

## CHEATING?

Old, dirty, poor quality oats exposed to too much moisture, mixed with average quality oats. This doesn't happen too often, but should you ever purchase such a mix, the fact should be brought to the attention of your feed dealer in direct and uncompromising terms.

of husk to kernel. They should appear bright in color. Oats are most commonly white, but they may also be black or gray, depending on the locale in which they were grown, and the particular variety. Contrary to popular opinion among many horsemen, the color does not affect the quality of the oat, and a gray or black oat should not be considered inferior **if that is its natural color.** (2)

The cleanliness of the oat is of great importance. Oats should be cleaned and recleaned several times at the mill where they are processed. This removes foreign materials, weed seeds, and broken or inferior kernels. The presence of dust in the oats may indicate that they have aged. Since aging destroys vitamins and increases perishability, dusty oats should not be considered to be of high quality. Dust may also indicate that the oats were not properly cleaned, or have been stored without sufficient protection. Dusty feeds may aggravate a tendency toward heaves and other congestive problems. This is another reason that dusty oats should not be purchased.

Weight is an important factor in judging the quality of oats. The higher the weight per bushel, the greater the proportion of kernel to husk. Since the main nutrient content of the oats is contained in the kernel, it is obvious that heavier oats will be more nutritious. Oats which have a large percentage of husk, are higher in fiber and lower in energy. Oats may be clipped to increase their weight. In this process, the points of the oat husks are clipped off by a special machine and separated by a blast of air. This removes more of the fiber, and raises the weight per bushel.

So-called "race horse oats" are top quality oats which normally have a weight of forty-two pounds per bushel or more. These oats are better oats for all horses, not just race horses. They received their name merely because they were of the high quality that top race trainers require. These oats generally should be considered to be the very best quality available.

Oats weighing up to fifty pounds per bushel may occasionally be found. Any oats weighing less than thirty-five pounds per bushel cannot be considered to be very good quality. More oats will have to be fed to produce the same results, and the price should be proportionately lower. However, even with lower price you still must sacrifice nutrient quality with the oat of lower weight. When choosing oats, it is best to buy the top weight available, and the cleanest possible. This may mean having them shipped in, rather than buying from local dealers, but it will generally prove to be worth the extra effort where the cost is not prohibitive. Since oats must generally be bought in carload lots when they are special ordered, it may be possible either to find a dealer who will handle this, or

*Equine Research Publications Staff Photo*

Top-quality "race horse oats" with clipped ends on right, (weight 42 lbs. per bushel). Average-quality oats on left, with unclipped ends, (weight 34 lbs. per bushel). The difference in these oats escape the scrutiny of many average horsemen.

to form a co-op with other horsemen in your area. Another advantage of buying top quality oats is that since their nutrient content is higher, lesser amounts of the top quality grains may need to be fed to produce the same results. In any case, the difference in price per ration will not be great. A slight increase in price when buying top quality grains usually pays for itself many times over in increased performance.

The smell is another consideration in choosing a good oat. High quality grains will smell fresh. There will be no musty odor associated with them. Mustiness indicates age and/or the presence of too much moisture. Both of these factors represent poor keeping quality.

Finally, the appearance of the individual kernel itself is important. It should be plump and firm. Large kernels indicate high feeding value. Tasting a few of the kernels yourself will also help determine whether or not they are of high quality. There should be no sour or bitter taste associated with them.

## Methods of Feeding Oats

Oats may be fed either whole or processed. The different methods of processing include crushing, crimping, and steam-rolling. For many years, horsemen have debated the merits of processed oats compared to whole oats. While there are valid arguments for both sides, after careful consideration it is generally concluded that whole oats are more advantageous.

Whole oats are the natural form of a nutritious, easily digestible grain. They are palatable, nourishing, and have good keeping qualities in their natural state. Unlike other grains, such as barley, oats can be easily chewed and properly digested without additional processing. It is true that processing the oat breaks the outer coating of the grain, and makes the kernel and the nutrients it contains more accessible to the digestive juices of the horse. This reduces chewing requirements slightly, and may increase the digestibility of the oats by a small amount, up to about five percent. (3) However, it also exposes these nutrients to the deteriorating effects of the air. The aging process of the grain is accelerated, and the nutrients are lost more rapidly. (4)

While it is true that when whole oats are fed a few of the kernels will pass through the horse undigested, this does not substantially lower the amount of nutrients ingested. When oats are processed they begin to lose nutrients. Vitamins, for example, may rapidly be depleted. The concentrate ration as a result may then become deficient in a few essential components. Thus, the digestibility of processed grains is increased initially, but this advantage is lost as nutrients become depleted. Further, the processed oats are more subject to fermentation and deterioration, with

Kelso, the world's money-winningest Thoroughbred, with earnings of $1,977,896.00, is shown driving to the wire in one of the many outstanding races which earned him "Horse of the Year" honors for five straight years.

**High quality steam-rolled oats often appear as palatable as oatmeal for human consumption.**

subsequent loss in palatability and quality. When processed oats are fed, a good rule of thumb would be to feed them within two to three weeks of processing.

Unless grains are processed on the premises where they are to be fed, their freshness cannot be guaranteed. Further, processing of oats significantly increases their cost. This cost is not offset by the slight and temporary increase in feeding value. Some processed oats are flavored with molasses. Since oats are highly palatable, this is unnecessary, and might serve to disguise the flavor of poor quality oats.

The consensus of modern thought would seem to conclude that processing of oats is not necessary. Only in a few extreme cases, such as horses of advanced years whose teeth are of such poor quality as to be unable to chew properly, or with animals recovering from illness that may be too weak to chew feed sufficiently, are processed oats of any great advantage. And then it is necessary to ensure that they are absolutely fresh. But in lieu of special problems, whole oats in their natural form are generally recommended. When oats are processed, the best method would seem to be coarse crimping.

## Nutrient Value of Oats

Oats contain between twelve and thirteen percent protein on the average (calculated by weight). (5) This protein is not complete, but is superior to the protein in corn. Oats contain about eleven to twelve percent fiber, **but this varies greatly with weight.** Laboratory analysis is useful in determining the actual proportion of husk to fiber when this information is required. This is done by husking a number of oats,and weighing the husks and kernels separately.

Oats contain about 1300 to 1400 kilocalories per pound, which is moderately high for the cereal grains. The carbohydrate content is about sixty percent on the average. (6) Oats are low in calcium, and moderately low in phosphorus. Oats contain virtually no carotene, and are not a good source of B vitamins. If they are cut when fully ripe, the moisture content is about ten percent.

## Other Facts

Oats are grasses of the cereal group. There are numerous varieties, and they may be grown throughout the world. The best varieties are grown in cool, moist climates, such as the American Northwest. (7) These oats tend to be higher in weight and nutrient value than oats grown in warmer climates. Oats may be home grown for feeding without great difficulty, but unless the climate is ideal, as previously discussed, there will be a sacrifice in quality. Good soil and adequate fertilization are also

### HOW TO DETERMINE OATS ARE DUSTY

Oats being poured from one bucket to another, at a height of approximately two feet. (There is almost as much dust here as oats!)

*photo courtesy of M. J. Pritchard Inc.*

Oats should be checked and re-checked many times throughout the growing season to protect against disease and to make certain they are harvested at the proper time.

required. Oats may also be grown for a hay crop. When grown for hay, they should be cut at the soft-dough stage, which is the point at which the seeds are fully formed, but are not yet mature and hard. (8) When oats are grown for grain, they should not be cut until they are fully ripe and the straw is no longer green.

## Advantages of Feeding Corn

Corn is the most widely grown cereal grain in the United States today, and is second only to oats in its use as a feed grain for horses. Corn is a very high energy feed because it contains a large amount of carbohydrates. It can easily be grown for local use since it grows well throughout the United States and is relatively inexpensive to grow. Corn is very low in fiber, making it a highly concentrated feed. Care must be taken not to overfeed corn when it is first introduced into a horse's diet. It is highly recommended that small amounts are fed at first, with gradual increases over a period of time. A sufficient amount to represent a good ratio to other grains fed, can generally be reached safely in 3 to 4 weeks.

## Judging the Quality of Corn

Corn is judged primarily by its moisture content and the percentage of unsound kernels it contains. The class of corn usually fed to horses is dent corn, which gets its name because the mature kernel has a dent in the surface when it dries. Although there are seven classes of corn in all grown in the United States, the use of the other varieties as a feed is not common, even though they do not vary greatly from dent corn in composition. The color of corn may range from white to yellow, and this does not affect the quality so long as the corn is ripe and does not have a pronounced green color. However, yellow corn has a higher vitamin A content.

Naturally, the higher the quality of the corn, the fewer damaged kernels it will contain. This can be determined easily by visual inspection of the grains. The kernels should be plump, firm, and separated, but they should not be too hard. Very hard corn is difficult to chew, and may pass through the alimentary canal undigested. Corn may be bought either on the ear or in shelled form. If it is shelled, it requires much less storage space, but it is more perishable and should be protected from light and moisture. Corn which shows signs of insect damage or mold should not be bought under any circumstances. Since the grain is high in starch, it can ferment rapidly if damaged, and will become toxic. A musty odor indicates a high moisture content which increases perishability.

**Even when it's not the very best quality, it is still an excellent source of energy.**

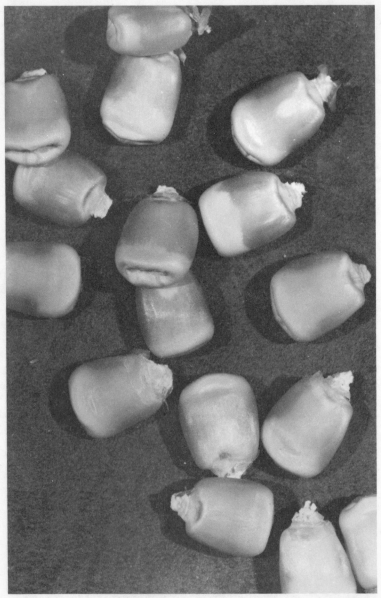

**Now you know where the term "dent" corn came from.**

An excellent "close-up" of properly-cracked yellow dent corn. (*Photo 2¼ times actual size.*)

# Methods of Feeding Corn

Corn may be fed on the cob, in whole shelled kernel form, or it may be cracked or crushed. It should never be finely ground. When it is fed in whole ears, horses tend to chew it more slowly and mix it with saliva more thoroughly before swallowing it. This increases the percentage of nutrients assimilated. Whole ears will also keep much longer than shelled or processed corn. These advantages are offset to a great degree, however, by the much greater amount of storage required for whole ear corn. This increases costs, and may not justify the slight increase in nutrient value. Since horses will eat shelled or processed corn more rapidly than whole ear corn, the tendency to colic may increase slightly, and animals should be carefully watched when corn is first added to their diet. Aged horses with dental problems may be unable to satisfactorily digest ear corn or whole shelled corn, and processing may be necessary for these animals.

Most commonly, corn is crushed or cracked before feeding. This greatly increases digestibility. It lowers keeping quality somewhat, but if the moisture content is tested and found to be below fourteen percent, or if there is air circulation through storage bins, this should not be a problem. Cracked corn is the superior variety of these two. It is rolled lightly with heavy rollers to crack the outside of the kernel, allowing penetration of the digestive juices and easier mastication, but the kernels are not fully broken, and thus, not nearly so subject to deterioration. Also, it should be mentioned, when corn is crushed or ground, the particles are smaller. This increases the tendency for rapid fermentation in the digestive tract, **and the possibility of colic.** Unless one is dealing with a horse which has extremely poor teeth or some digestive problem, cracked corn is sufficiently processed for easy digestion. Occasionally, corn is ground and mixed with ground cobs as a feed for horses. This increases the fiber content, and lowers the energy and overall nutrient value.

# Nutrient Value of Corn

The composition of corn may vary greatly within different regions of the United States, due to differences in the soil. If bought from a reputable, and quality conscious feed company, rather than home-grown however, it should be fairly standard in value. If it is home-grown, it should be laboratory tested for nutrient content. Corn is a valuable ingredient in the total ration even though it is a low protein feed, containing only about ten percent protein. In addition, this protein is of low quality because it is deficient in several essential amino acids, notably lysine.

**THREE CHOICES**

Whole, shelled, yellow dent corn (top left), cracked yellow dent corn (top right), and finely ground yellow dent corn (bottom). Corn in top left is very popular, corn in top right is very digestible, finely ground corn, at bottom, is very conducive to digestive upset.

And, the amount of protein in hybrid corn may be lower due to higher yields, and heavier planting rates. If corn is used as the primary grain in a ration, a protein supplement or high-protein hay should always be added. This is especially true for the growing foal and the young horse, where protein requirements are very high.

Corn is extremely low in fiber, having a fiber content of from two to two and one-half percent. This makes it highly digestible, and very rich. It contains from sixty-five to seventy-five percent starch, which is a higher percentage than other cereal grains. It has a caloric value of approximately 1800 kilocalories per pound, depending on the variety. Corn is also high in fat, containing about four percent. It is the only cereal grain which can supply significant amounts of vitamin A. This is due to the high carotene content, indicated by the yellow color of the corn. It supplies a moderate quantity of vitamin E, and it is a good source of thiamine, niacin, and riboflavin.

For many years, horsemen have considered corn to be a "hot" feed. Many have felt that it is too rich to feed except in winter, and that it will cause a horse to overheat or sweat. It is true that corn is a "hot" feed, from the standpoint that it is very high in energy, but this does not mean that it causes the horse to feel hot, or raises body temperature (unless of course the horse is overfed and becomes too fat). Corn has the highest energy content of the cereal grains. However, this should be considered an advantage rather than a disadvantage. It requires about fifteen to twenty percent less corn to yield the same amount of energy as a given measure of oats.

Whenever too much energy is fed, in whatever form, it may cause weight gain and digestive upset. But this is caused by overfeeding, rather than by the use of a particular grain. It does not cause a rise in body temperature in any case. Corn can be fully utilized as the excellent source of energy that it is, on a year-round basis.

## Other Facts

Corn grows easily on fertile, well-drained loam. It is generally grown in a crop rotation system, but this is not always necessary if the soil is carefully prepared. It is subject to numerous pests and blights. There are over a thousand varieties of corn grown in the United States today. (10) These may be divided into seven categories. Dent corn is the category generally used for livestock feeding. Corn should be harvested when it is fully ripe, and must be dried slightly before storing. It should never be stored until the moisture content is below fourteen percent.

# Summary

Corn and oats are the two most common feeding grains for horses in this country. Oats are considered to be an all-purpose feed for horses because they are moderately high in protein (compared to other cereal grains), they are palatable, easily digestible, moderate in price, and have good keeping quality. Oats should be judged on weight and appearance. A good oat is heavy, ripe, bright, plump, and clean. Oats may be fed in their natural state, or they may be coarsely processed. Processing is not necessary except for horses with dental or digestive problems. Oats are moderately high in energy, and are a fair source of protein. They are not a good source of vitamins. Oats may be grown throughout the country, but are of highest quality where the climate is cool and moist.

Corn is the most commonly grown grain in the United States today. It should be low in moisture, not too hard, and contain few damaged kernels. It may be fed whole, shelled, or cracked. Cracked corn has many advantages. Corn is the only cereal grain which contains a significant amount of vitamin A. It is a poor quality source of protein. It should not be considered a "hot" feed, but should be appreciated for its high energy value. Corn is easily grown throughout the country, and there are more than a thousand varieties in the seven classes.

## REFERENCES CITED

1. Morrison, Frank B., **Feeds and Feeding, Abridged, Ninth Edition.** The Morrison Publishing Company, Claremont, Ontario, Canada, (1958)
2. Hayes, M. Horace, F.R.C.V.S., **Stable Management and Exercise.** Arco Publishing Company, Inc., New York, (1968)
3. Morrison, Frank B., **Op. Cit.**
4. Montgomery, E. S., **The Thoroughbred.** Arco Publishing Company, Inc., New York, (1971)
5. Morrison, Frank B., **Op. Cit.**
6. Morrison, Frank B., **Op. Cit.**
7. United States Department of Agriculture, **Crops in Peace and War, the Yearbook of Agriculture, 1950 — 1951.** Government Printing Office, Washington, D.C., (1951)
8. National Research Council, **Nutrient Requirements of Horses.** National Academy of Sciences — National Research Council, Washington, D.C., (1973)
9. Morrison, Frank B., **Op. Cit.**
10. Seiden, Dr. Rudolph, **The Handbook of Feedstuffs.** Springer Publishing Company, Inc., New York, (1957)

# 9

# Other Grains

In addition to oats and corn, there are several other grains which are fed to horses. Each of these has different characteristics, and may be valuable under different circumstances.

## Barley

Barley is the most widely grown grain crop in the world today, and the fourth most common crop grown in the United States. (1) A few horsemen find it useful as a primary grain for their horses, because it is inexpensive, readily available, and plentiful in most areas of the United States, except in hot, humid climates.

Barley is comparable to oats in many respects, as it contains about twelve percent protein, and the fiber content usually ranges from five to six percent. As with oats, the lower the fiber content, the smaller the percentage of husk to kernel, and the higher the nutritive value. Good barley should be clean, heavy, ripe, and free from weed seeds and foreign material. The husk should be small and light, and the kernels should appear full and plump. Many other nutrient values of barley also resemble oats, except that barley is higher in niacin and can be considered a fairly good source of this vitamin.

Barley is relatively low in fiber, and is commonly classified as a "heavy" feed. That is, it is low in bulk, very compact, and can upset the digestive system. These are the probable reasons why barley has not replaced oats as a concentrate. If barley is not crushed or ground, it is hard to digest. And, when it is crushed or ground, it should be mixed with a bulkier feed so that it does not cause a tendency to colic. (2) Barley is occasionally fed in steam-rolled form, and is often included as an ingredi-

The pellet, (in center), contains the ingredients surrounding it. Cottonseed meal (top left), heavy oats (top right), yellow dent corn (bottom right), and wheat bran (bottom left).

ent in "sweet" feeds where it does not form a major part of the ration. Barley may tend to be less palatable than oats for horses which are not used to it, and it may be desirable to mix it gradually with the feed in increasing proportions until the horses become accustomed to its taste.

In areas where it is available and inexpensive, barley may also be fed to horses in the form of malt sprouts or brewer's solubles. These are by-products of the brewing industry. However, since they have been processed and much of the carbohydrate is extracted into the beer, brewer's by-products have a relatively low feeding value and nutrient content. They should not form a large part of the concentrate ration for this reason. However, they may be satisfactorily used in combination with higher protein feeds.

# Wheat

Wheat is a highly important grain for human consumption, but it is not widely fed to horses in this country. It is also, like barley, a "heavy" feed. The main reason that its use for horses is limited is that it is generally processed for flour, and only the by-products are available. It is almost never fed to animals in the whole-kernel form, since the cost of purchasing it in this form would be prohibitive. The two forms of wheat which are usually used are wheat bran and wheat middlings. The bran is the shiny, dark-colored coating of the wheat kernel. It is highly laxative and is frequently fed to horses on a regular basis for this reason. It is extremely high in phosphorus, containing about 1.3 percent. It should contain about eleven to thirteen percent digestible protein, between four and five percent fat, and a moderate amount of fiber (about ten percent or more). Bran is sometimes fed in the form of a mash, but it is more commonly mixed with other feeds. Since it is ground or crushed, it is difficult to judge the quality by its appearance. It should, however, be clean, and should not have a musty odor. Bran should never be considered a primary feed for a horse, and in fact should form only a small part of the grain ration. It may be considered a useful feed both because of its laxative effect, and for its phosphorus content.

Wheat middlings are more valuable as a general purpose grain than wheat bran. Middlings are the fine particles of the wheat kernel obtained in the milling process. (3) They must contain ten percent or less of crude fiber, depending on the variety. They are higher than whole wheat in protein, since the husk portion of the grain is not included, and they are a good source of niacin and vitamins $B_1$ and $B_2$. However, they do not have the laxative effects of wheat bran.

Because wheat middlings are fine and powdery, it is hard to judge their quality by appearance. Another factor worth mention, is their tend-

*photo courtesy of ADM Grain Company*

**Top quality wheat is cultivated for many uses: grain, hay, straw, etc. Wheat bran is the most popular use of wheat in horse rations.**

ency to pack in the stomach and cause digestive disturbances if they are not mixed with a coarse, bulky feed. These factors, together with their somewhat limited availability, are the probable reasons that wheat middlings are not more widely fed. It is possible to obtain the same nutrients more easily from other grains without the side effects.

# Rye

Rye is another member of the cereal grain family. Generally speaking, the drawbacks associated with rye are the same as those for wheat. Rye is grown as a crop for the milling industry, to be made into flour for human consumption. The only available rye products for livestock feeding, in most cases, are the mill by-products, and these are usually only available in the milling area. When rye is fed, it is most commonly in the form of rye middlings. These are the fine particles of the kernel left after the whole rye grain is milled into flour. Rye middlings are relatively low in fiber and must be fed in the fine, ground form. Like wheat middlings, therefore, they are usually extended with a bulky feed to promote ease of digestion. Rye middlings are not a good source of any vitamins or minerals in particular, and their digestible protein content (twelve to thirteen percent) can be matched by other grains that are more palatable and otherwise more nutritious. For this reason, rye is not particularly recommended as a feed unless local availability makes it superior in cost per unit of nutritive value.

# Milo

The only other grain used in large amounts as a feed for horses is milo. Milo is a sorghum grain. It is a low-growing plant which has heavy heads when it ripens, and ranges from yellow to white in color. The more yellow varieties have slightly higher amounts of carotene.

The protein content of milo may vary from 8 to 16 percent. However, its protein content is only about nine percent in most cases. It is very low in fiber (less than three percent), and contains only about three percent fat. Since it is high in carbohydrates, about seventy-five percent, it is considered to be a high energy feed. However, it cannot be considered a good source of vitamins or minerals.

The main consideration when using milo is that it is a heavy feed, and must be fed carefully to avoid colic and founder. Many horses find it difficult to chew, and it is relatively low in palatability for most horses. On a comparative nutritional basis, milo is similar to corn in its content except that it contains less carotene. It is slightly less palatable than corn however, and unless it is considerably lower in price than corn in a particular area, corn would be a preferable substitute.

A popular "sweet feed" from a major feed company with some of the ingredients in pelleted form.

## Other Concentrates

The listed grains; oats, corn, barley, wheat, rye, and milo are the prevalent grains fed in this country as part of the concentrate ration. Many other substances have been mixed into the concentrate ration for one reason or other, but with no real nutritive benefit. These include peanut hulls, mesquite beans, buckwheat, vegetables, and many different substances. An adequate, reasonably priced, and highly nutritious concentrate ration can be easily formulated from the listed cereal grains, however, and the addition of any other feed substances can only provide the same nutrients at higher cost, or a reduced nutritional quality.

## Summary

Although corn and oats are by far the most commonly fed cereal grains, several others are also widely used, and may have a valid place in the ration. These include barley, milo, wheat, and rye. Barley is comparable to oats except that it is slightly harder to digest. It is the third most common feeding grain for horses. Wheat and rye are usually available only as by-products of the milling industry, so they are not usually fed as the major portion of the concentrate ration. An exception is wheat bran, which is often fed regularly for its laxative effects. Milo is comparable to corn in content, but it is lower in carotene and harder to digest unless cracked or flaked. Any other feeds which might be included in the concentrate ration would be lower in quality for price, and would not have any beneficial effects which cannot be found in the common cereal grains.

### REFERENCES CITED

1. Morrison, Frank B., **Feeds and Feeding, Abridged, Ninth Edition.** The Morrison Publishing Company, Claremont, Ontario, Canada, (1958)
2. Morrison, Frank B., **Op. Cit.**
3. Seiden, Dr. Rudolph, **The Handbook of Feedstuffs.** Springer Publishing Company, Inc., New York, (1957)

**Top Deck, a Thoroughbred son of Equestrian, influenced the running Quarter Horse industry in legendary fashion through his siring accomplishments.**

# COMPOSITION OF POPULAR GRAINS USED IN HORSE RATIONS*

| GRAIN | DRY MATTER (%) | DIGESTIBLE ENERGY (Calories per lb.) | FIGURED ON A DRY BASIS (moisture free) | | | | | | | | |
| | | | TDN (%) | CRUDE FAT (%) | PROTEIN (%) | DIG. PROTEIN (%) | SOLUBLE CARBOHYDRATE (%) | CRUDE FIBER (%) | CALCIUM (%) | PHOSPHORUS (%) | ASH (%) |
|---|---|---|---|---|---|---|---|---|---|---|---|
| BARLEY (overall avg.) | 89.0 | 1660 | 83. | 1.9 | 13.0 | 8.2 | 67.2 | 6.7 | .09 | .47 | 3.4 |
| U.S. #1 mn. wt. 47 lbs. per bushel | 89.0 | ---- | -- | 2.1 | 13.6 | 8.7 | 67.2 | 5.6 | .27 | .41 | 2.9 |
| U.S. #3 mn. wt. 43 lbs. per bushel | 88.0 | ---- | -- | 2.0 | 13.4 | 8.5 | 66.5 | 6.8 | .06 | .39 | 3.0 |
| U.S. #5 mn. wt. 36 lbs. per bushel | 88.0 | ---- | -- | 2.3 | 11.7 | 6.9 | 62.7 | 11.4 | --- | --- | 3.7 |
| Pacific coast | 89.0 | 1642 | 82. | 2.1 | 10.9 | 6.2 | 69.2 | 7.0 | .07 | .45 | 2.7 |
| CORN (overall avg.) | 87.0 | 1819 | 91. | 4.7 | 10.9 | 8.5 | 74.7 | 2.4 | --- | --- | 1.6 |
| ground ears | 87.0 | 1560 | 78. | 4.0 | 9.3 | 4.6 | ---- | 9.2 | .05 | .31 | 1.7 |
| #2 Dent Yellow mn. wt. 54 lbs. per bushel | 89.0 | 1819 | 91. | 4.6 | 10.0 | 5.3 | 74.7 | 2.2 | .02 | --- | 1.4 |
| COTTONSEED MEAL solv-extd, 41 % protein | 91.5 | 1501 | 75. | 1.0 | 44.8 | 38.4 | 25.2 | 13.1 | .17 | 1.31 | 7.0 |
| LINSEED MEAL mech-extd | 91.0 | 1619 | 81. | 5.6 | 38.8 | 32.6 | ---- | 9.9 | .48 | .98 | 6.2 |
| MILO (Sorghum Milo) (overall avg.) | 89.0 | 1601 | 80. | 3.2 | 12.4 | 7.6 | 74.8 | 2.2 | .04 | .33 | 8.1 |
| OATS (overall avg.) | 89.0 | 1402 | 70. | --- | 13.3 | 8.4 | 51.6 | 13.2 | .09 | .33 | 3.0 |
| U.S. #1 Heavy mn. wt. 36 lbs. per bushel | 89.0 | ---- | -- | 5.8 | 14.2 | 10.2 | ---- | 10.0 | --- | --- | 3.0 |
| U.S. #1 mn. wt. 34 lbs. per bushel | 91.0 | 1402 | 70. | --- | 13.3 | 8.4 | 51.6 | 13.2 | .09 | .33 | 3.0 |

**OATS (continued)**

| | | | | | | | | | | |
|---|---|---|---|---|---|---|---|---|---|---|
| U.S. #2 mn. wt. 32 lbs. per bushel | 89.0 | 1402 | 70. | --- | 13.2 | 8.3 | 51.3 | 12.4 | .07 | .30 | 3.7 |
| U.S. #4 mn. wt. 27 lbs. per bushel | 91.2 | 1302 | 65. | --- | 12.7 | 7.9 | 46.4 | 16.5 | --- | --- | 4.9 |
| Pacific coast | 91.2 | 1402 | 70. | 5.9 | 9.9 | 5.2 | 52.4 | 12.1 | .10 | .36 | 4.1 |
| Rolled oats | 90.7 | --- | --- | 6.5 | 18.1 | 13.8 | --- | 2.5 | .09 | .47 | 2.3 |
| Groats | 91.0 | 1678 | 84. | 6.6 | 18.4 | 13.3 | 53.9 | 3.3 | .08 | .47 | 2.4 |

**OATS, WHITE**

| | | | | | | | | | | |
|---|---|---|---|---|---|---|---|---|---|---|
| Canadian #2 mn. wt. 36 lbs. per bushel | 86.5 | 1402 | 70. | 5.0 | 13.2 | 8.3 | --- | 12.0 | .09 | .38 | 3.5 |

**RYE**

| | | | | | | | | | | |
|---|---|---|---|---|---|---|---|---|---|---|
| (overall avg.) | 88.2 | --- | --- | 1.7 | 12.8 | 8.9 | --- | 2.3 | .08 | .39 | 2.0 |
| middlings (fine sift) | 90.6 | --- | --- | 3.9 | 18.2 | 13.9 | --- | 4.6 | --- | --- | 3.6 |

**SOYBEAN MEAL**

| | | | | | | | | | | |
|---|---|---|---|---|---|---|---|---|---|---|
| solv-extd, 7% fiber | 89.0 | 1601 | 80. | 1.3 | 51.5 | 44.7 | 27.7 | 6.7 | .36 | .75 | 6.6 |
| solv-extd, w/o hulls, 3% fiber | 89.8 | 1678 | 84. | 1.2 | 56.7 | 49.7 | --- | 3.2 | .29 | .69 | 6.5 |

**WHEAT**

| | | | | | | | | | | |
|---|---|---|---|---|---|---|---|---|---|---|
| grain, (overall avg.) | 89.0 | 1760 | 88. | 2.1 | 14.3 | 9.4 | 72.1 | 2.8 | .09 | .41 | 2.1 |
| bran, dry milled | 89.0 | 1166 | 65. | 4.8 | 18.0 | 12.9 | 48.2 | 11.2 | .16 | 1.32 | 6.7 |
| middlings, 4% fiber | 89.0 | 1701 | 85. | 3.9 | 20.2 | 15.0 | --- | 2.2 | .09 | .58 | 2.8 |

**YEAST, BREWERS**

| | | | | | | | | | | |
|---|---|---|---|---|---|---|---|---|---|---|
| dehy. grnd., mn. 40% protein | 93.0 | 1402 | 70. | 1.1 | 47.9 | 41.3 | --- | 3.2 | .14 | 1.54 | 7.4 |
| irradiated, dehy. | 94.0 | 1338 | 67. | 1.2 | 51.2 | 44.4 | --- | 6.5 | .83 | 1.36 | 6.6 |

* Data derived from *Nutrient Requirements of Horses*, National Research Council, 1973, and *Atlas of Nutritional Data on United States and Canadian Feeds*, National Academy of Sciences, 1971

# 10

# High Protein Concentrates

In most cases, cereal grains and average quality hay will not provide enough protein in the diet of the growing horse, pregnant or lactating mare, and performance horses in high-stress situations. For these horses, it becomes necessary to balance the ration with the addition of a protein supplement.

## Amounts of Protein to Feed

Protein is the nutrient most often lacking in the diet of the growing, pregnant, lactating, or working horse. (1) It is an essential component of healthy tissue, and a horse with insufficient protein in the diet will lack good muscle development. It is also an essential component for a healthy, glossy hair coat.

Foals may require as much as eighteen to twenty percent protein in the diet to support their rapid growth rates. Thirteen to sixteen percent is desirable for the yearling, twelve to fourteen percent for the two year old, and about twelve percent for mature horses. Additional allowances should be made in mature horses for breeding, gestation, lactation, and heavy performance requirements.

Excess protein in the ration is converted to energy, and extreme care should be taken to meet the individual protein requirements of each horse. This is essential for good health and top performance. However, protein is an expensive and inefficient method of providing energy, and a well-balanced ration will not include protein in such excess that it will be used to meet energy requirements. Small excesses of protein are not dangerous to the horse. However, extremely large amounts of protein, such as rations containing thirty percent or more total protein, may cause metabolic stress and digestive disturbances.

# Soybean Meal

The most commonly fed protein supplement is soybean meal, also called soybean oil meal. It is the by-product of the soybean oil industry. The whole soybeans are the richest in protein of all the common seed feeds, averaging about thirty-four percent protein. (2) However, these whole beans are not usually fed to horses. They contain a trypsin inhibitor, which prevents the proper breakdown of the amino acids in the protein. This inhibitor is destroyed by the heat used in the oil milling process, and the meal remaining after oil extraction is an excellent, easily digestible source of protein.

Three different processes are used for manufacturing soybean oil, and each produces a slightly different type of soybean meal. These processes are the hydraulic process, the expeller process, and the solvent process.

In the hydraulic process, no longer commonly used, the seed is crushed, cooked, and pressed by hydraulic presses until no more of the oil can be forced out. The resulting cakes are ground into meal. In the expeller process, the soybeans are first cracked and dried, and then cooked by a steam process. The oil is removed from the beans by screw presses. The residue is then ground into meal. The solvent process is the newest and most commonly used of the three. The soybeans are first rolled into flakes by heavy rollers. Then chemical solvents are used to extract all the oil possible from the soybean flakes. The flakes are dried, cooked, and ground into meal.

The soybean meal which results from this oil extraction varies from forty-one to fifty percent protein or more, and the fat content from one and one-half to five percent. (4) Solvent extracted meal is the lowest in fat and highest in protein, and the reverse is true for hydraulic process.

Soybean meal is a good source of phosphorus, a fair source of calcium, and provides moderate amounts of riboflavin and thiamine. Its primary value, however, is as a source of protein. As a protein supplement it has become the most widely used throughout the country. It is highly digestible, low in fiber, readily available, and economical in price per unit of protein. It provides a high quality protein that offsets most of the essential amino acid deficiencies in a grain and hay ration. It must be labeled according to its protein content, and it should have a clean, light colored appearance. It should not taste raw or bitter. It can be readily mixed into

*photo courtesy of ADM Grain Company*

**Soybeans being processed into soybean meal, one of the richest sources of protein for the horse.**

the feed in whatever amounts are necessary to balance the protein content of the ration. Since the texture of soybean meal is finer than cracked or whole grains, extreme care should be used to ensure that the soybean meal is thoroughly blended with the ration.

## Cottonseed Meal

Cottonseed meal, also called cottonseed oil meal, ranks second to soybean meal in its use as a protein supplement in the United States. It is the by-product of the large cotton industry in the South. Extraction methods are similar to those used for soybeam meal. Total protein varies from thirty to forty percent, and the fat content ranges from two to six percent in an inverse relationship to protein. Cottonseed meal is usually higher in fiber than soybean meal, having a fiber content of about eleven percent. It is low in lysine, an essential amino acid, and is not as complete a protein supplement as soybean meal. Cottonseed meal contains gossypol, a chemical substance which may be toxic when fed at high levels. This chemical is largely destroyed by the heat used in the oil extraction process.

## Linseed Meal

Linseed meal (linseed oil meal) is derived from the seed of the flax plant. It contains thirty to thirty-two percent protein and from one to five percent fat. It is not as high in protein quality as soybean meal, however, since it is low in several essential amino acids. In addition to being used as a protein supplement, it is possible that linseed meal has a laxative effect and may also be slightly more beneficial to the appearance of the coat than the other oilseed meals. However, these benefits are somewhat offset by a less favorable palatability factor, and it should be borne in mind that adequate amounts of protein enhance coat appearance, regardless of the protein source.

## General Properties of the Oilseed Meals

All of the oilseed meals are very concentrated since they are low in fiber. They should be fed to offset protein deficiencies and to balance the ration, and excessive amounts should not be fed. It is best to introduce horses to high protein feeds gradually, since sudden intake of large amounts may cause digestive upsets.

Since the oilseed meals do not usually form a large portion of the ration, they cannot be depended upon to supply vitamins or minerals in large quantities. For this reason, they should serve as a supplement to good quality grain rather than a substitute for it.

## The Commercial Protein Supplements

There are many supplements on the market today which are designed to be added to a ration to raise its protein content. There are several methods for judging the quality of these supplements. First, of course, is the reputation of the company. It must be one that has fully tested its product and will stand behind it. It should make no unreasonable claims that cannot be justified or proven. Second is the amino acid quality of the supplement. It should be a complete source of protein. If it is lacking in essential amino acids, the growing or highly productive horse will suffer as a result. Third, the cost should be reasonable for the amount of protein furnished per pound when compared to other supplements on the market. Fourth, it should contain the essentials necessary to balance the diet, but it should not contain unnecessary ingredients. That is, it should not contain large amounts of vitamins and minerals if the diet is already adequate in these respects, but if essential vitamins and minerals are lacking, it would be helpful to purchase a protein supplement that would contain these needed nutrients. Finally, it should be palatable. No matter how high the quality of the supplement, it is worthless if it is not eaten.

## When to Use Protein Supplements

Protein supplements should be used whenever a ration is lower in protein than the required amount for the particular class of horse to which it is fed. The amount to be added is that which will bring the total average protein content of the ration up to the required level. As previously stated, protein supplements should not be used as a substitute for good energy sources and high quality hays. Protein supplements should instead be used as a supplement to increase the protein content of an otherwise well-balanced ration. The particular variety of supplement to be used depends on availability and costs. If one of the oilseed meals is used, soybean meal contains the most complete balance of amino acids when mixed with cereal grain and hay.

## Summary

Protein supplements can be divided into two classes: the raw oilseed meals, and the commercial supplements which contain these. The oilseed meals are primarily soybean meal, cottonseed meal, and linseed meal, although others may be used. They are by-products of the oil-milling industry. They may be produced by any of three processes: the hydraulic method, the expeller method, and the solvent method. Fat and protein content will vary slightly depending on which method is used, but the difference is not significant. Of these meals, soybean meal is the highest in quality. The commercial supplements vary widely, and the user must depend to a large degree on the label and the manufacturer's reputation to judge the quality.

## REFERENCES CITED

1. Bullard, T. L., D.V.M., "Nutrition — Some Basic Thoughts on Horse Feeding," Paper presented to Southwestern Planning Conference for Livestockmen, Waco, Texas, March 1973.
2. Morrison, Frank B., **Feeds and Feeding, Abridged, Ninth Edition.** The Morrison Publishing Company, Claremont, Ontario, Canada, (1958)
3. Seiden, Dr. Rudolph, **The Handbook of Feedstuffs.** Springer Publishing Company, Inc., New York, (1957)
3. Seiden, Dr. Rudolph, **Op. Cit.**

## PROTEIN COMPOSITION OF POPULAR HORSE FEEDS*

| FEED | DRY MATTER (%) | PROTEIN (%) | DIG. PROTEIN (%) | AMINO ACIDS ESSENTIAL TO THE HORSE | | | | | | | | | |
| | | | | Argi-nine (%) | Histi-dine (%) | Isoleu-cine (%) | Leucine (%) | Lysine (%) | Methio-nine (%) | Phenyla-lanine (%) | Threo-nine (%) | Trypto-phan (%) | Valine (%) |
|---|---|---|---|---|---|---|---|---|---|---|---|---|---|
| ALFALFA s-c, (overall avg.) | 91.4 | 17.0 | 12.2 | 0.70 | 0.30 | 0.80 | 1.00 | 0.60 | 0.10 | 0.60 | 0.70 | 0.10 | 0.70 |
| BARLEY grain, (overall avg.) | 89.0 | 13.0 | 8.2 | 0.64 | 0.30 | 0.60 | 0.90 | 0.52 | 0.20 | 0.70 | 0.40 | 0.18 | 0.70 |
| CORN #2 Dent Yellow mn. wt. 54 lbs. per bushel | 89.0 | 10.0 | 5.3 | 0.50 | 0.20 | 0.50 | 1.10 | 0.20 | 0.20 | 0.50 | 0.40 | 0.10 | 0.50 |
| COTTONSEED MEAL solv-extd, 41% protein | 91.5 | 44.8 | 38.4 | 4.79 | 1.12 | 1.32 | 2.38 | 1.74 | 0.54 | 2.20 | 1.33 | 0.53 | 1.80 |
| LINSEED MEAL | 91.0 | 38.8 | 32.6 | 3.51 | ---- | ---- | ---- | 1.32 | 0.71 | ---- | ---- | 0.61 | ---- |
| MILK, (skimmed, dried) | 94.0 | 35.6 | ---- | 1.23 | 0.96 | 2.45 | 3.51 | 2.73 | 0.96 | 1.60 | 1.49 | 0.45 | 2.34 |
| OATS grain, (overall avg.) | 89.0 | 13.2 | 8.3 | 0.64 | 0.10 | ---- | ---- | 0.38 | 0.20 | ---- | ---- | 0.14 | ---- |
| grain, rolled | 90.7 | 18.1 | 13.8 | 1.00 | 0.30 | 0.60 | 1.00 | 0.50 | 0.20 | 0.60 | 0.50 | 0.20 | 0.70 |
| RYE grain, (overall avg.) | 88.2 | 12.8 | 8.9 | 0.64 | 0.30 | 0.60 | 0.80 | 0.53 | 0.21 | 0.70 | 0.40 | 0.14 | 0.70 |
| SOYBEAN MEAL solv-extd | 89.0 | 51.5 | 44.7 | 3.81 | 1.44 | 2.77 | 4.31 | 3.43 | 0.67 | 2.80 | 2.22 | 0.66 | 2.76 |
| WHEAT grain, (overall avg.) | 89.0 | 14.3 | 9.4 | 0.80 | 0.30 | 0.60 | 1.00 | 0.50 | ---- | 0.70 | 0.40 | ---- | ---- |
| bran | 89.0 | 18.0 | 12.9 | 1.12 | 0.34 | 0.67 | 1.01 | 0.67 | 0.11 | 0.56 | 0.45 | 0.34 | 0.79 |
| middlings | 89.0 | 20.2 | 15.0 | 1.01 | 0.45 | 0.89 | 1.34 | 0.79 | 0.20 | 0.73 | 0.67 | 0.22 | 0.89 |
| YEAST, BREWERS dehy/grnd/mn. 40% protein | 93.0 | 47.9 | 41.3 | 2.35 | 1.18 | 2.25 | 3.43 | 3.21 | 0.75 | 1.93 | 2.25 | 0.53 | 2.46 |

*FIGURED ON A DRY BASIS (moisture free)*

* Data derived from Nutrient Requirements of Horses, National Research Council, 1973, and Atlas of Nutritional Data on United States and Canadian Feeds, National Academy of Sciences, 1971

# 11

# Pelleted Feeds

One of the new and popular feed processing methods is pelleting. This consists of taking one particular feed component, or even an entire ration, and processing it into the form of round, oval, or, most commonly, cylindrical pellets. These can then be accurately measured and fed to the horse with little or no waste. They can be compactly stored, easily measured, and most are highly digestible.

## Types of Pelleted Feeds

Pellets are widely produced commercially, and may include any conceivable feed ingredient. Wormers are now available in pelleted form, as are vitamin and protein supplements. Hay may be pelleted, and it is possible to feed the entire ration in pelleted form. Many feed companies do in fact market pelleted feeds that contain a complete ration in one bag.

## The Pelleting Process

Pellets are produced in a pelleting mill. First, ingredients are carefully selected and mixed together in measured amounts. Most companies have highly automated equipment that measures exact amounts of ingredients by weight with computer precision. Formulas are controlled within minute tolerances.

Then, the selected ingredients are carefully mixed together. If they have not been ground, grinding may be done at this point. It is important that ingredients be thoroughly mixed so that each pellet has a uniform content. Molasses may be added to produce a mixture of the desired consistency, and the entire vat is then cooked by a steam process. This makes the pellets resistant to mold and decay and enhances their overall keeping quality. After the mixture is cooked, it is then forced through dies of a given diameter. As the pellets are extruded, they are dried by heating, and are cut off automatically at the desired length. (1)

This automatic process allows high standards of quality control, and uniform distribution of the ingredients in the ration. It may be done economically with modern technology. Pelleting is relatively new to horsemen however, and it remains somewhat controversial as a method of processing feed. Arguments can be presented both for and against the use of pelleted feeds.

## Advantages of Pelleting Feeds

Pelleted feeds are generally highly digestible unless they contain some poor quality roughage. They are compact, easy to store, and are not subject to the spoilage problems of fresh ingredients. For this reason, high quality pelleted feeds are very convenient for the small owner who does not have large storage facilities.

Another advantage of pelleted feeds is simply that they are well mixed. The taste of individual ingredients is not readily apparent, therefore, and horses cannot eat only selected ingredients while leaving others. Also, the addition of molasses may give pellets a desirable flavor of their own. Pelleted feeds often prove to have special usefulness in dealing with the horse which is a picky eater or has a particular dislike for the taste of a necessary ingredient.

One of the greatest uses for pelleted feeds is for the horse with heaves. (2) Since dusty or moldy feeds will greatly aggravate this condition, the use of pelleted feeds may help to alleviate the problem. Pelleting keeps the feed from being dusty, and increases resistance to mold.

Probably the greatest advantage of pelleted feeds, however, is that **if they are of high quality,** they are one of the safest methods of ensuring a standard nutrient content within a ration. That is, the horseman who mixes his own feeds must depend on day to day variance within the ingredients he uses, but pelleted feeds are scientifically tested, and their nutrient content should remain the same for every horse fed from a particular batch. The horseman can be sure of the protein, vitamin, and mineral content that he is feeding, and know that the energy value of a ration does not vary significantly. Each portion from a batch should equal the nutrient content specified on the label.

## Disadvantages of Pelleted Feeds

One problem often associated with the feeding of pelleted feeds is that

**PELLETS OF ALL SIZES**

Pellets pictured are (from top to bottom), large, "all-in-one" concentrate and hay pellet, next is an alfalfa pellet, next another "all-in-one" pellet, next is a popular vitamin supplement pellet, next is a popular high-protein supplement, and last is one of the new wormers in pellet form. (*Photo is 2¼ times actual size.*)

it encourages a horse with tendencies toward cribbing or wood chewing. This problem is usually detected when horses are fed their entire ration in pelleted form. It has been suggested that the problem may be alleviated by feeding a partially pelleted ration. If the concentrates are fed in pelleted form and long hay is fed in its natural state, wood chewing should not be a problem.

Another problem worth consideration is the highly concentrated form of the pellets. For this reason, they tend to expand in the stomach when mixed with saliva. When horses are fed individually in measured amounts, this does not present a problem. However, when several horses are fed from the same trough, or if horses are fed a pelleted ration on a free-choice basis, overeating with resultant problems could possibly occur.

Another problem with pelleted feeds is the cost. Some horsemen find that the advantages of the pelleted ration are not sufficient to offset the increase in cost. This decision is one which must be made by the individual.

Since pelleting involves a heat process, and heat destroys some vitamins, any guaranteed vitamin content analysis on the label should be carefully considered. (Vitamins which are destroyed by heat are covered separately and in detail, in the chapter on vitamins.) If the feed company is reputable, however, there should not be problems in this area, since the normal vitamin content of the feed can easily be supplemented during the pelleting process. However, the horseman should always **carefully** evaluate the feed bag label, regardless of the reputation of the company. Another suggested practice is to compare labels of different companies before a choice is made.

## How to Select a Pelleted Ration

When choosing a pelleted ration, the horseman must first consider which ingredients he wishes to feed in pelleted form. It is probably advantageous to feed all ingredients except the hay in pelleted form, and the hay in its loose, natural state. If good quality hay is fed with pelleted concentrates, the horse is allowed more chewing time, and a greater total quantity of feed, which may give a greater feeling of satiety.

When choosing a particular variety of pellets, the nutrient content of the feed should be checked, and also the reputation of the feed company. Pellets cannot be visually inspected like grains for quality and freshness. The buyer must instead depend on the label. Labeling regulations of the United States Department of Agriculture have made analysis of nutrient content much easier for the buyer, but the reputation of the manufacturer must be relied on for freshness and quality control. Also, it should be remembered that even among reputable companies, **all standards of quality are not the same.**

The large breeder, owner, or trainer may wish to consider formulating his own ration, and having a commercial mill pelletize it for him. In this way, he can process a formula to meet his exact needs, and still retain the advantages of a pelleted feed. It is suggested, however, that the services of a professional nutritionist be utilized in formulating the ration to be pelleted. (Remember, it has been suggested that feeds subjected to the pelleting process require supplementation to maintain the nutritional integrity of the ingredients.)

# Summary

Pelleted feeds are one of the new and popular innovations in the horse industry. They are convenient, and offer certain advantages to the horse owner. If chosen with care from a reliable company, they may meet the complete needs of the average horse, as well as the special case. They offer palatability, ease of storage, and exact certification of nutrient content. It might be suggested, however, that only the concentrate portion of the feed be pelleted, and hay be fed in its natural state.

### REFERENCES CITED

1. The Blood-Horse, **Feeding the Horse.** The Blood-Horse, Lexington, Kentucky, (1969)
2. Ensminger, M.D., Ph.D., **Horses and Horsemanship.** Interstate Printers and Publishers, Inc., Danville, Illinois, (1969)

**12**

# Feed Bag Labels
# And Feed Analysis

When buying a commercial feed mix, whether pelleted or not, the primary measuring tool the horseman has is the feed bag label. This tells him what he is buying, and roughly what he can expect it to do for his horse. He must know how to read the label, what it is required to say, and what it means. He must also learn how to "read between the lines". For instance, he should not be satisfied with knowing the minimum protein content. He should go further, and determine the quality of this protein. In other words, he should check the ingredients to see if they offer a good variety of essential amino acids.

## Requirements of the Feed Bag Label

The primary requirement of the feed bag label is that it show all of the ingredients in the feed. There can be no hidden components, according to United States Department of Agriculture regulations. This is primarily to ensure the safety of the animal. If there is a reaction to a particular type of feed, the ingredients should be known in order to determine what the proper treatment should be. Also, this prevents a company from misleading the public by using fillers or hidden substances. The quality or quantity of many ingredients cannot be determined to any great degree by the label, however, and the consumer must rely on visual examination to verify that the ingredients were actually fresh, wholesome, and top quality. Of course such visual examination is virtually impossible with feeds that have been pelleted. Therefore, more emphasis must be placed on the reputation of the company, and the text of the feed bag label.

The second requirement of the label is a listing of basic nutrient content of the feed. Minimum protein content, minimum fat content, and maximum fiber content *must* all be shown. Minimum and maximum values for calcium and phosphorus and the minimum amounts of each vitamin and mineral found in the feed *should* be displayed.

The third component of a feed bag label is the feeding instructions. Any possible hazards must be listed, and if there are any possible side effects, emergency treatment should be specified.

A careful reading of the feed bag label can show the horseman what the feed should be able to do for his horses. It cannot, however, serve as a guide to standards of quality. It does not guarantee that the ingredients listed are of the highest quality — it only certifies what the ingredients are. It is important to remember, therefore, that label analysis is not the ultimate criterion upon which purchasing decisions should be made. Label analysis must be supported by visual examination, where possible. Another very important test, after you have decided on a particular feed, is the performance, appearance, and the overall health of the animals to which the feed is being fed. If any doubts arise in these areas, perhaps laboratory analysis (explained carefully in Chapter 19) may be in order.

No matter what criteria is used in determining what feeds you purchase, they should look, smell, and taste fresh. They should have no visible damage, foreign material, or molds. They should be manufactured by a company which guarantees its products and will stand behind them. Another good point when trying a new feed mix, is to buy in small quantities at first and test it for palatability before ordering in large amounts. The label cannot guarantee the taste.

## What to Look for on a Feed Label

The first thing to look for on the label is the company name. Whether the company is large or small, it should be either one with which you are familiar, or one with which you may become so through reasonable investigation. No one should be suspicious of a feed company simply because it is new. By the same token, one should not be willing to accept the new brand without reasonable scrutiny.

Second, one should not buy a mix simply because it is claimed it will do "wonderful things for your horses". Read the description of the feed and its purpose. Classify it generally as a protein supplement, sweet feed, etc. Determine where it will fit into your feeding program, and if you actually have a need for it.

Third, read the list of ingredients. Check for hazardous ingredients, low quality substances, fillers, drugs, and thoroughly consider all the components. Determine if there are any ingredients you consider harmful, or you do not want. Determine if there are ingredients (such as minerals), which are normally desirable, but if included in excessive amounts would be harmful. Also, determine if there are ingredients you require, which are lacking. After these careful considerations, then you may determine whether or not the feed fits your feeding program.

Fourth, check the nutrient analysis of the feed carefully. Does it supply adequate amounts of the nutrients that you need? Will the addition of this feed cause a surplus of some ingredient in your feeding program? If so, can you adjust your ration easily to accommodate for this? If not, you must consider another variety of feed. If the feed is pelleted, you must make sure, as was previously mentioned, that the variety and amount of vitamin supplementation is at least equal to the depletion caused from the heating of the ingredients in the pelleting process.

Finally, read the cautionary remarks, if there are any. Also, see if there is any information that you feel is incomplete or lacking. If so, mention it to your dealer, and ask him to look into it for you. Should you fail to gain satisfactory results from this effort, then it would be advisable to contact the feed company direct.

By carefully analyzing the feed bag label, the buyer has a much better chance of getting what he pays for. But even more importantly, he has a better chance of properly feeding the animals in his care. He can make sure that he will balance his feeding ration adequately, and that he will be feeding something of real nutritional benefit.

The feed bag label is not foolproof, and it cannot say everything about the contents of the bag on which it is located. If properly used, however, within the framework of an all-out common sense program of securing the highest quality rations available, it is a valuable tool.

## Summary
There are certain Federal requirements for feed bag labeling. Basic nutrient analysis, all ingredients, feeding instructions, and cautionary measures must be listed. By carefully reading these labels and interpreting them in the light of an entire feeding program, sound buying decisions can be made. While visual analysis of the feed after purchase will always be important, use of the feed bag label can save much time and avoid much waste.

# 13

# Drying, Curing, Storing, And Processing Of Feeds

Proper processing and storage of feedstuffs is essential if quality levels are to be maintained. The horseman needs a basic knowledge of the proper curing and processing methods if he is to recognize and purchase good quality feedstuffs. He must also provide proper storage facilities to prevent the loss of this quality.

## The Effects of Curing on Nutrient Value

Curing is the method by which hay is reduced in moisture content before storing. It is left in the field after it is cut, or stored in a special drying barn, so that the circulation of air removes moisture from the hay until a safe moisture level is reached. The method and rate of curing will greatly affect the appearance and value of the hay.

The major factor in curing hay is that it should be cured as rapidly as possible until it reaches a safe moisture level. Safe moisture levels for storage of hay are considered to be a maximum of twenty-five percent, and preferably between twelve and eighteen percent. (1), (2) If the hay is cured too slowly, especially when it is sun-cured, it loses many vitamins. Even when it is barn-cured slowly, it begins to ferment, and much of the energy value is lost. However, if hay is cured rapidly, most of the nutrient content is retained. Hay should not be cured below recommended moisture levels, because it becomes too dry. When the hay becomes too dry many of the leaves, which contain most of the nutrients, are lost due to shattering. Further, the hay loses palatability.

The merits of sun-cured hay and barn-cured hay are approximately equal. If hay is sun-cured, it has higher vitamin D levels. However, it is more subject to loss of vitamin A, and it may be exposed to the weathering effects of rain. Barn-cured hay, on the other hand, does not have the high vitamin D levels of sun-cured hay, but it retains more vitamin A. It is protected from fading and weathering, but it is more subject to heating and fermentation. It is also higher in price, because it requires more processing facilities.

It is possible to recognize visually most of the characteristics of properly cured hay. It should contain a high proportion of leaves to stems, and it should be clean and free from foreign material. (3) It should have a bright green color indicating that it has not been overcured or weathered, and maximum protein and carotene contents have been preserved. The moisture content of the hay should also be tested. This may be done either with an electronic testing device, or by hand. When testing by hand, a handful of hay should be twisted several times to partially break the stems, and the hay should be placed in a glass jar. A teaspoon of salt should be added, and the lid placed on the jar. The jar should be shaken for thirty seconds, and the salt poured out into the lid. If the hay is below twenty-five percent moisture, the salt will still be granulated, but if the moisture content is higher, the salt will form lumps. (4) Breaking the stems will also indicate overcuring. If the hay is too dry, the stems will break easily. If the moisture content is within the proper range and is not too low, the stems will be somewhat flexible and difficult to break.

## Safe Moisture Levels for Grain

The moisture content for safe grain storage is of vital concern. If the moisture content of the grain is above safe levels, the feed will ferment and mold. Properly dried grains should have a moisture level of ten to twelve percent. Since grain should not be harvested until the moisture level is below twelve or thirteen percent, very little drying should be required to achieve these safe levels. (5) It is always wise to test the moisture content of grains purchased in bulk, especially when they are home-grown or locally grown.

## Proper Storage Facilities

Grains and hays should be stored in a protected area where they will not be affected by wind and rain. If the feedstuffs are to be stored for long periods of time, they should be tightly covered so that they cannot

*photo courtesy of M. J. Pritchard, Inc.*

Crops are cut and put in a windrow formation to allow proper drying before being used as hay, straw, etc.

be affected by moisture. If covered, airtight storage bins are not available for storage, feeds should be bought in small quantities, and long term storage should not be attempted. With age, the flavor and nutrient quality of most feeds begin to deteriorate. Proper storage can minimize these losses, but inadequate facilities can make an entire season's feed worthless in a short time. Feed should also be stored so that it cannot be reached by rodents or insects, and so that it will not be contaminated by pesticides, chemicals, and other foreign substances. Since even well cured, properly stored feed tends to lose five to six percent of its nutrient value in a year, it is recommended that grains and hays not be bought for more than one season at a time. (6) No matter how good storage may be, it cannot guarantee that feed will still be wholesome and palatable after long periods of time.

## Storage of Hay

Special attention should be paid to storage facilities for hay. First, since hay is dense, it is important that the storage area be specifically constructed for hay storage. Beams and flooring must be sound enough to support the total weight. Stronger construction is required for the storage of chopped hay than baled hay, since chopped hay tends to pack more closely and be heavier. (7) Also important for hay storage is proper circulation of air. Because of its density, hay is especially subject to fermentation, molding, and even spontaneous combustion. For this reason, moisture levels and internal temperature of the hay should be frequently checked. Proper ventilation by placing racks under the hay, and by the use of a fan to promote air circulation, will keep the internal temperature of the hay from becoming too high, and will lessen the chances of heating, molding, and combustion.

## Storage of Processed Grains

Processed grains are much more subject to spoilage than whole grains. The kernel coverings have been broken, and the heart of the kernel is exposed to the air. When this happens, the kernel becomes subject to fermentation and molding. Vitamins and energy are lost rapidly. It is most desirable to process grains immediately before feeding, when possible. If this cannot be done, care should be taken that processed grains are very fresh when purchased, and they should be purchased in small quantities and used as rapidly as possible. Processed grains should not be stored for long periods of time without expecting loss of freshness and quality.

# Mashes and Cooked Grains

For many years, horsemen have been preparing elaborate cooked meals for their animals on regular occasions. It was believed that this cooking process in some way increased the nutrient value of the grains, and made digestion easier. Hot mashes were prepared by pouring boiling water over the grain and allowing it to steam. The mash was cooled slightly and fed to the horse. This practice has not completely died out, in fact, bran is still prepared this way by many owners.

The extra time involved in preparing a mash may be worthwhile in the case of an animal with poor teeth, or for a sick horse. A mash requires much less effort in chewing and swallowing. Otherwise, the increase in digestibility is not enough to show a measurable difference. In most cases, horses will eat the grain in its natural state as well as when it is processed into a mash. Cooking does soften small, hard grains, but generally speaking, there is no real increase in feeding value or palatability. (8) And if water is drained from the mash before feeding, some vitamin loss may be expected. Some vitamin loss may be suffered as the result of the heating also.

# Summary

Storing and processing of grains and hay is an important part of the feeding process. It is essential that the horseman be aware of proper processing methods, and know how to recognize feedstuffs that have been correctly processed. Adequate storage facilities that are relatively airtight, pest-proof, and safe from weather are necessary if grain is to be bought in bulk. During storage, it is important that moisture content be below safe levels. Otherwise, heating, molding, fermentation, (and even spontaneous combustion where hay is involved) may result. Overcuring, overdrying, and weathering will cause a loss of quality in grains and hays.

## REFERENCES CITED

1. Morrison, Frank B., **Feeds and Feeding, Abridged, Ninth Edition.** The Morrison Publishing Company, Claremont, Ontario, Canada, (1958)
2. Pratt, J. N., and Novosad, A. C., "Keys to Profitable Hay Production," United States Department of Agriculture, Agricultural Extension Service.
3. Pratt, J. N., and Novosad, A. C., **Op. Cit.**
4. Morrison, Frank B., **Op. Cit.**
5. Hodges, R. J., "Keys to Profitable Small Grain Production in the North Central Texas Area," United States Department of Agriculture, Agricultural Extension Service.
6. Morrison, Frank B., **Op. Cit.**
7. Seiden, Dr. Rudolph, **The Handbook of Feedstuffs.** Springer Publishing Company, Inc., New York, (1957)
8. Morrison, Frank B., **Op. Cit.**

# 14

# The Hays

Hay is the cured material cut from grasses, cereal crops, and legumes. It serves as the main source of roughage in the diet of the horse not on pasture. Hay is high in fiber, and it is not quickly digested. Its bulk helps to move other feeds through the digestive tract by stimulating peristaltic action. Hay may be classified as one of two varieties: grass hay, (which includes the cereal grains), and legume hay. Sun-cured hay furnishes a primary source of vitamin D for horses. It is also high in calcium. Good quality hay contributes significantly to energy, protein, calcium, trace mineral and vitamin content of the horse's ration.

## The Grass Hays

The grass hays include many varieties of grasses and grains. They vary greatly in quality and palatability, depending on the particular variety and the location where it was grown. The grass hays are lower in protein than the legume hays, with a protein content that may be as high as fifteen percent, but averages closer to eight percent or less in most cases. The grass hays may safely be fed free-choice, because of their high fiber content and relatively low nutrient content. This gives them a low Total Digestible Nutrient content, so that they are not too rich. If the hay is of good quality, and not stemmy, there is little likelihood of over-feeding, colic, or founder from feeding unlimited amounts of the grass hays. The only danger is when the hay is moldy, fermented, or weedy, when it may contain toxic compounds, or when it is very coarse and stemmy. However, these would be poor quality hays that should not be fed in the first place, even in small amounts. Grass hays are frequently mixed with legume hays to provide a hay of moderate protein content that is safe to feed freely, high in vitamins, and very palatable.

# Timothy

Timothy is one of the most popular of the grass hays for horsemen. Timothy is average in nutrient content. The best quality timothy is grown in the northern parts of the country. It is especially valuable for horses because it tends to remain free from dust and mold. (1) Timothy is highest in nutrient content, quality, and palatability in the pre-bloom stage, or early bloom stage. (2) With maturity, the grass loses nutrients and becomes higher in fiber. Therefore, it is best to purchase timothy hay which was cut at pre-bloom, or early bloom. Timothy cut at full bloom or after, has lost most of the protein and many of the minerals and vitamins, and is not recommended. One of the reasons that timothy is a popular crop is that it can be harvested over a long period of time, providing several cuttings of hay from the same field in one year. The second and later cuttings are recommended, as they tend to be higher in nutritional value. This is largely due to the higher moisture content of the first cutting. Timothy is frequently grown in a mixture with a legume crop, such as alfalfa or one of the clovers, to increase the protein content and yet retain the freedom from dust and mold that makes timothy advantageous. Like all hays, the nutrient content of timothy varies greatly depending on the cutting and the stage at which it is cut. If cut very·late, after it has gone to seed, the digestible protein content is only 1.9 percent. However, high quality timothy, cut at pre-bloom, second-cutting, has a protein content of 12.3 percent, and a digestible protein content of 6.6 percent. The same hay, cut at mid-bloom or late bloom would have a protein content of 8.3 percent, and a digestible protein content of 3.6 percent. (2) The fiber content of all varieties is slightly more than thirty percent.

# Bermuda Hay

Bermuda grass hay is popular in the southern regions of the country, where it is plentiful and of good quality. Coastal Bermuda varieties are those which are most commonly used since they grow taller than Common Bermuda, which is too short for good hay yields. Bermuda hay may be cut four or five times in one year from the same stand of grass. The second and later cuttings are higher in quality. The nutrient content and feeding value of Bermuda hay closely approximates that of early bloom timothy. (3) Like timothy, its value is increased by seeding a legume crop, such as lespedeza or red clover, in the same field. Bermuda hay and timothy hay are grown in different regions of the country, but both can be high in quality in the areas where they grow well. For this reason,

Bermuda and timothy hays are frequently substituted for one another when feeding horses which are traveling. The protein quality of Bermuda, like timothy, is higher than that of the cereal grass hays, such as oat or barley hay.

## Bluestem Grass Hay

Bluestem grass hays grow throughout the Central Plains Region of the United States. There are a number of different grasses included in this classification. The two most commonly used for hay are big bluestem and little bluestem. (4) Bluestem hays are highly palatable for most horses. They have a digestible protein content of about three percent, and are slightly higher in fiber than timothy and Bermuda, containing about thirty-four percent.

## Bromegrass Hay

Bromegrass is a very hardy hay, and is highly palatable for most animals. The varieties most commonly used for hay are the smooth bromegrasses. These grow throughout the Great Plains Region, and do not do well in the southern states as a rule. Bromegrasses are frequently mixed with legumes for a higher quality hay and higher yields. The protein content of second-cutting, mid-bloom, smooth brome hay is 11.8 percent, with a digestible protein content of 6.2 percent. Mature smooth brome has a protein content of 5.8 percent, with a digestible protein content of 1.8 percent. The crude fiber content of mid-bloom smooth brome is 38.5 percent, and 34.2 percent in mature smooth brome. (2) The bromegrass-legume mix is more palatable for most horses than bromegrass fed alone.

## Wheatgrass Hay

Crested wheatgrass is normally grown for pasture, however it is often grown for hay in the Northern Plains states. It is hardy, and produces high quality roughage with a digestible protein content averaging 4.4 percent. The fiber content is about thirty-four percent. Wheatgrass hay requires a moist climate for good growth, and should be cut early, before it begins to bloom. As it matures, the quality drops sharply and it becomes very tough and fibrous.

## Sudangrass Hay

Sudangrass is easily grown throughout most of the United States, except the northern portions of the country. It likes warm climates, but will grow in most types of soil. Sudan hay should be cut at early bloom or slightly before, for greatest palatability and nutritional value. However, if cut too early, it may contain large amounts of prussic acid, which is toxic. Many of the newer Sudan varieties are low in prussic acid, but it is advisable to test hay before feeding if the prussic acid content is not known. Sudangrass produces two cuttings of hay per year if planted early, and may yield three cuttings in the South. It contains about five percent digestible protein and thirty percent fiber on the average.

## Johnsongrass Hay

Johnsongrass, like Sudangrass, is related to the sorghums. It is frequently grown in the Southern United States as a hay crop. It should be cut at the early bloom stage, and may yield two or three crops of hay in one year. It contains approximately three percent digestible protein.

## Orchardgrass Hay

Orchardgrass is grown in many different areas of the United States. If it is cut in the early bloom stage, it is of fairly good quality, but if cut later, it is unpalatable and low in nutrients. It produces a much better quality hay when mixed with a legume. On the average, orchardgrass contains 9 percent protein or more, with a digestible protein content of 4.2 percent.

## The Prairie Hays

The prairie hays are a mixture of wild native grasses. Many different varieties may be included. Prairie grass hay is of greatest importance in the Western states. If it is cut in the early stages of growth, it is high in nutritional value and palatability. The quality varies greatly, however, because of the many different grasses which may be included. On the average, **good quality** prairie hay contains from two to four percent digestible protein.

## The Cereal Grass Hays

The cereal hays are made from the common cereal grain crops. They have a high nutrient value, and are very palatable for most horses. Oat hay is the most popular, followed by barley and wheat. These cereal hays must be cut at an early stage, while still green, because the stems and leaves become coarse and unpalatable as the grain ripens. The cereal hays are lower in calcium than the other hays, and care should be taken that the calcium-phosphorus ratio is adequate when these hays are fed. The protein content of second-cutting oat hay averages 9.2 percent, with a digestible protein content of 4.3 percent. (2) It contains about one-third fiber. The digestible protein content of barley hay is about five percent,

*Equine Research Publications Staff Photo*

**Good quality, leafy, alfalfa hay.**

and it contains about twenty-seven percent fiber. The protein content of second-cutting wheat hay is 7.5 percent, with a digestible protein content of 3.4 percent. (2) Rye hay is considered to be low in palatability and quality. The digestible protein content is slightly above four percent, but it is not a good quality protein. Rye is higher than the other cereal hays in fiber content, containing about thirty-eight percent fiber.

## The Legume Hays

The legume hays are higher in nitrogen content than the grass hays because of their different root structure. The roots of legumes are covered with nodules containing bacteria that fix nitrogen out of the air. As a result, they are higher in protein and may be considered a richer feed than the grass hays. Legumes are good sources of vitamins A, B, and D, and are higher in calcium and phosphorus than the grass hays. They tend to be more laxative than most of the grass hays, especially when cut at an early stage. Since the legumes are so much higher in protein and lower in fiber than the grass hays, they are richer and there may be danger of colic if animals are given a legume hay free-choice when they are not used to it. Therefore, if switching from a grass hay to a legume hay, it is best to make the switch gradually and limit amounts of the legume at first. The legume hays are generally higher yielding than the grasses, but may be harder to cure since they grow densely. For this reason, and also to provide a hay that is not too rich, the legumes are often seeded in mixtures with grass hays.

## Alfalfa

Alfalfa is the most widely fed legume hay. Its use varies within different regions of the country. Most horsemen find that it is highly palatable to their horses, but in some areas animals may refuse it at first. Good bright green alfalfa is an excellent source of carotene, or vitamin A for horses. Some growers do not cut alfalfa for hay production until it has reached the full bloom stage. They believe if it is cut earlier, it may be highly laxative. This is an "old wives tale" and does not bear up under scientific investigation. Also, much of the nutrient value of alfalfa is lost by waiting until the full bloom stage before it is cut.

Alfalfa is a popular hay among growers, because its yield is so great. It may produce up to three times as much hay per acre as many of the grass hays. In addition, it can be satisfactorily grown in most areas of the country. Many cuttings can be made on the same field in one year, up to eight in some cases. (5) Early bloom, second-cutting alfalfa hay has a

**High quality alfalfa pellets with a guaranteed minimum protein content of 16%.** (*Photo 2¼ times actual size.*)

protein content of 18.4 percent, and contains a digestible protein content of 12.3 percent. The same hay in mid-bloom has a protein content of 17.1 percent, and a digestible protein content of eleven percent. The same hay in full bloom has a protein content of 15.9 percent, and a digestible protein content of 9.9 percent. The same hay mature, has a protein content of 13.6 percent, and a digestible protein content of 7.7 percent. (2) It should also be mentioned that the protein in alfalfa is a very high quality protein. The fiber content is about thirty percent.

Many horsemen prefer to feed alfalfa in the form of alfalfa pellets. These are made from dehydrated alfalfa hay in some instances, and dehydrated alfalfa leaf meal in others. Alfalfa pellets made from dehydrated alfalfa leaf meal have a higher protein and carotene content than alfalfa hay. In addition, they are less dusty and are not as subject to mold, aging, and weathering. They may be fed either as roughage, or, in some cases, as part of the concentrate ration. Alfalfa hay is frequently mixed with grass hays to increase palatability, and lessen the susceptibility to gaseous colic. This method of producing hay also increases the yield per acre.

Some horsemen feel that alfalfa, because it has a higher energy content than the other hays, should not be fed in summer. They feel that it causes overheating and sweating of the horse. However, this argument is not valid when the total ration is considered. Feeding a ration that is excessively high in energy is not helpful and may actually be harmful to the horse. It can cause weight gain in the form of fat, and it may be indeed cause sweating because it increases body heat. However, this is not due to the use of a high energy feed, but rather to improper balancing of the ration. If alfalfa, with its high level of Total Digestible Nutrients, is the primary hay in the ration, then smaller amounts of hay may need to be fed, or the amounts of other feeds included in the ration may need to be reduced. However, there is no reason why alfalfa cannot be safely fed if the ration is properly balanced, and mixing alfalfa with grass hay is one way of assuring a safe balance. When properly harvested and stored, alfalfa hay fed with discretion, provides more nutrients per pound than any other hay. It is an excellent feed for horses!

## The Clover Hays

The clover hays are close to alfalfa in protein content and total nutrients. However, they are less frequently fed in pure form, because they are lower-growing, and the leaves tend to mat when they are cured. Instead, they are usually grown in mixtures either with alfalfa or with grass hays, particularly timothy. The varieties most commonly fed to horses are red clover, white clover, crimson clover, alsike clover, and ladino clover.

Red clover is the most important variety. It yields either one or two hay crops in a season, depending on the species. There are many different species, and they may be grown throughout the United States, but are particularly important in the northern regions. To make high quality hay, the crop should be cut between the half-bloom and full bloom stages. It is a good source of calcium, and second-cutting red clover contains 14.2 percent protein. It contains 8.3 percent digestible protein. (2)

White clover is a low-growing legume, and for that reason, is rarely grown for a hay crop alone. However, it is frequently used in mixtures with grass hays. It has a digestible protein content of about ten percent, and averages twenty-two percent fiber.

Crimson clover hay, second-cutting, contains 16.9 percent protein, or 10.9 percent digestible protein. It contains about thirty-two percent fiber. (2) It should be cut while it is still blooming, as it becomes tough and unpalatable as it matures. It is most commonly grown in the southeastern parts of the country, and will grow on a variety of different soils.

Alsike clover makes a high quality hay which is similar to red clover in nutrient content. It contains 14.7 percent protein, or 8.7 percent digestible protein, with 29.4 percent crude fiber content. (2) The stems are thin and do not stand upright, however, and for that reason it is frequently sown in a mixture with other hays, especially red clover and timothy. (6)

Ladino clover is actually a variety of white clover. It is primarily grown for pasture, but may be harvested for hay. It is larger than the other white clover, which is why it is sometimes considered as a separate variety. It is very palatable, and contains about 15 percent digestible protein. The fiber content is only about twenty-four percent.

## Lespedeza Hay

Lespedeza is widely grown as a hay crop in the South. It will grow in poor soil, and is drought-resistant. It should be cut at the half-bloom to full bloom stage. Some varieties are high in tannin, making them unpalatable. Pre-bloom, second-cutting, lespedeza contains 17.8 percent protein, and 11.7 percent digestible protein. Full bloom, second-cutting, lespedeza contains 13.4 percent protein, with 7.5 percent digestible protein. (2)

## Judging the Quality of Hay

Good quality hay is bright, clean, has a rich green color, and a pleasant, fragrant smell. Loss of color indicates that the carotene, of which hay is

photo courtesy of *The Blood-Horse*

The beautiful home at Meadow Stud, located near Doswell, Virginia, was the birthplace of C. T. Chenery's ancestors. Mr. Chenery re-purchased the house and adjoining land and set up operations for Meadow Stud.

the primary source, has been depleted by moisture, improper curing, or weathering. The cutting of the hay determines the quality to some degree. In a variety which produces several cuttings per year, the second and later cuttings tend to be lower in moisture and higher in nutrient content. Hay is also judged on freedom from weeds and foreign material. Hay which contains a large number of weeds is likely to be unpalatable, and may even be toxic. The moisture content may be tested, or may be judged by the flexibility of the stems. If the stems are not brittle, and the bark peels easily, the moisture content is probably too high for safe storage, and should be dried before it is stored. Hay which has an excessive moisture content is likely to heat, mold, and ferment, and may even catch fire spontaneously. Therefore, it is important to store hay so that there is adequate air circulation, and to check the moisture content and the temperature of the hay frequently.

## Buying Hay

When buying hay, it is important to buy the very best quality available. However, it should be pointed out that the values given different hays in this text are based on "all things being equal". In other words, where nutrient values are given, it is hypothetically assumed that each variety of hay discussed is of high quality. Unfortunately, the average horseman at the average hay market, is rarely faced with a wide selection of high quality hays. Therefore, his choices must often depend to a great degree on local availability. Should the horseman be faced with a choice between one hay which has a higher "textbook" nutrient value, but is obviously lacking in actual physical qualities, and another hay of lower "textbook" value, possessing excellent physical qualities, then obviously the latter hay is superior to the former. In other words, if the horseman is presented with a choice, for example, between a normally high protein content hay, such as timothy, and a lower protein hay, such as prairie, a marked discrepancy in the physical condition of the hays should be carefully considered. If the prairie hay is of top quality and good appearance, and the timothy is damaged, bleached, weathered, or suffering in other respects, then the prairie hay would obviously be the wiser choice. The physical condition of the hay is a good indicator of the amount of vitamins and other nutrients which have been retained in the hay. A good quality, low protein hay can be accommodated for by adding high protein concentrates to the ration, but there is no justification for feeding hay which is fermented, weathered, moldy, stemmy, or full of weeds and foreign material.

Since the purchase of hay generally depends on local availability, top quality hay may not always be available. For this reason, it is advisable to buy large quantities, (up to a year's supply) when good, high quality, nutritious, palatable hay can be found, (assuming you have sufficient storage facilities). It is not recommended that more than one-year's supply be purchased, however, since hay does lose some nutrients during storage. But, wherever feasible, it is always well to have a good supply of high quality hay on hand in case local supplies are limited, or good quality hay becomes scarce late in the season.

## Summary

Hay is an important part of the equine diet, and so it is vital that good quality hay be fed. The hays may be divided into the grass hays and the legume hays. The legumes tend to be richer, and have a higher protein content. The type of hay that is chosen should depend on protein needs, palatability, and local availability. Hays are high in fiber, and have a high calcium-phosphorus ratio which balances the low calcium content of the cereal grains. It is important that hay be of high quality, bright color, free from foreign material, and fresh. The moisture content should be checked and found to be at a safe level before the hay is stored.

### REFERENCES CITED

1. Morrison, Frank B., **Feeds and Feeding, Abridged, Ninth Edition.** The Morrison Publishing Company, Claremont, Ontario, Canada, (1958)
2. National Research Council, **Nutrient Requirements of Horses.** National Academy of Sciences — National Research Council, Washington, D. C., (1973)
3. Morrison, Frank B., **Op. Cit.**
4. Seiden, Dr. Rudolph, **The Handbook of Feedstuffs.** Springer Publishing Company, Inc., New York (1957)
5. Morrison, Frank B., **Op. Cit.**
6. Seiden, Dr. Rudolph, **Op. Cit.**

## COMPOSITION OF HAYS COMMONLY USED IN HORSE RATIONS*

| HAY | DRY MATTER (%) | DIGESTIBLE ENERGY (Calories per lb.) | FIGURED ON A DRY BASIS (moisture free) | | | | | | | | |
|---|---|---|---|---|---|---|---|---|---|---|---|
| | | | TDN (%) | PROTEIN (%) | DIG. PROTEIN (%) | SOLUBLE CARBOHYDRATE (%) | CRUDE FIBER (%) | CALCIUM (%) | PHOSPHORUS (%) | PROVITAMIN A (Carotene)** (milligrams per lb.) | ASH (%) |
| **ALFALFA** | | | | | | | | | | | |
| hay, s-c, early bloom*** | 90.0 | 1057 | 59. | 18.4 | 12.3 | 27.8 | 29.8 | 1.25 | .23 | 57.7 | 8.7 |
| hay, s-c, mid-bloom | 89.2 | 1021 | 57. | 17.1 | 11.0 | 28.2 | 30.9 | 1.35 | .22 | 15.1 | 8.6 |
| hay, s-c, full bloom | 87.7 | 953 | 53. | 15.9 | 9.9 | 28.3 | 33.9 | 1.28 | .20 | 16.8 | 8.9 |
| hay, s-c, mature | 91.2 | 880 | 49. | 13.6 | 7.7 | 21.9 | 37.5 | .71 | .16 | 7.2 | 7.4 |
| hay, pelleted, s-c, grnd. (overall avg.) | 92.2 | ---- | --- | 18.4 | 13.1 | 30.0 | 25.6 | 1.57 | .24 | 28.9 | 10.9 |
| **BARLEY** | | | | | | | | | | | |
| hay, s-c, (overall avg.) | 87.7 | ---- | --- | 8.7 | 5.0 | ---- | 27.0 | .29 | .25 | ---- | 7.6 |
| **BERMUDAGRASS, COASTAL** | | | | | | | | | | | |
| hay, s-c, (overall avg.) | 91.5 | 880 | 44. | 9.5 | 4.5 | 12.5 | 30.5 | .46 | .18 | 16.5 | 4.9 |
| **BLUEGRASS, KENTUCKY** | | | | | | | | | | | |
| hay, s-c, (overall avg.) | 88.9 | ---- | --- | 10.2 | 6.2 | ---- | 30.0 | .45 | .30 | 153.2 | 6.6 |
| **BLUESTEM** | | | | | | | | | | | |
| hay, s-c, (overall avg.) | 90.9 | ---- | --- | 5.4 | 2.1 | ---- | 34.3 | ---- | --- | 18.9 | 7.0 |
| **BROME, SMOOTH** | | | | | | | | | | | |
| hay, s-c, mid-bloom | 89.7 | 866 | 44. | 11.8 | 6.2 | 10.5 | 38.5 | .40 | .20 | 5.4 | 9.2 |
| hay, s-c, mature | 92.8 | 839 | 46. | 5.8 | 1.8 | ---- | 34.2 | .43 | .22 | 2.2 | --- |
| **CLOVER, ALSIKE** | | | | | | | | | | | |
| hay, s-c, (overall avg.) | 87.9 | 1002 | 56. | 14.7 | 8.7 | ---- | 29.4 | 1.31 | .25 | 84.8 | 8.7 |
| **CLOVER, CRIMSON** | | | | | | | | | | | |
| hay, s-c, (overall avg.) | 87.4 | 989 | 55. | 16.9 | 10.9 | ---- | 32.2 | 1.42 | .18 | 15.9 | 9.2 |
| **CLOVER, LADINO** | | | | | | | | | | | |
| hay, s-c, (overall avg.) | 89.5 | ---- | --- | 20.7 | 15.1 | ---- | 24.1 | 1.71 | .32 | ---- | 9.3 |

| | | | | | | | | | | | |
|---|---|---|---|---|---|---|---|---|---|---|---|
| CLOVER, RED<br>hay, s-c, (overall avg.) | 90.1 | 980 | 55. | 14.2 | 8.3 | 26.9 | 29.5 | 1.45 | .23 | 15.8 | 7.9 |
| FESCUE, MEADOW<br>hay, s-c, (overall avg.) | 88.5 | 889 | 49. | 10.5 | 5.3 | ---- | 31.2 | .50 | .36 | 9.4 | 9.2 |
| JOHNSONGRASS (Sorghum, Johnsongrass)<br>hay, s-c, (overall avg.) | 90.6 | ---- | --- | 7.6 | 4.0 | ---- | 33.1 | .89 | .30 | 19.4 | 8.9 |
| LESPEDEZA<br>hay, s-c, pre-bloom | 92.1 | 1012 | 56. | 17.8 | 11.7 | ---- | 23.7 | 1.14 | .26 | ---- | --- |
| hay, s-c, full bloom | 93.2 | 939 | 52. | 13.4 | 7.5 | ---- | 31.0 | 1.04 | .23 | ---- | --- |
| OATS<br>hay, s-c, (overall avg.) | 88.2 | 889 | 49. | 9.2 | 4.3 | ---- | 31.0 | .26 | .24 | 45.8 | 8.2 |
| ORCHARDGRASS<br>hay, s-c, (overall avg.) | 88.3 | 839 | 46. | 9.0 | 4.2 | 12.6 | 34.5 | .45 | .22 | 7.7 | 7.4 |
| PRAIRIE HAY<br>hay, s-c, (overall avg.) | 91.0 | ---- | --- | 6.4 | 2.9 | ---- | 33.7 | .35 | .14 | ---- | 8.0 |
| SUDANGRASS (Sorghum Sudangrass)<br>hay, s-c, (overall avg.) | 89.6 | ---- | --- | 9.7 | 5.8 | ---- | 30.7 | .40 | .30 | 2.4 | 9.6 |
| TIMOTHY<br>hay, s-c, pre-bloom | 88.6 | 1061 | 53. | 12.3 | 6.6 | ---- | 32.9 | .66 | .34 | ---- | 7.1 |
| hay, s-c, mid-bloom | 88.4 | 880 | 49. | 8.3 | 3.6 | 14.7 | 33.5 | .41 | .19 | 4.9 | 6.9 |
| hay, s-c, late bloom | 88.0 | 862 | 44. | 8.3 | 3.6 | ---- | ---- | .38 | .18 | 4.4 | 5.4 |
| WHEAT<br>hay, s-c, (overall avg.) | 85.9 | 866 | 47. | 7.5 | 3.4 | ---- | 27.8 | .14 | .18 | 50.6 | 6.8 |
| WHEATGRASS, CRESTED<br>hay, s-c, (overall avg.) | 90.8 | ---- | --- | 8.1 | 4.4 | ---- | 34.5 | ---- | ---- | ---- | 8.0 |

* Data derived from Nutrient Requirements of Horses, National Research Council, 1973 and Atlas of Nutritional Data on United States and Canadian Feeds, National Academy of Sciences, 1971

** One mg of carotene equals 400 IU of vitamin A

*** s-c is abbreviation for suncured

131

# 15

# Pasturing Horses

Before the horse was domesticated, his diet consisted of growing plants. As time has passed and horses in general have become more confined, use of pasture has become increasingly supplemental, to the point that many horses are now grazed largely for exercise, and minimally for nutrition. However, the healthy, mature horse in a stress-free situation can graze on pasture and require little or no supplementation, if the quality of the pasture is very high. For other horses, pasture can be an important ingredient in the total ration. Whenever a horse is grazed, no matter for how short a time, it is desirable that the pasture be lush and growing, free from toxic weeds and chemicals, and low in parasite infestation if efficient use of grazed feed is expected.

## Types of Pastures

Originally, pastures were composed of native grasses and grass-legume mixes. Since they were naturally adapted to the area in which they grew, they were hardy and ideally suited to land and climatic conditions. While there are still many native pastures in use, many of these have become depleted by heavy grazing or by recurrent stands of grasses which have removed the necessary minerals from the soil. For this reason, more and more horsemen have turned to improved, planned, and managed pastures. (1) When planting pasture, it is best to consult County Agricultural Agents before choosing the types of plants. The different varieties should be compatible with each other, so that less hardy plants will not be crowded out. If the pasture includes low-growing clo-

*photo courtesy of Meadow Lands Farm*

Foals are most likely to reach their full growing and performance potentials, when allowed to graze and move about in a fairly large pasture area, with high quality forage.

vers and tall grasses, the tall grasses may shade the clovers and prevent them from developing properly. It is important to choose grasses that are comparable in palatability and rate of growth, so that horses do not eat only certain plants while leaving others. Many pastures today are grass-legume mixes. Wherever it is possible to include legumes in the pasture mix, it is advantageous. (2) The legumes add nitrogen to the soil, and promote the life of the pasture and the growth of other plants. They are also better protein sources than the grasses. Some of the most common mixes are alfalfa-timothy, clover-Bermuda, and other similar combinations. Mixing different varieties of grasses has an additional advantage. When a pasture becomes affected by disease or infested by insects, if there are a variety of plants, it is not likely to be completely depleted. However, if grasses have widely divergent growing seasons, lengths of maturity, or nutrient needs, it is not advisable to mix them. Instead, these grasses should be planted in separate pastures where they can be managed according to their specific agronomic requirements.

Every region of the country has native grasses which are particularly adapted for pasture in that region. Examples are Kentucky bluegrass, Coastal Bermuda in the South, the Western mountain grasses, and the prairie grasses. These grasses should form an important part of the pastures in the regions where they grow well. Often, little if any reseeding is needed to maintain these native varieties.

Pasture is higher in protein, vitamin, and mineral content than early-cut hay of the same variety. It is the best source of carotene available. It is also rich in B vitamins and vitamin E. Although it is not a good source of vitamin D, grazing animals receive large amounts of sunlight and readily synthesize vitamin D within the body. Although pasture is rich in these nutrients, it is also moderately high in fiber (about twenty percent on a dry weight basis), and is therefore lower in Total Digestible Nutrients than the concentrate feeds. The TDN of pasture is higher than hay on a dry weight basis, but pasture has a higher moisture content than hay, and so larger quantities must be consumed. Nutritional analyses of different pasture plants are given in the table at the end of this chapter. Nutritional composition depends on the specific plant mix included in the pasture, the soil, climate conditions, and the time of year at which the pasture is tested. Nutrient analysis of pasture is therefore a valuable laboratory procedure. County Agricultural Agents can also furnish information on the nutrient content of specific pastures in a given locale.

## Grazing Patterns and Pasture Rotation

Generally speaking, horses will select the more nutritious, more tender

*Equine Research Publication staff photo*

This hardy, "bottom-land", native Bermudagrass could provide excellent forage. However, because it is over-mature, it will offer low nutritional value unless it is mowed. (Photo taken in Fall.)

grasses from the mixture within a pasture. Areas which have unpalatable weeds or rank, coarse, overmature grasses may be completely avoided. For this reason, it is important to control weeds within a pasture, select grasses which are comparable in palatability and maturity, and watch pastures carefully for signs of selected grazing. Regular weeding of pastures can check weeds before they become established. Toxic weeds can become established in a pasture very quickly, and their effects may not be noticed until several horses become ill. Policing the boundaries of a pasture is usually sufficient to note weed growth and ungrazed areas. If there are areas of desirable grasses which have overmatured and become unpalatable, so that they are being avoided, mowing of the pasture will usually solve this problem. It will allow young, tender new growth that will be eaten readily.

Pasture rotation is very important for two main reasons. First, it is a useful method of reducing and controlling the spread of internal parasites. If pastures are used continuously by the same animals without rotation or rest, they will become heavily infested with worms, and will continue the breeding cycle of these parasites. This is poor pasture use, and is not only unhealthy, but actually dangerous. Rotational grazing for parasite control is discussed fully in the chapter covering internal parasites.

There is a second major reason for pasture rotation. If animals graze continuously in the same pasture, the grasses may become depleted. Grasses which are grazed down close to the roots cannot effectively maintain nutrient value and support new growth. The total nutrient yield of a pasture will be lower if it is heavily grazed and new growth is cut back frequently than if it is grazed moderately and has time to replenish and re-establish itself in between grazing. This is particularly important in the spring of the year, before the herbage is completely established in the field. If grazed too early in the life cycle, the plants may soon die out.

## Good Pasture Maintenance

Pasture maintenance includes spring plowing when necessary, mowing, weed control, fertilization, reseeding, and the control of dung.

Whenever it appears that the quality of pasture is dropping severely and cannot be brought back, the pasture should be plowed and reseeded. If this is not done, several things may occur. First, pasture yield may begin to drop sharply. The quality of forage will be low, and the soil will become depleted of essential minerals. Also, undesirable plants with different soil requirements will move in as the desired plants wear out the soil. These unwanted plants may take over the entire pasture within a

*Equine Research Publications Staff Photo*

Four months before this picture was taken the pastures on both sides of the fence looked identical. Since then the pasture on this side was mowed once per month. (Picture taken in Fall.)

few years. Reseeding allows plants within a pasture to remain evenly mixed, whereas they may be restricted to specific locations and highly concentrated within these locations if pasture is never reseeded. Whenever pastures are reseeded, it is desirable to have the soil analyzed to see if fertilization is necessary, and if the character of the soil has changed significantly, a different plant mix might be desirable. Another beneficial measure when reseeding is to allow one year of rest for every two years of grazing within a pasture so that the soil does not become depleted too rapidly. Whenever a pasture is reseeded, it should not be grazed until the new plants are at least three inches tall. (4) This allows the new plants to become established and firmly rooted. However, grazing should not be delayed too long, as the plants may begin to grow very rapidly once they become established. In this case, horses may not be able to keep the plants grazed down enough, and the pasture may become tall and mature. If this happens, it should be cut for hay and allowed to grow again, rather than expecting horses to eat the mature pasture plants.

Fertilization of pasture is necessary if it is to maintain strong, healthy plant growth. Soil should be analyzed before seeding, and whenever plants appear to be deficient, or mineral deficiencies are suspected in horses being grazed. After analysis, careful fertilization is important to correct any deficiencies which may appear. If this is not done, the pasture will be of low quality, and will rapidly become depleted of nutrients. If legumes are grown in the pasture, nitrogen in the soil is not likely to become depleted, but in a grass-only pasture, nitrogen fertilization is especially important to maintain high protein levels. Potassium and phosphorus are the other substances most likely to be required for pasture fertilization. If the soil is too acid to support the desirable plants, lime may be added to neutralize it.

Controlling manure piles in pastures is another important measure in a high quality pasture maintenance program. This is especially important if the number of horses grazing per acre is high. Horses frequently will not graze in the same areas where they defecate, and this may leave areas of tall, mature, untouched grass. In addition, if manure piles are left in pastures, the spread of parasite infestation is much greater. Spreading of fresh manure is not advised. It is likely to spread both parasite eggs and larval forms, and also weed seeds. If spread, manure should first be composted. In some cases, horses will avoid the areas of pasture where manure is first spread. Dragging, or harrowing pastures, once or twice per year will scatter manure piles, which will help break the parasite cycle and will prevent much of the selective grazing.

Good pasture management includes supplying adequate water and salt where horses are grazed. High quality pasture can supply most essential

This "close up" offers some perspective of what a horse must face as he struggles to extract a few blades of grass from a weedy pasture.

minerals, but will probably not contain enough sodium and chloride, the minerals contained in salt. For this reason, if pasture forms a large part of the diet of the horse, salt blocks or well-protected salt boxes in pastures are essential. If soil and feed analysis so indicates, then other mineral supplementation may be necessary. A good water supply is also essential. The important thing is that the water be fresh, clean, and readily available. Horses will tend to graze more heavily in the areas where water and salt supplies are located. (5) This should be considered when choosing the locations for these. If a natural water supply, such as a stream, is the primary source of water in a pasture, then it is advisable to place salt blocks as far away as possible from the water, so that horses will move throughout the entire pasture. If temporary or movable sources of water and salt are used, their locations should be changed occasionally so that even grazing results.

## Miscellaneous Notes on Pasture Management

A high quality, clean pasture may provide the entire ration for some horses if salt and minerals are supplied as necessary and the pasture is well-maintained. Animals for which this is true are barren and maiden mares before breeding season, and mature, idle horses in good health. For most horses, however, pasture alone will not be sufficient. Young, growing horses will need a higher protein content and Total Digestible Nutrient content in the ration than pasture alone can furnish. This is also true for broodmares in foal, lactating mares, and performance or hard-working horses. Even where pasture cannot provide the complete diet, however, it can be a valuable addition to the balance of nutrients, digestive action, and behavioral expressions of horses.

There are great psychological advantages for the horse which is grazed at least a short time each day where good quality pastures are available. This is also an unsurpassed source of vitamins, and it is a good method of exposing the horse to the sunlight, which satisfies his vitamin D requirements. If pasture is not high in nutrient content, it should not be counted on to supply much of the horse's daily requirements, but it can still be useful.

Pasture should be analyzed along with the rest of the ration, to determine exactly what nutrients it does supply, and the ration should be balanced accordingly. If a complete balanced ration is fed, grazing will be minimal, and overgrazing is not a problem. The only instance when pasture grazing should be avoided, is in the case of heavy parasite infestation, or when toxic weeds or minerals are present, such as a high selenium content in the soil. In these instances, the benefits of grazing are offset by the hazards to health. However, except where toxic mineral content is high, pastures can be maintained in safe, healthy, clean condition by following simple, common sense management practices.

One of the most important points in good pasture management practice is to make sure that all horses are receiving the benefits of regular periodic worming.

## Summary

Pasture may provide the major part of the diet for some horses, and serve as an important supplementary ingredient for others. It is important for this reason that it be well maintained. Pasture plants should be chosen for their local adaptability, hardiness, and palatability, and should be mixed only with plants that are compatible. Grass-legume mixtures are especially advantageous. Nutrient content of pasture varies greatly, but it is generally high in vitamins, especially vitamin A, and also has a high protein content. Since horses tend to graze selectively, it is important that pastures be weed-free, and they should be mowed when grasses become mature and less palatable. Pasture rotation helps keep pastures free of parasites and maintains healthy, well-established herbage. Plowing and reseeding of pastures when necessary will also help to maintain high quality forage. Pastures must be fertilized, or the soil is likely to become depleted in essential elements. Soil analysis is helpful in choosing necessary fertilizer. Manure should not be allowed to lay in piles in pastures since selective grazing will result. Manure should be composted before spreading on a pasture. Adequate water and salt should be supplied in the pasture, and these may be moved to also reduce selective grazing. Good quality pasture may furnish all or an important part of the diet for many horses, but even when it forms only a small part, good quality pasture is an excellent source of vitamins. Horses will benefit from grazing whenever pasture is clean and healthy.

### REFERENCES CITED

1. Morrison, Frank B., **Feeds and Feeding, Abridged, Ninth Edition.** The Morrison Publishing Company, Claremont, Ontario, Canada, (1958)
2. United States Department of Agriculture, **Soil, The Yearbook of Agriculture, 1957,** The United States Government Printing Office, Washington, D.C., (1957)
3. Morrison, Frank B., **Op. Cit.**
4. Ensminger, M. E., Ph.D., **Horses and Horsemanship.** Interstate Printers and Publishers, Inc., Danville, Illinois, (1969)
5. United States Department of Agriculture, **Op. Cit.**

# COMPOSITION OF FORAGES COMMONLY FED GREEN TO HORSES IN PASTURE*

| FORAGE | DRY MATTER (%) | DIGESTIBLE ENERGY (Calories per lb.) | FIGURED ON A DRY BASIS (moisture free) | | | | | | | |
| | | | TDN (%) | PROTEIN (%) | DIG. PROTEIN (%) | CRUDE FIBER (%) | CALCIUM (%) | PHOSPHORUS (%) | PROVITAMIN A (Carotene)** (milligrams per lb.) | ASH (%) |
|---|---|---|---|---|---|---|---|---|---|---|
| **ALFALFA** | | | | | | | | | | |
| pasture, fresh, pre-bloom | 21.1 | 1070 | 60. | 20.5 | 14.3 | 26.0 | 2.30 | .31 | 49.7 | 9.8 |
| pasture, fresh, full bloom | 25.3 | 971 | 54. | 16.9 | 10.9 | 31.7 | 1.53 | .27 | ---- | 9.8 |
| **BERMUDAGRASS** | | | | | | | | | | |
| pasture, fresh, (overall avg.) | 36.7 | 1007 | 56. | 11.6 | 6.8 | 25.9 | .53 | .22 | 127.5 | 12.4 |
| **BERMUDAGRASS, COASTAL** | | | | | | | | | | |
| pasture, fresh, (overall avg.) | 28.8 | ---- | -- | 15.0 | 10.3 | 28.4 | .49 | .27 | 149.9 | 6.3 |
| **BLUEGRASS, KENTUCKY** | | | | | | | | | | |
| pasture, fresh, immature | 30.5 | 1107 | 62. | 17.3 | 12.2 | 25.1 | .56 | .47 | 173.7 | 9.4 |
| pasture, fresh, milk stage | 35.0 | 989 | 55. | 11.6 | 6.8 | 30.3 | .19 | .27 | 90.8 | 7.3 |
| **BLUESTEM** | | | | | | | | | | |
| pasture, fresh, immature | 31.6 | ---- | -- | 11.0 | 5.6 | 28.9 | .63 | .17 | 99.4 | 8.5 |
| pasture, fresh, mature | 71.3 | 871 | 48. | 4.5 | 0.8 | 34.0 | .40 | .11 | ---- | 3.9 |
| **BROME, CHEATGRASS** | | | | | | | | | | |
| pasture, fresh, immature | 21.0 | 1070 | 60. | 15.8 | 10.9 | 22.9 | .64 | .28 | ---- | 9.6 |
| pasture, fresh, dough stage | 30.0 | 889 | 49. | 5.3 | 1.4 | 34.8 | .38 | .27 | ---- | --- |
| **BROME, SMOOTH** | | | | | | | | | | |
| pasture, fresh, immature | 32.5 | 1070 | 60. | 22.1 | 16.3 | 22.4 | .62 | .57 | 264.4 | 9.6 |
| **CLOVER, ALSIKE** | | | | | | | | | | |
| pasture, fresh, (overall avg.) | 22.5 | ---- | -- | 18.1 | 12.9 | 23.3 | 1.36 | .29 | ---- | 9.3 |
| **CLOVER, CRIMSON** | | | | | | | | | | |
| pasture, fresh, (overall avg.) | 17.7 | 1057 | 59. | 16.7 | 10.7 | 28.3 | 1.62 | .35 | ---- | 9.5 |
| **CLOVER, LADINO** | | | | | | | | | | |
| pasture, fresh, (overall avg.) | 18.0 | ---- | -- | 24.7 | 18.5 | 14.1 | 1.27 | .42 | 144.9 | 10.8 |

| | | | | | | | | | |
|---|---|---|---|---|---|---|---|---|---|
| CLOVER, RED<br>pasture, fresh, (overall avg.) | 22.7 | ---- | -- | 18.3 | 13.1 | 22.3 | 1.80 | .26 | 83.6 | 8.7 |
| FESCUE, MEADOW<br>pasture, fresh, (overall avg.) | 27.6 | 907 | 50. | 15.1 | 10.3 | 27.1 | .51 | .38 | 153.1 | 8.6 |
| JOHNSONGRASS, (Sorghum Johnsongrass)<br>pasture, fresh, (overall avg.) | 24.8 | ---- | -- | 14.4 | 9.8 | 29.6 | .91 | .26 | 89.9 | 11.2 |
| LESPEDEZA<br>pasture, fresh, immature | 31.1 | ---- | -- | 18.7 | 13.4 | 27.3 | ---- | -- | ---- | 10.6 |
| ORCHARDGRASS<br>pasture, fresh, immature | 23.8 | 1070 | 60. | 18.4 | 13.1 | 23.6 | .58 | .55 | 153.0 | 11.3 |
| pasture, fresh, mid-bloom | 30.0 | 939 | 52. | 9.1 | 4.2 | 31.9 | .23 | .23 | ---- | 7.5 |
| pasture, fresh, milk stage | 30.0 | 871 | 48. | 8.4 | 3.7 | 35.2 | .23 | .22 | ---- | 6.0 |
| MILO, (Sorghum Milo)<br>pasture, fresh, (overall avg.) | 67.0 | ---- | -- | 7.9 | 4.3 | 30.8 | .40 | .21 | .9 | 6.2 |
| SUDANGRASS (Sorghum Sudangrass)<br>pasture, fresh, mid-bloom | 22.7 | 871 | 48. | 8.7 | 3.9 | 36.1 | ---- | -- | ---- | 10.4 |
| TIMOTHY<br>pasture, fresh, (overall avg.) | 27.6 | ---- | -- | 12.8 | 8.4 | 26.8 | .59 | .38 | 101.6 | 8.0 |
| WHEATGRASS, CRESTED<br>pasture, fresh, immature | 30.8 | 1070 | 60. | 23.6 | 17.5 | 22.2 | .46 | .35 | 196.7 | 9.6 |
| pasture, fresh, full bloom | 50.0 | 839 | 46. | 9.8 | 4.8 | 30.3 | .39 | .28 | 69.6 | --- |
| pasture, fresh, over-ripe | 80.0 | 707 | 38. | 3.1 | 0.0 | 40.3 | .27 | .07 | 0.0 | 7.8 |

\* Data derived from Nutrient Requirements of Horses, National Research Council, 1973, and Atlas of Nutritional Data on United States and Canadian Feeds, National Academy of Sciences, 1971

\*\* One mg of carotene equals 400 IU of vitamin A

# 16

# Good Feeding Management

In a sound program of equine nutrition it is important not only to know what to feed but also how to feed. Proper equipment and stable management are essential to a system of good nutrition.

## When And How To Feed

When and how often to feed should not be affected by the physical limitations of the stable work force nor by the activities of the horses involved. These things should be adjusted to fit the demands of a sound feeding program. There are some fairly specific guidelines which should be followed. The horse is basically a grazing animal, and his digestive system is geared to that activity. This means that he was designed to eat frequent small meals rather than a few large ones. (1) Any good feeding program will therefore include feeding as frequently as is possible within reasonable limitations. An ideal feeding program for the horse which is not turned out to pasture would probably include four feedings per day, separated by at least six hours each. Assuming, however, that few of us will follow a program which requires a late night feeding, three feedings per day should be considered essential. Two feedings per day should be considered an absolute minimum. Feeding less frequently results in imperfect digestion of the feed and may increase the tendency toward digestive upsets. Although it is true that many horses have survived adequately for years on one or two feedings per day, these horses are certainly not receiving the maximum benefit from their feed rations. Food

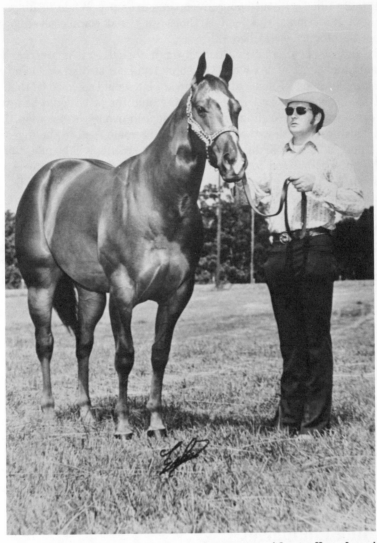

*photo courtesy of Quarter Horse Journal*

Magnolia Gay, owned by Norman Ruback of Omaha, Nebraska and Gail Ross of Barrington Hills, Illinois was named Honor Roll Halter Horse by the American Quarter Horse Association for 1972. She is an excellent example of the conditioning required for the top halter events in the United States.

is forced through the digestive system too rapidly as the stomach is repeatedly filled without being given time to empty. When feedings are frequent and small, the feed is thoroughly and completely digested before the stomach is refilled. (2)

The horse should not be rushed through a meal, so it is preferable to feed at quiet times of day when the animal will not be distracted and will have ample time to finish eating. A good plan would seem to be that the first feed should be early in the morning, and the last should be late in the evening. Other feedings should be spaced evenly in between these two. This provides that there will always be some food in the digestive tract, and full bacterial digestive action in the cecum will be maintained. If the horse is not fed for long periods of time, the cecal bacteria may diminish in quantity and activity, and digestion in this portion of the alimentary canal is inhibited.

Another very important point is that **horses be fed exactly the same time each day.** They learn to anticipate feeding times, and become expectant. Failure to feed at regular hours can cause psychological and digestive problems. Adhering to this simple but important rule of good husbandry can make a significant difference in the appearance and physical well-being of every horse.

Feed should be divided between the feedings in a logical manner, and it would seem to be unadvisable to feed only hay or only grain at one feeding. The grain should be divided equally between the feedings, and small amounts of hay should be given at the morning and afternoon feeding, with the remainder at night. This is because hay is bulky and will distend the digestive tract. (3) Since hay is high in fiber, it is harder to digest than grain. It should be fed before grain at each feeding (preferably fifteen minutes before). This allows the hay to remain in the stomach longer, and be more fully broken down by the digestive juices. It should be noted that the horse should have plenty of leisurely time to digest his rations before being put to work. A good rule of thumb would be to allow one hour between when the horse finishes a meal, and when he is put to work.

## Feeding Equipment

Hay may be fed from a rack, net, manger, or on the ground. Many horsemen have for many years fed hay from the ground because it is logically assumed that the horse being a natural grazing animal, would receive certain benefits from eating hay in this position. However, feeding from the ground may not be so advisable when the fact is taken into consideration that hay can become mixed with dirt, sand, or other foreign particles, which might cause digestive impaction. Also, hay fed from the ground can easily become scattered over the floor of the stall, and ruined by the horse walking on it. Obviously, there is more waste when this occurs. Another good point is, that if the hay is contaminated with manure it will compound the parasite problem.

Whether a rack, net or manger is used depends on the preference of the individual horseman. However, since the horse is naturally a grazing animal, as mentioned above, it would probably be awkward and unnatural if he were forced to reach up very high to obtain his hay ration. There is some evidence to indicate that a lower positioning of the hay ration is an aid to digestion. Therefore, it would seem logical to place the rack, net or manger in something less than an elevated position.

Grain should be fed from a clean trough of adequate size protected from water and weather with no sharp edges or projecting points. It is important that grain troughs be scrubbed and thoroughly rinsed routinely, and where possible on a daily basis. Uneaten grain left in the trough may ferment where it comes into contact with saliva. This can cause colic or poisoning if the horse is allowed to eat the fermented grain. The feed trough should be designed to fit comfortably into the stall space, and there are a number of different sizes and shapes to meet this need. (The new patented feed troughs, manufactured by several different companies, appear to be superior to anything the horseman might build himself.) The feed trough should not be set at an awkward height, as it may cause the horse to eat more rapidly and uncomfortably. An ideal height would seem to be on a level with the lower portion of the horse's chest.

Automatic waterers are discussed in the chapter on water. If automatic watering devices are not used, however, water should be changed at regular intervals, and the water bucket should be cleaned out thoroughly at least once a day. Fresh water should always be available in ample quantities.

## The Effects of Grooming on Nutrition

Obviously, an entire book could be written on the arts and sciences of good grooming. However, within the confines and purposes of this text, brief mention of the relationship between grooming and nutrition must suffice.

Good grooming is essential to the health and well-being of every horse. It also seems to have an improving effect on appetite. That is, brushing and rubbing the horse increases blood circulation and, thereby, seems to stimulate appetite. It is also beneficial psychologically.

Each horse should be groomed at least once daily. This includes brushing, combing, rubbing, and thorough cleaning of the hooves. This proce-

## CLEAN YOUR OWN OATS

**When dusty oats are all that is available, you can shake them thoroughly on screen-wire, as shown in illustration. (Notice dust sifting out on bottom ¾ of photo.)**

dure should also include a careful wiping with a clean rag of the area around the eyes, the nostrils, and the anal and genital areas. To ensure good sanitation measures, brushes and rub rags should be cleaned frequently. Unsanitary rags can spread disease and infection.

Basic equipment for minimal good grooming consists only of a good curry comb, a soft bristle brush, (for the more tender areas of the horse's body), and a slightly stiffer brush, (for the mane, the tail, and very dirty or very muddy areas). Also, several old cotton or wool rags, and a hoof pick are required. More elaborate systems may include electric vacuum cleaners, and other equipment, but basic grooming procedures can easily be performed with the items listed. A complete minimal daily grooming regimen can take as little as ten minutes, and any person who fails regularly to provide his horses the benefits of this procedure cannot in any sense be considered a serious horseman. And, further, it may be stated with conviction: *The horse which is not regularly groomed is not in the optimum state of health.*

## Effects of Exercise on Good Nutrition

Before the horse was domesticated, it was allowed to run free and exercise at will. The practice of confining horses to stalls is a direct contradiction to this natural state. (4) Because this is true, it is essential that every horse receive regular exercise to compensate for this loss of freedom. Exercise is vital for several reasons. First and foremost, it is a facet of good nutrition. The horse receiving insufficient exercise will not eat well. He will have reduced appetite, and will not properly utilize the energy portion of the ration. The underexercised horse will be much more prone to digestive disturbances, and is likely to have poor muscle tone resulting in inefficient digestion.

Furthermore, exercise is important to healthy feet and legs. It builds good muscle tone and allows proper development of the hoof. A third major reason that sufficient exercise is required is for its psychological effect. It relaxes the horse, and lessens the feeling of confinement from being in the stall. (5) The stalled horse receiving insufficient exercise is also much more likely to develop stable vices, such as stall weaving, wood chewing, and cribbing.

A good rule of thumb for the average stalled horse, not working or in training, would include at least one hour of forced exercise per day. This may include riding, hand walking, or exercising on a mechanical walker. For horses receiving no other exercise than walking, there would appear to be psychological advantages to dividing the hour into two thirty minute periods, one each in mid-morning, and mid-afternoon. It is important to realize that if walking is the only exercise the stalled horse receives over an extended period of time, then one hour per day should be considered an absolute minimum. If the horse is working or in training, his exercise program would need to be adjusted by the owner or trainer, according to the individual needs of the animal involved.

The amount of exercise a horse receives should be directly correlated with the ration that is fed. A horse which is heavily exercised on the weekend and ridden lightly during the week, for example, should receive larger amounts of energy feeds and concentrates on days of heavy exercise. A horse that is taken out of training and put on light exercise, should have his ration reduced proportionately. Proper exercise and good nutrition are directly related, and should always be considered together in good feeding management.

## Good Stable Design

Good stable design includes many facets. One of the first is adequate space for each animal. An optimum or "ideal" stall size is impossible to give, simply because stalls must be held to a reasonable size in order that a reasonable number of animals may be housed within the same building. Therefore, a reasonable "ideal" stall size for the average size horse is usually considered to be from 12' x 12' to 14' x 14'. 11' x 11' is considered by some to be satisfactory. Anything smaller than 10' x 10' is definitely not satisfactory. The horseman should keep in mind the smaller the stall, the higher the likelihood of horses being "cast" in their stalls. Also it would seem to be a logical assumption, all other things being equal, the smaller the enclosure, the greater the risk a horse may develop psychological problems.

Ventilation is an important factor in good stable design. The horseman should be careful to see that stalls are well ventilated in warm weather, but not overly ventilated in cold weather. Common sense planning in this area can prevent many equine health problems. Proper stall drainage is another stable problem which must be carefully checked. A well designed stable is a composite of many factors. Careful consideration of these factors is a "must" if good stable design is to be achieved.

## Fly Control

Fly control within the stable is essential. Regular fogging with commercial products is valuable. Horses may also be individually wiped or sprayed with fly repellent if flies are a serious problem. The feeding of small amounts of vinegar in the rations, (less than 1/4 cup) is thought by some horsemen to reduce the the fly problem, but this has not been proven. Horses bothered by flies will be distracted and unable to eat properly. Flies may also spread disease within a barn.

1973 made it two years in a row that the Meadow Stable of Virginia was the owner of the Kentucky Derby winner. Secretariat, pictured above, not only swept to victory in the Churchill Downs classic, but also ran the fastest derby in history.

# Feeding Horses in Groups

There are many situations when horses cannot be fed individually, and must instead be fed in groups. The horseman should recognize that group feeding raises several potential problems, and should be prepared to deal with these problems.

One particular problem caused by group feeding of horses is jealousy and fighting over feed. Unless horses within the group are completely familiar with each other, and there is no jealousy, special care must be taken to prevent fighting. Hay should be placed in individual bundles, one for each horse, and these should be widely spaced, (at least 50 feet where possible). In addition, several extra piles should be provided so that a horse is not required to eat next to or between horses that he is afraid or jealous of.

Grain troughs should be separated whenever possible, and the ideal situation is to have an individual trough for each horse and each trough should be separated by at least 50 feet. Sometimes, however, it is not possible to provide individual troughs, but it should be borne in mind, that as many troughs as is possible should be provided. Where animals must eat from common troughs, they must be closely watched to ensure that each horse gets a fair share of the grain. Timid horses may be pushed away by others and may not receive sufficient amounts of feed. Bolder horses may overeat. It is important to watch horses frequently when they are fed from a common trough to make sure that problems of this type are not existent.

If horses which are fed in a group situation are carefully supervised and reasonable safety measures taken, they can usually be fed without serious problems.

# Creep Feeding

Designing and maintaining a creep feeding program is one of the very best management tools for any horse breeding operation. The creep feed is an enclosure that is designed to let foals eat a specific diet while keeping their dams out. Generally, it is a fenced enclosure with an opening that is large enough to permit foals to enter, but small enough to keep their dams from following. The size of the opening should be variable so that it may be enlarged as the foals grow if necessary. Inside, there should be adequate feeding space for the expected number of foals to eat without crowding, so that timid eaters will not be pushed away by larger or bolder animals. The creep feed allows the foal to become accustomed to a solid ration prepared especially for him. He does not have to eat from his dam's box, and yet she can stand just outside the rail, where they can still see each other and not feel isolated. A ration designed espe-

**Shavings on left have ideal size and consistency for stall bedding. Shavings on right are too fine and too dusty for good bedding.** (*Pencil is used for frame of reference.*)

cially for the growing foal should be placed in the creep. Troughs should be cleaned out regularly, and the foals should be observed frequently to make sure that all are eating their fair share. The creep fed foal is accustomed to eating independently at weaning time, and therefore does not suffer as great a setback when he is removed from his dam.

# Bedding

Stall bedding should always be of top quality. It should be selected with the same exacting care that is exercised in buying feed. Once good bedding is selected, manure should be picked up from stalls twice daily, and under no circumstances less frequently than once per day. Soiled and wet bedding should be replaced with clean bedding each time manure is picked up.

The best type of bedding is clean bright straw or wood shavings. (6) It should have a fresh smell and be free from foreign material. Rice hulls, sawdust, and peanut hulls are occasionally used for bedding purposes, and they should meet the same standards. Sand is sometimes used for bedding, however, it is usually not recommended. It is very easy for the horse bedded on sand to ingest part of the sand and develop impactions in the colon and cecum. Also, it is difficult to keep the hair coats of horses bedded on sand clean and shiny. Bedding should provide a dry, warm, comfortable, clean surface at all times.

# Summary

The good stable manager is consistently maintaining high standards. He feeds often and in small amounts, to allow the digestive system of the horse to perform as it was intended. He feeds at regular hours at quiet times of the day and the horse is never rushed through a meal. Feed should be divided between the feedings, with some hay and some grain at each meal.

Good equipment is an important part of good stable management. The proper equipment is the right size, it presents no safety hazards, and it is kept clean.

Good grooming must be considered an essential part of stable management. The horse should be groomed regularly to maintain a healthy coat and a good appetite. Grooming equipment should also be cleaned often.

Proper design of stables is important. They should be designed with adequate space, equipment, ventilation, and sanitation. Otherwise they may promote the spread of disease. The good stable manager involved in a breeding operation will also want to consider a creep feed as part of the buildings. This provides many advantages for the foal and dam.

Finally, the good stable manager is well aware of the importance of clean stalls and high quality bedding. He will clean out stalls regularly and frequently, and will make sure that bedding is always clean and dry.

## REFERENCES CITED

1. Catcott, E. J., D.V.M., Ph.D., and Smithcors, J. F., D.V.M., Ph.D., Editors, **Progress in Equine Practice, Volume Two.** American Veterinary Publications, Inc., Wheaton, Illinois, (1970)
2. Ensminger, M. E., Ph.D., **Horses and Horsemanship.** Interstate Printers and Publishers, Danville, Illinois, (1969)
3. Ensminger, M. E., Ph.D., **Op. Cit.**
4. Rossdale, Peter D., M.A., F.R.C.V.S., **The Horse.** The California Thoroughbred Breeders Association, California, (1972)
5. Montgomery, E. S., **The Thoroughbred.** Arco Publishing Company, Inc., New York, (1971)
6. Ensminger, M. E., Ph.D., **Op. Cit.**

# 17

# Nutrition and
# Veterinary Care

For any sound program of nutrition and health to function at optimum levels, the services of a qualified, interested veterinarian are required. By maintaining open communication and good rapport with the veterinarian, the conscientious horseman ensures that his programs will function at more efficient levels.

## The Need for Regular Veterinary Care

Every horse should have periodic veterinary checkups even when the animal appears to be in excellent health. In this way, the veterinarian learns what is normal for each particular horse in the stable, and small problems can be detected before they increase in scope. Temperature, pulse, and respiratory rate should be checked, and a rapid visual and manual examination made of the animal to determine potential problem areas. The entire examination requires only a few minutes, and should, ideally, be repeated at least twice a year.

Regular veterinary services are also needed to maintain a good immunization program. The owner should maintain records for each animal showing immunizations given and the date for future injections. If planned well in advance, the owner can be sure that all of his animals will be well protected, and the veterinarian can better schedule his time for giving the injections.

A valuable side effect to the horseman, gained through the periodic visit by the veterinarian, is picking up information on new scientific data. The veterinarian is kept abreast of many new drugs and procedures through various veterinary manuals, representatives from drug companies, etc. What may be the best drugs and procedures today could very well be outmoded tomorrow. The veterinarian is usually the horseman's best source for learning this new information.

Another regular service provided by veterinarians is dentistry. As discussed in Chapter 22, healthy teeth are an important part of good nutrition. Regular semi-annual dental checkups for every horse should be performed and corrective work done as needed.

Another regular function of the veterinarian is to periodically tube each horse for worms. This also should be set up in advance on a regular basis, and the scope of the entire program planned jointly by owner and veterinarian.

By performing the regular services, the veterinarian can do much preventive work and save many emergency calls. He can also, as previously mentioned, become familiar with the normal condition of each horse, when it is in a state of good health. The conscientious horseman will want to learn as much as possible about routine veterinary care in order to handle small problems. He should be well-informed about emergency procedures and treatment of routine illnesses. The veterinarian can supervise the horseman and teach him proper methods of dealing with many routine problems himself. However, the intelligent horseman would be well advised to not overestimate his own medical skills. *When in doubt call the vet!*

## The Role of the Veterinarian in Planning a Feeding Program

The owner who wishes to plan and administer the best possible equine nutrition program will use the services of his veterinarian here also. The veterinarian can often serve as a source of new information and advice. If laboratory tests are to be made to determine the adequacy of the feeding program, as is discussed fully in the chapter on laboratory analysis, these tests need to be supervised by a veterinarian. Most reputable laboratories prefer that testing work be handled through a veterinarian rather than an individual owner for several reasons. First, the laboratory personnel can be sure that samples were taken under specified conditions. Second, they can discuss the medical aspects of the test results with someone trained in the field. Third, veterinary supervision ensures that tests are made when they are necessary and will provide useful results, rather than when they might be superfluous.

Having a veterinarian fully informed about the nature of a nutritional program allows him to be alert for changes in the condition of the animals which may be a result of feeding techniques or dietary imbalances. Correction can then be made as soon as it becomes necessary, before serious symptoms appear.

## Emergency Services

The wise owner will maintain a good rapport with his veterinarian. Thus, when emergencies arise, such as a horse that founders, the veterinarian is already familiar with the horse and the stable conditions. He will know exactly what equipment to bring, and what type of space he will have available in which to work. Because he has treated all the animals in the stable for routine immunizations and preventive care, he will know at once whether the illness of one horse will endanger others. The horseman who is a good stable manager will provide convenient treatment facilities in his barn for the vet's work.

By maintaining a good working relationship with the veterinarian, the stable manager or owner will save many hours for both the vet and himself. He will be sure he is providing top quality treatment for his horses, and that the routine care he gives them may save many emergencies.

## Summary

The horseman who is careful and cautious will work with his veterinarian at many levels to ensure the finest of care for his animals. He will depend on the vet for reliable information. He will establish routine immunization, dentistry, health checkups, and worming programs, and schedule them in advance. He will work closely with his veterinarian to devise a high quality nutritional program and to continually evaluate the results of the program. Finally, he will provide necessary facilities in an emergency. By following these steps, he can feel more confident that his horses will remain sound, healthy, and well-nourished.

# 18

# The Role Of
# The Research Foundation
# And Laboratory

Many organized groups of horsemen have expressed sincere concern due to the lack of information available in the realm of equine nutrition. Although these groups presented their problems ambitiously, the merits of their arguments were severely diluted by the lack of sufficient protagonists to present a large and impressive front. Such groups were unable to catalyze any major breakthroughs in this relatively barren field until about ten years ago. Within the last ten years, however, several major strides have been made, narrowing the gap between equine nutrition and the nutritional studies of other domesticated animals.

## The Colleges and Universities
More and more colleges and universities are offering programs in horse science and nutrition. These are generally through the Animal Science Departments in Land-Grant Colleges of Agriculture, or in Schools of Veterinary Medicine. Many of these schools present continuing educational programs designed especially for horsemen. In addition, some schools make their laboratory services available at cost, in order to provide training for students. Continuing research is done by professors and students, and this research information is field tested, and made available for public distribution. Such colleges and universities provide valuable information and services that might otherwise be unavailable. The

role of these institutions and the highly skilled professionals who implement their programs, are of inestimable value to the serious horseman.

## Cooperative Extension Service

The Cooperative Extension Service maintains an Agricultural Extension Agent in each county. These agents are equipped to deal with local conditions and problems. They can provide many helpful booklets, on request, dealing with problems which are local in scope, or which are common to all horse owners. They are especially useful for those who maintain pastures for grazing, and those who wish to raise their own feeds. They can provide information on soil conditions, expected rainfall, common tests, and necessary fertilizers. In addition, state Extension programs are conducted through the college of agriculture in the Land-Grant University in each state. These programs provide courses and information briefings throughout the state at regular intervals. By calling the local County Extension Agents office, an individual can become acquainted with the programs and services in any given area. (1)

## The National Research Council

One outstanding and highly qualified research group is the National Research Council, funded by the Agricultural Research Institute, and composed of leaders in the field of agriculture. The Council is a division of the National Academy of Sciences, and is primarily composed of individuals from colleges and universities, governmental agencies, and trade and industrial organizations. (1) This group meets at assigned intervals to determine dietary standards and nutritional analyses for horses and other animals, and these standards are released in printed form to the public. The Council is an important source for factual data used in planning a balanced diet. In fact, much of the scientific material in this text is based upon data gathered by N.R.C. and published in their 1973 report. The headquarters for the Council is in Washington, D.C.

## The Feed Companies

Most of the major feed companies now maintain completely modern testing and research laboratories staffed by competent nutritionists. These measures help to ascertain whether or not their products meet existing standards, and to ensure that they will be able to meet additional dietary needs as they are discovered. Most of these companies publish booklets or reports occasionally, which give nutritional information. In addition, many will answer questions about basic nutrition. While these laboratories provide a useful service to horsemen, it must be recognized that the feed companies are in business, and thus, logically must pursue a goal of profit making. Consequently, they are loathe to recommend products other than their own! Therefore, the information any company provides, can be considered to be only as good as its reputation, and the quality of the products it manufactures.

## The Private Foundations

Two private organizations sponsor research in the field of equine nutrition. These competent, and very worthwhile organizations are the Morris Animal Foundation, and the Grayson Research Foundation. These foundations have provided invaluable service to the horseman, and have often led the way in lighting theretofore darkened scientific paths. Although these organizations do not conduct the actual research themselves, they initiate the original programs for research by funding universities or other laboratories, and also coordinate the research activities.

Research sponsored by the Morris and Grayson Foundations is on a continuing basis, and reports are released as conclusions are reached. Because both of these groups are non-profit, and are funded largely by grants and public contributions, they can present conclusions in an unbiased manner, and are free to devote all of their income to research projects. There are numerous other private foundations, but they are smaller and usually local in nature. Many are sponsored through local universities and colleges. Others are headed by well-known researchers.

Some good sources for staying abreast of the latest scientific developments include the "horse" magazines. Many of these magazines are published under the auspices of various breed groups, and breed registries. Others are general in scope, and are written for all horsemen. A good rule of thumb for choosing magazines for this purpose, is to stick with the publications that regularly feature helpful, scientifically oriented articles, rather than just occasionally. In addition to the magazine publishers, companies such as Equine Research Publications, publish books and other materials designed to acquaint the conscientious horseman with the latest scientific developments in all areas of equine research.

## The Private Laboratories

The private laboratories are a valuable tool for the horseman. While they charge for their services, the valuable role they play in the horse world should not be minimized. They provide quick and efficient service in many areas of analyses. (These tests are described in Chapter 19.) The horseman normally utilizes the services of these laboratories through a veterinarian or other professional, and consequently, has little, if any personal contact with them. But we should not forget the vital role they play.

## Summary

The concerned horseman is searching for the newest, most up-to-date information on feeding and nutrition. In order to stay in touch with new developments as they occur, you should follow closely the work of the research organizations. Most of these organizations welcome the interest and support of those in the horse industry.

## 19

# Laboratory Analysis To Determine Nutritional Adequacy

As the study of equine nutrition becomes more scientific, it is possible to rely more and more on the laboratory to determine the adequacy of feeding programs. As the good horseman has always known, it is important to use visual observation to determine problems and overall health, but the laboratory can now offer you the last word in this determination. Further, it is now possible to make diagnoses of problems much sooner; that is, before they affect the horse's visible condition.

There are five major types of laboratory analysis now being done. These are blood analysis, hair analysis, feed analysis, soil analysis, and water analysis. Each of these is done with a different purpose in mind, but the overall intention is the same: to make sure that the diet of the horse is nutritionally adequate, and that his health is good and will remain so.

## The Blood Analysis

It is recommended that a blood analysis be done routinely on all horses at regular intervals; at least annually for the average horse, and twice a year for race and show horses. Blood analysis should also be performed whenever illness or deficiency is suspected. The blood analysis can determine a number of problems before they become serious, and is also a good indicator of the healthy horse when the results are normal.

In performing a blood analysis, a blood sample is taken from the animal by a veterinarian under sanitary conditions. The blood sample is carefully sealed in a collection vial or test tube, and either it is clotted and the serum drawn off, or anti-coagulants are added, depending on the specific tests which are to be performed. The collected blood is then taken or sent to a licensed testing laboratory. At the lab, a series of chemical tests and microscopic analyses are performed.

For most horsemen, the most important test performed in a blood analysis is the hematocrit analysis. (1) The hematocrit is an instrument which centrifuges the blood for approximately thirty minutes, separating it into three components. These are the erythrocytes, the leukocytes and thrombocytes, and the blood plasma. Erythrocytes are the red blood cells. They are the oxygen carrying portion of the blood. The leukocytes are the white blood cells, which primarily serve to fight infection and maintain resistance. Found with the leukocytes, but in very small numbers, are the thrombocytes. These are the platelets, which are flattened disks of protoplasm that aid in clotting of the blood. Plasma is the clear, straw colored, fluid portion of the blood. It is the medium of transporting the blood cells.

From the hematocrit separation of the blood, several values can be determined. These include packed cell volume, red blood count, hemoglobin value, and white cell count. The packed cell volume (PCV) is the volume of erythrocytes, and is expressed as a percentage in the blood. The PCV is determined not only by the **number** of red blood cells, but also by their **size**. This percentage is frequently referred to as the "hematocrit value" when evaluating the results of a blood analysis. The average PCV should be considered to be about thirty-five percent of the blood volume. But this figure varies greatly. (2) The horse stores large volumes of erythrocytes, primarily in the spleen, and may release them into the bloodstream during periods of excitement, increasing the PCV by as much as sixty percent. For this reason, it is important that blood samples for analysis be collected under calm circumstances. The result of the PCV analysis is one indicator of whether or not the horse is anemic.

The red blood cell count (RBC) is simply a microscopic count of the number of erythrocytes in the blood. The distinction between the RBC and the PCV should be carefully noted. The RBC can only provide the number of red blood cells, whereas the PCV, which takes into consideration the size of the red blood cells, offers you a value consideration. The RBC is not affected by the size of the individual cells.

A range of values has been determined, and the red cell count should fall somewhere within this range. However, because this range varies so greatly, it is difficult to give specific values which are generally applica-

The incomparable Three Bars, Thoroughbred son of Percentage, out of Myrtle Dee, proved to be the most successful out-cross for Quarter Horse mares in the entire history of the Quarter running horse industry.

ble. Therefore, it would seem advisable to have a veterinarian evaluate test results and determine whether or not they are normal for a particular horse. It is interesting to note that the normal range has been found to differ with age, sex, and breed. Thoroughbreds in particular are noted for having higher erythrocyte counts than other horses. In actuality, this is true for all "hot-blooded" horses (Thoroughbreds, Arabians, and those horses which contain a high percentage of Arabian blood). Other light horses and horses containing draft blood, will have red blood counts which are somewhat lower.

It is also notable that a horse whose normal red blood count, when in good health, is somewhat higher than average, will tend to be more successful as a race horse than horses of the same breed whose normal RBC values are low. This was discovered by comparing the blood analyses of successful race horses with those having poor racing records. The probable explanation for this difference is that if the red blood cell count is higher, more oxygen can be carried through the body, and oxygen therefore reaches the tissues more effectively. This gives the horse more stamina, and results in better race performance. (3)

Two year old horses have lower red blood counts than older horses, a difference of slightly less than one million cells per millimeter. In addition, two year old geldings have significantly lower red cell counts than two year old colts and fillies. Among older horses, stallions tend to have slightly higher values than mares or geldings. (4) Because of variances, such as these, analysis by a veterinarian is always recommended to determine whether the red blood count is within the normal range for the particular animal being studied. As a rule, however, the number of red blood cells, in millions, per cubic millimeter of blood is approximately ten to twelve for most horses. (5) If the red blood cell count is low, it indicates, as does a low PCV, that the horse is suffering from some form of anemia, which may be nutritionally caused, or a result of illness.

An interesting and little known fact is that when the erythrocyte count is extremely high, (say more than fifty percent above normal), illness may be indicated. Normally, the first step, when such a situation is discovered, is to have the blood test repeated to see if excitement or nervousness caused a temporary rise in the number of erythrocytes. If the count remains excessively high, the condition is known as polycythemia, or excessive numbers of red blood cells in the bloodstream. This may be caused by a limited supply of oxygen, or it may be the result of excessive fluid loss. In either case, the blood is thicker and more concentrated, and heart and liver damage may result if it is not treated. (6)

The hemoglobin analysis is another very important test which is performed during the hematocrit process. Hemoglobin is a protein sub-

Claiborne Farm near Paris, Kentucky has consistently been one of the leading Thoroughbred breeding establishments in the country, and had the distinction of being the home of Bold Ruler at the time of his death. Bold Ruler, of course, has proven to be one of the most influential sires in the history of the Thoroughbred industry.

stance which is a component of the red blood cells, and it is this substance which is responsible for the red color of the blood. Hemoglobin analysis is important because it indicates the health of the red cells. A hemoglobin analysis reveals the amount of iron in the blood, and it also reveals the ability of the red blood cells to transport oxygen through the blood. This makes it especially important in determining the fitness of race horses, and other endurance horses. Hemoglobin concentration is measured in grams of hemoglobin per milliliter of blood. It will fall within a range of 11 to 13 grams per milliliter for most horses. (7)

The white cell volume in the blood is also important. A high leukocyte count indicates the presence of illness or infection within the body.

Another test which can be performed is the blood film analysis. A smear is made with fresh blood soon after collection. A small drop of whole blood is spread thinly across a slide, so that only one layer of cells is present. This is analyzed under a microscope for three primary factors. These are the degree of variation in size and shape of erythrocytes and the presence of abnormal or diseased red blood cells, the percentage of leukocytes in the blood, and the distribution of thrombocytes. (8)

Blood analysis can also reveal the amount of nitrogen in the blood, which is indicative of proper kidney and respiratory function, the vitamin levels, (particulary the B vitamins), and the concentration of most required minerals, such as calcium, phosphorus, magnesium, sodium, chloride, and potassium. (9)

When having a blood analysis performed, it is important to have a complete analysis which tests all of the critical values. Of particular importance are PCV, red blood count, and hemoglobin. A blood analysis which tests only one value is insufficient. For example, a horse which suffers from polycythemia may have a normal red blood count if the horse is also anemic, and this has been known to happen. (10) If a hemoglobin test had also been performed, however, the anemia would have been revealed and a correct diagnosis could be made. To determine the true health picture of the horse, all of the major tests should be performed and the results should be analyzed by a qualified veterinarian.

The blood analysis can pinpoint many illnesses before they become symptomatic. It can also point out changes that should be made in a feeding program. It serves as a hallmark of the overall health of the horse.

## The Hair Analysis

In the hair analysis, a small amount of hair is clipped from a thoroughly brushed horse. The hair is then sent to a laboratory under sterile conditions, and it is then microscopically analyzed. The analysis will give a rapid estimate of the mineral levels within the body. Deficiencies

## A WIDE SPREAD PROBLEM

A fat, and healthy-appearing horse which, in reality, is nutritionally starved from a diet of poor-quality forage.

quickly become apparent, and the need for supplementation can be adequately met. It is also possible to determine toxic mineral levels, and corrective measures can be taken. (11)

Both of these tests should be made by a veterinarian, and the samples should be sent to a recognized laboratory for the tests. A complete analysis will be returned to the veterinarian within a short time, and diagnosis can be made and corrective measures taken.

## The Feed Analysis

The feed analysis is a more complicated procedure. It involves collecting samples of all the feeds used in the complete ration, and sending them to a laboratory to be analyzed for nutrient content. Protein, carbohydrate, fat, fiber, vitamin, and mineral levels can all be measured by laboratory analysis. Steps can then be taken either to balance the ration if it is deficient, or to maintain it if it is satisfactory. (12) This type of analysis is time consuming and expensive. It therefore cannot be recommended for the average small owner. However, the large breeding farm would certainly find it worthwhile. It is also a step worth considering for the owner whose feeding program has inadequacies which cannot be pinpointed or successfully corrected. If a feed analysis can be conducted, it can provide a valuable tool in providing the most nutritionally sound ration possible.

## The Soil Analysis

The soil analysis is quick and inexpensive. It can be readily performed by either the Department of Agriculture Extension Office, or by many agricultural colleges. The purpose of the soil analysis is to reveal mineral and chemical deficiencies and excesses in the soil so that they may be corrected. Proper fertilizer can then be added to supplement or correct these imbalances. (13) The main advantage for running a soil analysis is when horses are kept on pasture or feeds are raised for on-farm use. A soil sample is collected in a jar and mailed to the appropriate facility. The test results are then returned by mail, along with appropriate recommendations in most cases. The time required to receive results may vary, but it is usually about one to two weeks.

## The Water Analysis

The water analysis, like the soil analysis, is simple and inexpensive, and can usually be performed by the same laboratory. A sample of water is collected in a sterile container and tightly sealed. It is then mailed to the laboratory. An analysis is done to show purity, mineral content, and hardness. The results are returned within a short time. Since the water in an area is an important factor if there are unusually high levels of minerals, the water analysis can be extremely valuable. Flourine and calcium are particularly important. For example, if the water shows a high fluorine content, then a low fluorine hay must be fed.

## When to Use Laboratory Testing

Laboratory tests should become an important preventative measure for the average horseman. A blood analysis should be performed on each horse once a year, or twice for race or show horses, and whenever there are signs of illness. Water and soil tests should also be performed at yearly intervals. Although there is likely to be little change from year to year, depletion of soil nutrients should be corrected as soon as it becomes visible, and pollution may rapidly affect water supplies in some areas. A hair analysis should also be performed yearly, and may be used with value whenever mineral deficiencies are suspected. Feed analysis should be performed if possible whenever there is a major change in the ration, or whenever nutritional deficiencies seem to affect several animals and the cause cannot be determined by other means.

## Summary

Modern laboratory procedures have provided a new tool for horsemen interested in sound nutrition. Blood, hair, soil, water, and feed may all be analyzed. The results can pinpoint disease, nutritional inadequacy, toxic amounts or deficient levels of vitamins and minerals, and the proper methods for balancing a ration. Tests should be conducted on a regular basis under the supervision of a licensed veterinarian through a recognized laboratory.

# REFERENCES CITED

1. Schalm, Oscar W., D.V.M., Ph.D., **Veterinary Hematology.** Lea and Febiger, Philadelphia, (1965)
2. Schalm, Oscar W., D.V.M., Ph.D., **Op. Cit.**
3. Schalm, Oscar W., D.V.M., Ph.D., **Op. Cit.**
4. Catcott, E. J., D.V.M., Ph.D., and Smithcors, J. F., D.V.M., Ph.D., **Equine Medicine and Surgery.** American Veterinary Publications, Inc., Wheaton, Illinois, (1972)
5. Montgomery, E. S., **The Thoroughbred.** Arco Publishing Company, Inc., New York, (1971)
6. Catcott, E. J., D.V.M., Ph.D., and Smithcors, J. F., D.V.M., Ph.D., **Op. Cit.**
7. Schalm, Oscar W., D.V.M., Ph.D., **Op. Cit.**
8. Schalm, Oscar W., D.V.M., Ph.D., **Op. Cit.**
9. The Blood-Horse, **Feeding the Horse.** The Blood-Horse, Lexington, Kentucky, (1969)
10. Schalm, Oscar W., D.V.M., Ph.D., **Op. Cit.**
11. The Blood-Horse, **Op. Cit.**
12. Crampton, E. W., and Harris, L. E., **Applied Animal Nutrition.** W. H. Freeman and Company, San Francisco, (1969)
13. United States Department of Agriculture, Extension Office, Dallas, Texas.

# 20

# Digestive Disturbances In The Horse

Digestive disturbances in the horse can range from minor discomfort to fatal illnesses. It is important to know the nature, cause, and treatment for the most common digestive disorders.

Many digestive disorders are related to improper feeding management or feeding spoiled feed. Since the stomach of the horse is relatively small, undigested food residues will pass to the lower intestine rather quickly when large amounts of feed are fed at one time. This may cause excessive gas production and/or accumulation of residues in small constricted areas — either of which will generate pressure buildup in the intestine and subsequent colic. Also, if the lower intestine is gorged with grain feed, laminitis, or founder, may result, due to excessive fermentation and toxin production. Therefore, it is essential that horses be fed small amounts of feed at regular intervals, and the higher the level of food intake, the more important this practice becomes. A good horseman feeds his horses by weight, and at regularly scheduled intervals every day.

Feeding spoiled, or moldy feed may result in some toxicity to horses if mold-produced toxins are present in the feed. Also, wet grain feed can become partially fermented and cause excessive gas production when ingested by the horse. For these reasons, and others, horses should not be fed spoiled or partially spoiled feed.

Where cereal grains and oil seed meals and other supplements are fed together, it is essential that ingredients be thoroughly and evenly mixed.

Feeds that are finer in texture are generally rapidly fermentable, and will segregate in a feed mixture if precaution is not taken. This can result in intake of an abnormally high amount of one of these feeds, when horses are fed from a sack or bin, and gas colic may result. Therefore, it is necessary to do a good job of mixing feed ingredients of different consistency to ensure proper composition of the ration.

# Colic

Colic can be broadly defined as any abdominal pain. In this text, only colic as related to digestion is considered. It may be differentiated into three categories: spasmodic colic, flatulent colic, and colonic impactions. Colonic impactions result when large masses of food pack together and block a portion of the colon so that food cannot pass out into the remainder of the digestive tract. Fibrous feeds or feeds which have been contaminated with sand may be a primary cause. Colic may be caused by these factors or others including overexertion, overeating, sudden changes in the diet, spoiled or toxic feeds, eating or drinking while overheated, or working immediately after eating. Windsucking may also be a cause of flatulent colic. The most common cause of flatulent colic is excessive gas production resulting from a large intake of rich, rapidly fermentable feed.

The symptoms of colic may appear gradually. The horse becomes restless. He may turn his head to look at the flanks. As pain becomes more acute, he may even try to kick the flanks. Pawing the ground, alternately getting up and lying down, rolling on the ground, and profuse sweating also indicate an attack of colic. The horse may attempt to defecate frequently, but may pass only a small amount of manure, or will be unsuccessful. Spasmodic colic is differentiated from flatulent colic in that there may be frequent attacks that will last for a few minutes and then pass. In flatulent colic, large amounts of ingested air, or gas given off by the fermentation of spoiled feeds fills the digestive tract and distends the stomach or intestines.

In all cases of colic, a veterinarian should be called. Intermediate treatment consists of trying to make the horse comfortable, restrain him from injuring himself, and relieve the pressure in the colon. The horse should not be allowed to lie down. If necessary, the horse should be walked to prevent lying down. Otherwise, walking is not necessary. Oral medications or drenches should not be given without guidance, and water should be withheld except in small sips. Frequent irrigation of the rectum and colon should be performed in an attempt to get the animal to pass fecal material. Usually, the symptoms will be relieved within twelve to twenty-four hours.

# Twisted Intestine

Sometimes, a case that starts as simple colic will develop into a case of twisted intestine. The horse may roll excessively to relieve pain due to gas or obstruction and cause a twisted intestine that results in blockage and interruption of blood supply. The mesentery that supports the intestine in the body becomes torn due to trauma, and the intestine twists, cutting off the blood supply to a portion, and completely blocking the passage of digestive products. If the condition is diagnosed early enough, surgery can be performed and the animal's life may be saved. But because the risks of surgery are extremely high, the diagnosis of a twisted intestine should be fairly positive before surgery is begun. Without surgery, twisted intestine is usually fatal. This is one reason why a veterinarian should be called when obvious colic appears in a horse.

# Founder (Laminitis)

Founder, or laminitis, appears as soreness in the feet due to an inflammation of the laminae in the hoof. These are the thin layers of tissue in the hoof from which the horn develops. It is a common disease, and varies in seriousness. In some cases, the horse either dies in the acute stage, or must be put down later because of hopeless lameness.

Little is actually known about the causes of laminitis. It appears that there is a histamine reaction in the body resulting from excessive fermentation of feed, or from stress, but this has not been conclusively proven. Many of the predisposing causes can be pinpointed, however. These include overeating, infection of the uterus after foaling, allergic reactions to feed, overtiring, and traveling. Sometimes a perfectly healthy horse will be affected for no apparent reason.

The initial symptoms may parallel those of colic, except that there is often diarrhea. Temperature may rise. Immediate veterinary treatment is essential if the horse is to be saved. Emergency procedures include administration of purgatives to remove the affective substance from the body (in the case of grain founder). Another step that is frequently of help is to walk the horse in water so that his feet and legs are immersed. This slows blood circulation in the feet, and apparently slows the imflammatory process in the laminae.

If the horse survives the acute phase of laminitis, he may pass into the chronic phase. In this condition, the walls of the hoof become brittle and are marked with rings after a period of time. The feet are sore and sensitive. In severe cases, the sole may drop and the coffin bone rotate. A horse this severely afflicted probably faces permanent lameness.

There are some therapeutic measures that are helpful in treating a foundered horse, but prevention is the best approach. Good feeding management, refraining from overfeeding, and paying attention to details will go a long way toward preventing founder.

## Choke

Choke is a partial or complete blockage of the esophagus. It may frequently be a result of eating feed too fast. A mass of dry grain or other feed becomes lodged midway in the esophageal passage. Choke occurs most often in older horses, and may occur repeatedly in horses that have malformations of the esophagus.

When choke occurs, the horse should be kept calm. A veterinarian should be called at once. He can usually dislodge the mass of food without further problems. Feeding in large shallow containers to prevent gulping mouthfuls of feed will help prevent choking.

## Diarrhea

Diarrhea is characterized by frequent, watery fecal discharges. Fever and abdominal discomfort may be present. Diarrhea is usually a result of eating rich, toxic, or dusty feeds, but may be caused by infectious disease organisms. Impure water may also be a causative factor. Frequently, symptoms will last only a short time, and will disappear without treatment. If diarrhea lasts for more than twenty-four hours, however, and if a very foul odor is noticed, a veterinarian should be called. He can give medication to relieve the symptoms. If diarrheal discharges contain blood, the condition should be considered serious, and the veterinarian should be called without waiting.

The horseman should be aware of the consistency of fecal material during different feeding programs. Feces will be dry or soft depending on type of feed eaten. The feces of horses on pasture in early spring will be looser than those on dry feed. In any event, the horseman should determine normal conditions and be on the alert for abnormal color, odor, or consistency of feces.

## Susceptibility of Horses to Digestive Diseases

The length and configuration of the equine digestive tract, discussed in Chapter One, predisposes the horse to digestive problems. The tract suddenly enlarges and narrows again in several places. It twists and turns many times along its length. This makes intestinal blockage and partial obstruction a not uncommon illness. However, most horses, if fed a healthy diet, can overcome this limitation. A poor diet will almost assure digestive trouble.

## Summary

Digestive disturbances in the horse include colic, founder, and choke among others. Diarrhea also occurs but is usually not serious. All of these diseases can be brought about by dietary conditions. Emergency measures should be followed in the colic, founder, and choke, and a veterinarian should be called at once. Diarrhea is less serious, and a veterinarian need not be called unless the condition lasts or unless there is a very foul odor that suggests infection.

# 21

# Internal Parasites

All horses, at some time in their lives, are infested with internal parasites. Most horses, in fact, are never completely free of worms throughout their entire lives. The main problem, therefore, is not one of eradication but of control. Since different species can best be controlled by different methods, it is first necessary to identify the particular varieties of internal parasites and to understand the stages in their life cycles.

## The Strongyles

The strongyles, often called red worms or bloodworms, are among the most prevalent and most dangerous of the equine internal parasites. (1) They are broken down into two groups: the large strongyles, and the small strongyles. Among these groups there are several classifications.

Strongylus Vulgaris, a variety of large strongyles, is a highly common and dangerous parasite. Fecal examinations performed in an important, but not uncommon experiment on a large group of horses that were chosen at random and appeared to be healthy, showed seventy percent to be infested with these worms. (2)

S. Vulgaris eggs are laid in the intestines of the horse, and are passed out with the feces. The eggs hatch in the grass, and develop into second and then third stage larvae. The entire developmental process takes from five to ten days, depending on climate and temperature conditions. In this third stage, they are infective. They climb up the blades of grass from the roots, and are ingested by the horse while grazing. Once they are ingested, they usually travel to the cecum and colon and live in these areas. They burrow into the mucosal linings, and grow to adult size, (about one inch in length). They sometimes will break free from the intestinal walls, and will migrate into the arteries, especially the mesenteric artery which leads from the heart to the stomach. If this migration occurs in moderate numbers, blockage of the artery may result. If this blockage is complete it will cause sudden death, but if it is partial, it may still cause portions of the intestinal lining to die from loss of blood supply and result in an aneurism, which is an abnormal dilation of the blood vessel wall. If this happens, infection and peritonitis can result. Adult stage strongyles lay eggs, which pass through the colon with the feces, and the cycle begins anew.

Another variety of large strongyles is Strongylus Edentatus. When these larvae are ingested, they also burrow into the cecum or colon walls, like S. Vulgaris. From this stage, they may migrate to the liver through the circulatory system. Or they may remain in the peritoneal lining where they may cause bleeding and tissue death. They are also capable of penetrating directly into other parts of the horse from the gut. (3) These parasites are also highly common, and may reach one and one-half inches in length at maturity.

The third variety of large strongyles is Strongylus Equinus. This variety is rare, and is not considered to be a significant problem in horses today. Its life cycle is parallel to those of other members of the strongyle family.

The small stronglyes consist of a number of different species. They are differentiated from the large strongyles by their smaller size, and are not considered to be as serious a problem. However, they are common enough that treatment is necessary. They are found most often in the cecum and colon, where they form cysts in the mucous membrane. If they occur in large numbers, inflammation and digestive upset may result. Their life cycle, like the large strongyles, varies from two to twelve months in length, depending on the variety of worm and the host conditions. The most favorable climatic conditions for development are mild, consistent temperatures with moderate sunlight and moisture. Excessive heat or cold can be fatal to larvae.

# Pinworms

Oxyuris Equi, the seat or pinworm, is not as serious a problem in horses as the bloodworms. (4) However, while it does not usually cause serious or dangerous illness, its presence may be a source of discomfort for the animal. The eggs are passed in the feces and are ingested by the horse while grazing. They hatch in the cecum and large colon. After maturity, the females are fertilized. They then crawl to the anus to lay their eggs. In this area they cause itching and irritation. The affected animal may rub against objects such as doors, fences, and trees to relieve the irritation. This may cause loss of hair and skin irritation. After several days, the eggs are released from the mucosal wall of the anus, and are passed out of the body.

## The Ascarids

The ascarids, Parascaris Equorum, are a highly migratory parasite. They are consumed in egg form from the pasture, and hatch inside the body. The larvae enter the bloodstream from the intestines, migrate to the liver, and from there may move to the heart and lungs. (5) In the lungs they may cause respiratory difficulties and pneumonia. From the lungs they pass upward to the pharynx, and from there are returned to the stomach with the ingested food. In the stomach they reach adult form and lay eggs, which are returned to the pasture with the feces. Ascarids appear in foals as early as eight weeks of age, and as the horse matures the infestation becomes lighter and less common. It appears that horses become immune to this parasite as they grow older, and ascarids are rarely found in horses over two years old. It is the presence of ascarids that is most likely to be responsible for the unthrifty appearance of parasitized young horses.

## The Strongyloides

The strongyloides, Strongyloides Westeri, are another parasite to which horses seem to develop immunity with age. Strongyloides may affect the foal within the first week of life, but immunity is usually complete by one year of age. The strongyloides live primarily in the small intestine. They may be a cause of diarrhea in the young horse, but this has not been conclusively proven. (6)

## The Bot Worms

There are several species of bots, of which the most common is Gastrophilus Intestinalis. The adult of this species is the bot fly. The fly lays eggs on the hairs of the horse's coat, and these eggs are licked off and carried into the mouth. The eggs develop into the larval form inside the body of the animal, and in this stage they attach themselves to the mucosal linings of the stomach and intestines. The exact location depends on the species. In the larval form, they cause irritation and bleeding, and may even penetrate the intestinal wall, causing peritonitis. (7) As the bot larvae mature, they are passed out of the body in the dung, where they hatch into adult flies. The other species of bots that commonly afflict horses are G. nasalis, and G. haemorrhoidalis. (8) Their life cycles are similar.

## The Dangers of Worm Infestation

Internal parasites are so common that prevention is almost impossible. If they are not controlled, however, they will produce weakness, disability, and even death. The horse with a large worm population within the body will exhibit signs of poor health. A blood count will usually reveal anemia, and the energy level will be low. The condition of the coat will be poor, and there may be digestive disturbances and predisposition to colic. Although not all horses with parasite infestation will show these symptoms, it can be conclusively stated that any horse with a large worm colony in the body cannot perform at its highest capabilities. In serious cases, internal hemorrhaging, peritonitis, or arterial and intestinal blockage may eventually result in the death of the animal.

## Methods of Parasite Control

The most essential step in parasite control is worming at regular intervals by a proven method. The two major medications for control of internal parasites are thiabendazole and piperazine. (9) If these medications are given in measured amounts at the proper time, they can effectively control all of the common worm species. Phenothiazine may also be used against some species. In order to determine which medications are necessary, a fecal analysis and culture should be done. The egg count in the feces will determine the approximate number of worms in the body, and will indicate the type. After concluding the nature of the parasite problem, a complete worming program should be begun. It is recommended that horses be tubed by a qualified veterinarian at least every six months, and that each treatment consist of two doses approximately three weeks apart. Worm medications in feed may be used as long as the horse will consume the drugs and the results are satisfactory. Obviously, horses that will not consume anthelmintics must be tubed. Tubing is generally considered the most effective method of eradicating parasites. Since tubing is a dangerous procedure if not properly undertaken by a qualified person, it should be done only by a veterinarian.

A complete worming program should be worked out and scrupulously adhered to. An exact method cannot be given that is universally applicable, because worming dates and medications vary with the worm population and the climate of a particular region. In all cases a veterinarian should be consulted to devise a complete program. There are several guidelines which can be successfully applied by everyone, however. These include the need for two doses, several weeks apart, at each treatment. This is because the initial treatment will kill the adult worms in the intestines. Unfortunately, however, the treatment is not effective against the eggs and the larval stages in the other parts of the body. Then, while the worm population in the cecum and colon may be temporarily depleted by the medication, within several weeks the larvae in other parts of the body will have migrated to the cecum and colon, and they will again be infested. Therefore it is necessary to administer two doses to effect full control.

Other methods of worm control which are applicable to all areas are the various forms of pasture control. Pasture control of parasites is often overlooked, yet it is one of the most effective and important methods of destroying the worm population in an area. There are several measures which are commonly used: pasture rest, rotational grazing, segregated pastures, feces removal, chain dragging, harrowing, and plowing. (10)

Pasture rest consists of alternately grazing and resting a pasture at six month intervals. During the resting period, the egg population in the pasture can be killed off in large numbers by sunlight, heat, cold, and lack of hosts. When the horses are returned to grazing in that pasture, there should be few or no worms to begin their life cycles. This measure is considered to be especially useful if the pasture can be left ungrazed for nine months, including both winter and summer.

Rotational grazing is a variation of pasture rest which allows the pasture to be put to use during the rest period. Since equine parasites tend to avoid cattle as hosts, and vice versa, alternate grazing with horses and cattle will allow the equine parasites to die out while cattle are grazing, and will also provide depletion of cattle parasites while being used for horses. There are rare examples of horses being affected by parasites normally found in cattle, but these cases are so rare as to be of no statistical significance. Rotational grazing can therefore be considered a useful control method.

Segregation of pastures implies that weanlings and yearlings will be grazed in separate areas from mature horses. If their dams are wormed within a month before foaling and parasites are carefully controlled while they have foals at side, this provides that parasites will not be passed from mature horses to young horses in the same pasture. (11) Since the foals are born free of worms, if they are grazed on clean pasture and kept away from horses already infested, the chances of developing internal parasites are greatly reduced.

Removal of feces from pastures and stables should always be done as often as possible. If dung is collected from pastures at least twice a week, eggs rarely have time to hatch into larval forms, and parasites cannot easily be spread. This involves more actual physical effort than other control measures in the pasture, but it should always be considered as worthwhile. In fact, it is probably the most valuable way to control parasites in the pasture.

Chain dragging of pastures has some benefits in worm control. Dragging chains behind a tractor through the pasture does not spread the feces too widely, but it does break up the manure piles and expose them to sunlight. This will reduce the worm population to some degree, but it will not completely eradicate it. While not the most successful measure of parasite control, chain dragging is nevertheless superior to harrowing or plowing of pastures.

Harrowing of pastures is a fair method of reducing the spread of worms. In this method the feces are spread through the pasture. This exposes the eggs and larvae to the sunlight which may be fatal to them. Spreading of **fresh** manure, by any method, is not advised. It is likely to spread both parasite eggs and larvae forms, and also weed seeds. if spread, manure should first be composted.

Plowing of pastures to spread feces and bury eggs and larvae has long been utilized in worm control, but it is doubtful that its effect is sufficient to warrant the trouble. In fact, it may actually be harmful. Like harrowing, it may act only to spread parasites from small scattered areas throughout the entire pasture, and it may also affect the flavor of the grass so that horses may refuse to graze in certain areas. And if the pasture is plowed deeply enough to inhibit worm development (to a depth of at least twelve inches), it may prove detrimental and disruptive to plant growth within the pasture. Probably the main benefit derived from plowing is that it allows the pasture to be rested while plant growth becomes re-established. Plowing is not recommended as a useful method of parasite control.

# Effect of Internal Parasites on Nutrition

It can always be assumed that the horse which is heavily afflicted with internal parasites is not healthy, and will not perform to the fullest of its capabilities. Since these parasites are most commonly found in portions of the alimentary canal, they may have a significant effect on digestion. They may reduce appetite in the horse, and they may produce colic. On the other hand, it has been proven that the well-nourished horse is far less susceptible to heavy parasite infection than the horse whose diet is lacking. (12) If the horse is healthy, it is less likely to become anemic, and the stomach lining is more resistant to penetration by parasites. Further, the horse that is well-nourished is better able to withstand the effects of being taken off feed before worming.

*photo courtesy of Al-Marah Arabians*

**The extremely versatile Arabian horse can perform any one of many activities, when placed on a well-balanced ration, enabling him to receive the proper energy requirements, as well as bone and tissue building components.**

# Summary

Internal parasites are a significant problem for every horse owner, because they can be found in every horse. The major types of internal parasites include strongyles, ascarids, strongyloids, pinworms, and bots. Their primary source of irritation is in the lining of the cecum and large colon, where the larvae burrow into the mucous membranes. Parasites cannot be eradicated, but they can be controlled. Control methods include fecal analysis, and subsequent dosage with anthelmintic drugs including thiabendazole, piperazine, and phenothiazine. Tubing is the most effective method, and this should always be performed by a veterinarian.

Pasture control of parasites is also important, and the primary methods include pasture rotation, pasture rest, segregation of foals and yearlings from older animals, and picking up of dung. Plowing, dragging, and harrowing of pastures is also done, but these methods should not be considered to be highly useful. Good nutrition is vital in increasing resistance to parasites and good response to worm-control treatment. A good worm-control program is essential to good stable management.

## REFERENCES CITED

1. Dunn, Angus M., Ph.D., M.R.C.V.S., **Veterinary Helminthology.** Lea and Febiger, Philadelphia, (1969)
2. Catcott, E. J., D.V.M., Ph.D., and Smithcors, J. F., D.V.M., Ph.D., Editors, **Equine Medicine and Surgery.** American Veterinary Publications, Inc., Wheaton, Illinois, (1972)
3. Rossdale, Peter D., M.A., F.R.C.V.S., **The Horse.** The California Thoroughbred Breeders Association, California, (1972)
4. Rossdale, Peter D., **Op. Cit.**
5. Dunn, Angus M., Ph.D., **Op. Cit.**
6. Catcott, E. J., D.V.M., Ph.D., and Smithcors, J. F., D.V.M., Ph.D., Editors, **Progress in Equine Practice, Volume Two.** American Veterinary Publications, Inc., Wheaton, Illinois, (1970)
7. Rooney, James R., D.V.M., **Autopsy of the Horse, Technique and Interpretation.** The Williams and Wilkins Co., Baltimore, (1970)
8. Ensminger, M. E., Ph.D., **Horses and Horsemanship.** Interstate Printers and Publishers, Inc., Danville, Illinois (1969)
9. Siegmund, O. H., Editor, **The Merck Veterinary Manual.** Merck and Co., Inc., Rahway, New Jersey, (1967)
10. Hayes, M. Horace, F.R.C.V.S., **Stable Management and Exercise.** Arco Publishing Company, Inc., New York, (1968)
11. Rossdale, Peter D., **Op. Cit.**
12. Miller, Wm. C., F.R.C.V.S., F.R.S.E., **Practical Essentials in the Care and Management of Horses on Thoroughbred Studs.** The Thoroughbred Breeders Association, London, (1965)

# 22

# Teeth And Digestion

The importance of healthy teeth and their role in the digestive process cannot be minimized. The teeth can be considered as accessory organs of the digestive tract, and unless they perform their proper function at the beginning of the digestive process, the entire system can be thrown out of balance. Healthy teeth are necessary to breakdown food into small pieces, and for crushing and grinding seed coats and stems. If this is not done, the saliva cannot begin the digestion of starch in the mouth, and the feed cannot move smoothly through the alimentary canal. (1)

## The Equine Dental System

The horse, like the human, has two sets of teeth. The first set, comparable to human "baby teeth," are the deciduous teeth. These consist of the first, second, and third incisors on each side, and the first, second, and third premolars on each side. Canine teeth may also be present. The first incisor and the first premolar are usually present at birth or shortly after, and the other deciduous teeth appear gradually until about nine months of age, at which time they will be through the skin. After the deciduous teeth have erupted, they take approximately six months to grow out fully, and they then remain in place until they are replaced by the permanent teeth.

The permanent teeth appear in the mouth more gradually than the deciduous teeth. The molars, which are located behind the premolars on each side, and which do not replace a deciduous tooth, are the first to

The American Quarter Horse Association named Poco Sugar Leo (above) as the Honor Roll Working Cow Horse of 1972. Owned by Marc Mogol of Roseville, California, the beautiful bay gelding maintains his active performance schedule at the age of 10, due to a well-balanced feeding program.

erupt. These usually penetrate the skin at about nine to twelve months of age (the first molar), and the second and third molars on each side appear at one to one and one-half year intervals thereafter. The first premolars, or "wolf teeth", will normally appear at about five to six months of age. These teeth appear in front of the deciduous first premolars in the mouth, rather than replacing them. In some horses, these teeth never appear, and they are usually extracted in those cases where they are present. The permanent first incisors, (central incisors), and second premolars usually replace the deciduous first incisors and second premolars at about two and one-half years, and these are followed at one year intervals by the permanent second incisors, (lateral incisors) and third premolars, and the permanent third incisors (corner incisors) and fourth premolars. Thus, the horse will have a full set of permanent teeth that are all in wear by about five years of age.

## Effect of Age on Teeth

In the mouth of the mature horse, there are thirty-six teeth. Three of these teeth are located on each side, both top and bottom, in the front part of the mouth, and six on each side, top and bottom, in the back part of the mouth. In addition, males may have four canine teeth, (occasionally called bridle teeth), located one on each side, both top and bottom, in the space between the third incisor and the second premolar. On occasion, mares will have these canine teeth, but they will only be vestigial. There are commonly two upper wolf teeth located directly in front of the premolars. Occasionally, there are lower wolf teeth as well.

After the horse reaches five years of age, and all the teeth are in use, the dental surfaces begin to change with age and wear. Because of these changes, it may be possible to determine a horse's age by examining his teeth with a fair degree of accuracy. The teeth at first are round on their cutting surfaces, and there is a "cup" or hollow on these cutting surfaces. As the age of the horse increases, these cutting surfaces begin to show wear, their shape changes from oval to triangular, and the cup disappears. (2) Also, as the surface of the tooth wears, the angle at which the top and bottom teeth meet begins to change. In the young horse, the teeth meet on a flat surface, flush with each other. As the horse ages, they meet less perfectly, almost at a right angle. In the very old horse, many pairs of top and bottom teeth meet only at the front edge of the cutting surfaces.

Other signs of age may be noted by examining the teeth. These include the appearance of a dark-colored groove on the upper third incisors at about ten years of age. This groove runs lengthwise on the teeth, beginning at the gum, and progresses downward with increasing age, until it covers the entire length of the teeth in the twenty year old horse. This groove is called Galvayne's Groove. (3) After the age of twenty, the groove begins to disappear from the top down, until by the age of thirty it is no longer visible. Another mark of age which appears on the teeth is the so-called "dental star", which is a pulp cavity in the tooth. The filling of this cavity is of a lighter color than the body of the tooth. As the teeth wear with age, the cavity becomes visible on the table surface of the tooth. It first appears at about eight years of age as a thin line across the chewing surface. With increasing age, it becomes more rounded and moves inward, until by fifteen years of age, it is a round, distinct mark on the center of the table surface of the teeth. (4)

## Wolf Teeth

The first permanent premolars, or "wolf teeth", appear in the top of the mouth in front of the deciduous first premolars at the age of about six months. And, as was mentioned earlier, they occasionally appear in the bottom of the mouth. They are interesting because of the many myths connected with them. It was formerly thought that the presence of the wolf teeth would in some way interfere with vision, and would eventually cause blindness in the horse if they were not removed. (5) For this reason, wolf teeth were routinely extracted shortly after they emerged. Since the teeth have very shallow roots, this causes little pain and no permanent damage to the horse. However, the procedure is completely unnecessary, unless the wolf teeth in some way interfere with the development of the other teeth. If they appear to impinge on the permanent teeth in any way, or if they cause discomfort or improper chewing, then they should of course be extracted, but they may otherwise be left in the mouth with no harm.

## Digestive Disturbances Caused by Dental Malformation

The primary problem that may arise concerning the teeth of the horse is any condition which prevents proper chewing. As previously discussed, this keeps the food from being properly broken down in the mouth and does not allow the primary breakdown of starches before digestion in the stomach. Improper chewing may be caused by sharp teeth edges, broken teeth, missing teeth, or congenital malformations. Improper chewing may first be apparent by horses "going off feed", or taking longer to clean it up. Drooling, or bleeding in the mouth is another symptom. Strong, foul odors from the mouth may indicate cavities or trapped food. Poor chewing should also be suspected if many unchewed grains are excreted in the feces.

If the teeth are too sharp, the edges may actually cut the cheek surfaces as the horse chews his food. In addition to causing bleeding and infection in the cheeks, the pain that results will in many cases cause the horse to bolt food without chewing it thoroughly. This can cause choke, if large mouthfuls of improperly chewed food become trapped in the esophagus. It can also in extreme cases cause colic, if large particles of improperly chewed food become impacted in the stomach. In less extreme cases, it merely means that the full nutrient value of the food is not received by the horse.

Broken teeth will also leave sharp edges that can cause the same problems, including cutting of the cheeks and tongue. In addition, broken teeth and missing teeth leave spaces in the mouth where there should be none. This can cause food to slip between the teeth and the cheeks and become trapped in that space. The food ferments, and the horse can become subject to infection or digestive disturbances if the trapped food is not frequently removed from the mouth.

Caries, (tooth decay), is rarely a problem in the horse, and when it occurs it is usually the result of trauma. (6) Unless the diet of the horse is varied greatly and includes far too many sweets, the teeth seldom decay unless they have received some injury that weakens them. If decay is present, however, it becomes recognizable by a strong odor on the animal's breath.

Congenital malformations of the mouth can usually be classified as either parrot mouth, (where the upper jaw extends past the lower jaw), and undershot jaw, in which the reverse is true. In these cases, the incisor teeth do not meet where they should. The incisors may become very long as a result of not being worn down properly, and will prevent proper grazing or grasping of food. Unlike the previously mentioned problems, however, there are no cures for these conditions. The problem may be minimized by filing the incisors to proper length periodically, but if the condition is serious there is little that can be done.

## Proper Dental Care

Regular dental check-ups by a veterinarian are a must for the healthy horse. If they are performed at regular intervals and in the proper manner, they will ensure that minor dental problems are handled before they can cause serious disturbances.

A complete dental checkup should include careful examination of the dental surfaces for proper, even wear. Teeth which have sharp edges should be floated, (rasped with a special file), to remove these points, and teeth which have not worn evenly with other dental surfaces should be filed until they are even. The mouth should be checked for any lacerations or cuts, and these should be treated with antiseptic. If possible, the cause of the lacerations should be determined, and if it results from some condition of the teeth, steps should be taken to correct it. Unhealthy teeth which cannot be saved should be extracted. It is recommended that these checkups should take place on a semi-annual basis, and should also be made whenever there is reason to suspect trouble with the teeth, as has been previously explained.

## Summary

Healthy teeth are vital to the proper digestion of food. The horse has two sets of teeth: the deciduous teeth, which are gradually lost, and the permanent teeth. There are thirty-six functional teeth in the mouth of the mature horse. In some horses, there may also be four canine teeth and two to four wolf teeth. The surfaces of the teeth are worn down with age, and show characteristic signs depending on the age of the horse. Complete dental checkups should be performed at six month intervals, or sooner if dental trouble is suspected. Lack of proper dental care can cause poor digestion, discomfort, and infection in the mouth, and can lead to a generally unhealthy animal.

### REFERENCES CITED

1. Catcott, E. J., D.V.M., Ph.D., and Smithcors, J. F., D.V.M., Ph.D., Editors, **Equine Medicine and Surgery.** American Veterinary Publications, Inc., Wheaton, Illinois, (1972)
2. Smith, A. F., D.V.M., "The Teeth of the Horse," Paper, presented to Southwest Planning Conference for Livestockmen, Waco, Texas, March, 1973.
3. Simmons, Hoyt, **Horseman's Veterinary Guide.** The Western Horseman, Colorado Springs, Colorado, (1963)
4. Smith, A. F., D.V.M., **Op. Cit.**
5. Jones, William E., D.V.M., Ph.D., Editor, **The Teeth of the Horse.** Caballus Publishers, East Lansing, Michigan, (1972)
6. Smith, A. F., D.V.M., **Op. Cit.**

# 23

# Feeding
# Problems, Appetite,
# And Psychology

## Stable Vices

The most common stable vices are cribbing, wind sucking, wood chewing, and stall weaving. Some of these may be considered to be nutritionally related, while others are most probably attributable to psychological problems such as boredom.

Cribbing should be considered an unsoundness in a horse. The cribber rests the teeth on an object such as the stall door, draws back the upper lip, arches the neck, and by depressing the tongue and elevating the larynx, pulls backward and upward, bears down with the teeth, and swallows air. Cribbing causes the edge of the front teeth to wear away on the outer surfaces. The cribber may be identified by careful examination of the upper front incisors for this characteristic wearing. (1)

Most horsemen assume that a cribber and a wind sucker are one in the same. This is not necessarily true. The horse that has been wind sucking for some time may not always crib simultaneously.

The cribber and wind sucker will frequently be underweight. He will generally be a hard keeper, and will pay little attention to his feed at times. Research on the subject suggests that there may be more to the problem than the simple fact that the nervous horse does not eat well. Some researchers believe when the horse draws air into the stomach, it results in a false feeling of fullness, causing loss of appetite and indifference to feed.

The cause of cribbing is not clearly identifiable. The vice probably begins as the result of boredom, and may be continued strictly from habit. (2) Boredom is normally the result of too much "stall time", and insufficient exercise, and attention.

Wood chewing is a habit in which the horse chews on all the wooden objects around him — fence posts, gates, and stall doors. Wood chewers should be distinguished from cribbers and wind suckers. Wood chewing is often attributed to insufficient oral satisfaction, or lack of things to chew on. Some horsemen claim that pelleted feeds may be one factor that encourages wood chewing, since the horse on a completely pelleted ration finishes a meal quickly, with little chewing required. Again, however, boredom is probably the primary motivating factor. Wood chewing may also result from a mineral deficiency that causes the horse to crave specific or unnatural foods. This theory might be validated by performing a blood and hair analysis on the horse in question to see if a mineral imbalance is in fact present. Phosphorus deficiency has been known to cause wood chewing in other animals, and this may also be true in the case of horses.

Whatever the initiating cause, cribbing and wood chewing can be discouraged to a large degree by treating all the wooden surfaces with which the horse comes in contact. Creosote may be used, or some commercial substance designed specifically for such purpose. Another fact to keep in mind is that the normal wood chewing animal is often discouraged when the only wood available to him is very hard, such as oak. The softer woods, such as pine, seem to encourage the wood chewing habit. Feeding good quality, long hay is often helpful, as it provides the horse with additional phosphorus, and allows more chewing. Cribbing and wind sucking may also be prevented with the use of a brace or strap that prevents the horse from holding its neck in the proper position for these vices. (3) Many such devices are widely marketed and the horseman is usually offered a fairly wide selection through his local tack shop.

Stall weaving is a condition in which the animal rocks back and forth on its front legs in the stall. It is usually the result of nervousness or boredom. Turning a horse out to pasture as much as possible, more time spent in grooming, and increased exercise are three suggestions generally found helpful. Also, the addition of a stall mate in the stall with him, such as a goat, will often serve to distract the weaver's attention and break the habit. Another trick sometimes found useful is hanging several plastic bottles or tether balls in the stall about head height from rafters. The stall weaver normally has one spot in the stall where he prefers to practice this vice, and the hanging objects should be hung in this area. A single dangling plastic bottle, or a tether ball is often found to be beneficial for any nervous horse. As he plays with the hanging object by batting it with his nose, he oftens works off nervous energy that might otherwise be spent developing a wood chewing, cribbing, or weaving habit. With stall weavers, however, it is usually recommended that several such objects be used.

Sometimes a horse which has developed stall weaving, in an isolated situation, can be helped by putting him in a stall where he is able to view other horses. However, should this procedure not work quickly, it should be borne in mind that stall weaving, like cribbing and wood chewing, is easily picked up by other horses, and the horse which continues in this vice, should probably be isolated from other horses.

The horse which possesses stable vices such as those mentioned above, is likely to be underweight, nervous, and a poor doer. On the other hand, the healthy, well-fed horse receiving adequate exercise and attention is not likely to be as subject to such stall vices.

## Easy and Hard Keepers; Good and Poor Doers

The easy keeper is the horse which is not prone to digestive troubles, and easily maintains a balanced weight and healthy appearance from a normal ration. The hard keeper, on the other hand, tends to lose weight easily. Even a slight change in rations may cause digestive disturbance. This horse is difficult to fatten and difficult to condition. These problems are often related to the metabolism of the individual horse. Although it is difficult to judge horses for these characteristics on the basis of appearance only, the easy keeper will appear sleek and healthy and well-nourished in most cases. The hard keeper may be underweight or poorly nourished, in spite of the fact that he cleans up his trough every night. These qualities, if no other problems are present, such as being infested with worms, are usually of metabolic origin, and they are innate, so there is little that can be done. However, the hard keeper should be closely watched to make sure that his diet is well-balanced and enriched as far as possible, and that he is wormed regularly. This may minimize his problems.

Good doers are those which clean up their feed tubs rapidly, and are not picky eaters. Poor doers, on the other hand, are horses which have choosy appetites, go off of feed easily, and do not clean up feed readily. Poor doers, like hard keepers, may appear under-nourished. Good doers will have a healthy, well-fed appearance. Unlike, hard and easy keepers, however, poor and good doers are often influenced by psychological causes, rather than by differences in metabolism. The good doer is not a problem as long as he is not allowed to overeat. The poor doer is frequently the result of poor feeding when young and/or the victim of psychological problems. If the horse is accustomed to a balanced ration, the likelihood of going off feed is greatly reduced. The poor doer may sometimes be treated by tempting with special delicacies to increase his appetite. Molasses, sliced carrots, and soaked beet pulp are "extras" which may be offered to a poor doer when he goes off feed. (4) These are flavorful and highly digestible, and may be mixed with the regular concentrate ration, or may be offered instead of the ration, (in extreme cases), until the horse has resumed eating regularly.

## "Nibblers"

Nibblers may be defined as treats given to horses that would not normally be part of the regular ration, and are high in flavor rather than necessarily in nutritional value. They are frequently fed to satisfy the psychological need of the owner to "be good" to his horse, rather than to meet the nutritional or psychological needs of the horse itself. However, no matter what the motive may be, the possible psychological value to the horse should not be underestimated. Acceptable nibblers include carrots, apples, lettuce leaves, etc. The use of sugar as a nibbler is not recommended.

Nibblers are rarely fed as part of a meal. For this reason they are a very small part of a total ration, and so have little nutritional significance. Instead, they are offered as rewards, treats, or psychological incentives. For example, many horseman may pass out carrots as they walk through the barn at a certain time of day. Trainers of trick horses may offer an apple as reward for performing a certain trick properly. Another may use some nibbler to tempt the horse in the paddock to come to the rail.

When nibblers are used properly as treats or training aids, they can be very useful. There are several drawbacks to the use of nibblers, however, and these should be carefully considered.

If the horse learns that an owner frequently carries treats in his pocket, the horse may begin attempting to nose through the pockets every time his owner walks by. This can become a source of irritation and inconvenience if it is continued. The logical solution to this problem would seem to be, to drop the nibbler into the trough, as opposed to hand feeding.

When nibblers are used as training aids, they should be offered for every success at first. They should then be presented less and less frequently, so that the horse learns that he must perform the test correctly, but does not know when to expect a reward. After the test is learned, rewards should be given occasionally, so that the learning process is reinforced, but they should be infrequent. If reinforcement is always given, instead of occasionally, response may be lost when the reward is withdrawn. (5) If nibblers are used judicially, and the possible drawbacks are recognized, they will not be harmful.

## Summary

Stables vices, including cribbing, wind sucking, wood chewing, and stall weaving may cause a horse to become underweight and nervous. It is possible that these vices originate from boredom, although mineral deficiences, lack of satisfaction in chewing, and nervousness have also been suggested as causes. There are no foolproof remedies, but treating wood, less stall time, more exercise and attention, and the use of restraining devices may have some effect.

Horses may be classified as good or poor doers, depending on whether or not they clean up feed rapidly. They may also be categorized as easy or hard keepers, according to whether or not they utilize feed well. Good doers and easy keepers pose no problems, but poor doers and hard keepers should be watched to make sure their diets are adequate, and that they maintain good health.

Nibblers are foods offered as treats. They form only a small part of the ration and would seem to have more psychological than nutritional significance. If they are not carefully used, however, they can encourage annoying vices.

### REFERENCES CITED

1. Straiton, E. C., **The Horse Owner's Vet Book.** J. B. Lippincott Co., Philadelphia, (1973)
2. Summerhays, Reginald S. **The Problem Horse.** A. S. Barnes and Company, New York, (1959)
3. Straiton, E. C., **Op. Cit.**
4. The Blood-Horse, **Feeding the Horse.** The Blood-Horse, Lexington, Kentucky, (1969)
5. Smythe, R. H., M.R.C.V.S., **The Mind of the Horse.** The Stephen Greene Press, Brattleboro, Vermont, (1965)

# 24

# The Art And
# Science Of Feeding
## (Expert opinions and practices)

The "arts" (practical methods), of horse feeding have been presented in this chapter through interviews with some of the leading breeders, trainers, and owners throughout the country. These interviews are composed of comments from leading horsemen representing several different breeds. The "science" of horse feeding is admirably represented in this chapter through interviews with leading scientists from different parts of the country, but whose scientific interests are the same . . . equine nutrition.

Our editorial policy in this chapter is to not comment pro or con on the material presented. Our goal has simply been to choose intelligent, qualified, high-ranking members from each category represented, and we leave it to the reader to agree or disagree with the various points as they are presented. The experts interviewed in this section were not chosen on the basis of whether or not they agreed with our opinions on the subject of equine nutrition. They were chosen strictly on the basis of their "standing" in the horse world.

Obviously, there are other fine and well-qualified horsemen, and scientists that could have been interviewed for this section. However, space limitations had to be considered.

Interviews were compiled on an objective basis by John M. Brown, Public Relations Director for Equine Research Publications. Through several years of turf-writing assignments and personality interviews for horse-oriented publications, Mr. Brown has come into contact with many of the leading individuals of the horse world. This experience proved to be very beneficial in the overall success of this chapter.

# Dr. Donald D. Nelson

*Being a recognized expert in his field of endeavor, Dr. Donald D. Nelson of Fresno, California conducts research in equine nutrition as part of his position at California State University.*

*Ten years of practice and research have placed him among the most qualified scientists in the country, in the field of equine nutrition. Having obtained his Ph.D. in equine nutrition, Dr. Nelson has continually kept abreast of all studies conducted in that field. In fact, Dr. Nelson has authored, and co-authored some of the most learned papers ever published on the subject of equine nutrition.*

**QUESTION:** What areas in the field of equine nutritional research do you feel are most in need of further study?

**ANSWER:** The effect of high-intensity exercise on the nutrient requirements of the horse. Also, the relationship of trace minerals to nutrition.

**QUESTION:** What do you think are the particular advantages or disadvantages of the popular grains fed today?

**ANSWER:** Oats are preferred by many horsemen because of the high fiber content, which makes it a relatively safe grain. Corn is the best grain from the standpoint of an energy source. Corn is also a good conditioner because of the natural oil content. Rolled barley is a widely used grain for horses in our area.

**QUESTION:** Which grains normally have the highest palatability factor for horses?

**ANSWER:** Corn, barley and oats.

**QUESTION:** When would you recommend using processed grains rather than natural grains?

**ANSWER:** Processed grains are not really necessary, but I use steam-rolled grains in concentrate mixtures.

**QUESTION:** What method of processing is most valuable for oats?

**ANSWER:** Crimping.

**QUESTION:** What method of processing is most valuable for corn?

**ANSWER:** Steam-rolling.

**QUESTION:** What about "race horse" oats? Are they worth the additional expense for the average horse?

**ANSWER:** The heavier the oat, and the higher quality the oat, the more nutritional value.

**QUESTION:** Which cutting of hay provides the highest quality?

**ANSWER:** I don't really care what cutting the hay comes from, so long as it is clean, (free of weeds) and it is harvested before it matures.

**QUESTION:** What are the advantages of mixing grass and legume hays?

**ANSWER:** Mixing legume hay with grass hay improves the nutritive value of the grass hay.

**QUESTION:** What varieties of hay available in your area are highest in nutritional value?

**ANSWER:** Alfalfa hay.

**QUESTION:** What varieties of hay available in your area tend to be most palatable?

**ANSWER:** High quality alfalfa hay is the hay of choice in this area.

**QUESTION:** What is the minimum amount of hay necessary for a balanced diet?

**ANSWER:** This depends on the individual horse and amount of work being done. However, I would not feed less than ten pounds of hay per day for a thousand pound horse.

**QUESTION:** Do you feel that it is best to feed hay from a manger, in a net, on the ground, or how?

**ANSWER:** Overhead mangers cause the horse to inhale too much dust. Feeding on the ground results in ingestion of parasite eggs, and in some cases sand, which can cause "sand colic."

**QUESTION:** Is pasture important to a complete ration?

**ANSWER:** It is a good feed, but it is not necessary.

**QUESTION:** How do you decide what are the best types of pasture to plant?

**ANSWER:** Legume, or legume/grass mixtures are best in our area.

**QUESTION:** What do you think of the practice of horsemen feeding "nibblers" to their stalled horses?

**ANSWER:** I do not recommend this practice, and I feel that they are used mainly to make the owner, rather than the horse, feel better.

**QUESTION:** How useful do you feel the protein concentrates soybean meal, linseed meal, and cottonseed meal are?

**ANSWER:** I feel that soybean meal has the highest quality protein in terms of amino acid content. Linseed meal is a good conditioner (i.e. bloom). Cottonseed meal is the most commonly used protein supplement in this area, and I would rate it second to soybean meal in comparing the three concentrates.

**QUESTION:** Are commercial protein supplements valuable and worthwhile?

**ANSWER:** If the commercial protein supplements are used properly, they are worthwhile. My main criticism is their cost, and the widespread improper, or excessive uses of them.

**QUESTION:** Should protein supplements be added to the diet routinely, or only under special circumstances?

**ANSWER:** With mature horses receiving high quality alfalfa hay, protein supplements are not normally required.

**QUESTION:** How can you determine most effectively how much of a protein supplement to feed?

**ANSWER:** Protein requirements are determined mainly by age and productivity of the animal. Young animals require more protein and higher quality protein (amino acid balance) than other animals. Lactating mares and breeding stallions also have increased protein requirements.

**QUESTION:** Is it preferable to feed mineralized salt, plain salt, or both?

**ANSWER:** The horseman should feed trace-mineralized salt free-choice.

**QUESTION:** In your opinion, what is the role of vitamin E in body function?

**ANSWER:** Vitamin E plays a vital role in muscle metabolism.

**QUESTION:** Do you feel that vitamin E can have a beneficial effect on racing, working, or breeding performance?

**ANSWER:** Therapeutic levels of vitamin E have not proven to increase fertility in large animals. Vitamin E and selenium combinations sometimes have been used in treatment of "tying-up" syndrome.

**QUESTION:** Are vitamin supplements necessary if the diet is well-balanced?

**ANSWER:** Not usually.

**QUESTION:** Are there any special activities that could necessitate vitamin supplementation, such as strenuous work or foaling? If so, what vitamins and under what circumstances?

**ANSWER:** Energy intake should be increased in working horses. This is usually done by increasing both the amount of feed and the energy density or content of the feed. The B-complex vitamins are involved in energy utilization, therefore as more energy is fed, more B vitamins may be required for efficient energy utilization. A good and economical source of all the B-complex vitamins, with the exception of vitamin $B_{12}$, is brewer's yeast. A couple of tablespoons at each feeding, or about five pounds per ton of concentrate should be adequate. Wheast is also a good source of B vitamins, and so is green pasture.

I also feel that concentrate rations should be supplemented with vitamins A and E if the horse does not have access to green pasture. The precursor of vitamin A, carotene, is very subject to oxidation and its content in stored feeds is unreliable. Any processing of the ration (i.e. steam-rolling or pelleting) that causes heating of the ingredients may also cause the destruction of vitamins A and E. I would recommend providing the horse's minimum daily requirement in the concentrate portion of the ration in the form of stablized vitamins A and E.

**QUESTION:** Do you feel that injected supplements are superior to oral vitamins?

**ANSWER:** No.

**QUESTION:** Do you know of any disadvantages with injected supplements?

**ANSWER:** For one thing, they are too expensive, also they are not as effective in most cases as oral administration via the feed.

**QUESTION:** Is the average horse owner today too concerned with supplements, not concerned enough, or does he usually have the proper attitude?

**ANSWER:** In my opinion, many horse owners today are too concerned. They are easy prey for high-pressure advertising and sales gimmicks.

**QUESTION:** If a balanced diet is fed, are mineral supplements necessary?

**ANSWER:** The calcium-phosphorus levels should be adequate in a properly balanced diet. Trace-mineralized salt with five percent magnesium oxide should be fed free-choice.

**QUESTION:** What do you feel is the ideal calcium to phosphorus ratio?

**ANSWER:** Somewhere between 1.5 and 2 to 1.

**QUESTION:** How would you explain the function and importance of the calcium-phosphorus ratio to a layman?

**ANSWER:** Calcium: essential for normal calcification of bones and teeth, and also for normal muscle function. Phosphorus: necessary for normal bones and feet and for energy utilization.

**QUESTION:** What are the easiest methods of balancing the calcium-phosphorus ratio, and how can you tell if the balance is correct?

**ANSWER:** As long as the minimum requirements for calcium and phosphorus are met, the horse can withstand calcium-phosphorus ratios of 4 or 5 to 1 with no apparent harm.

**QUESTION:** Do you believe mineral supplements should be fed free-choice or forced?

**ANSWER:** Calcium-phosphorus supplements should be fed free-choice separately from the free-choice trace-mineralized salt, which should have five percent magnesium oxide added to it.

**QUESTION:** Do you think that the Total Digestible Nutrient (TDN) system of balancing a ration is practical and valid? Is it a reasonable approach for the average horseman?

**ANSWER:** Yes, to both questions.

**QUESTION:** What factors do you think are most important in considering the preparation of the complete balanced diet?

**ANSWER:** Quality, palatability, cost, availability, and convenience.

**QUESTION:** Do sweet feeds have any advantages or disadvantages?

**ANSWER:** Molasses is a good energy source, it is palatable and reduces dustiness, and helps to prevent separation of ingredients.

**QUESTION:** How much molasses do you feel should be included in the sweet feed mix?

**ANSWER:** Five percent.

**QUESTION:** Are pelleted rations of value in a normal feeding program?

**ANSWER:** Our creep ration is pelleted, to prevent sorting of feed ingredients and to improve palatability.

**QUESTION:** Is pelleted hay an adequate substitute for loose hay?

**ANSWER:** Nutritionally, yes, psychologically no.

**QUESTION:** In your opinion, what are the major advantages and disadvantages of pelleted feeds?

**ANSWER:** The major disadvantage is that poor quality feed ingredients can be hidden in pellets. The advantages are, pellets are easy to handle, and feed ingredients cannot be sorted out by the picky eater.

**QUESTION:** In your experience, have you found commercial feed mixes from reputable companies to be usually adequate in quality?

**ANSWER:** Yes.

**QUESTION:** How can you judge the worth of a commercial feed?

**ANSWER:** Feed analysis, acceptance by horses, and condition of horses.

**QUESTION:** In your opinion, is it ever worthwhile to have a commercial mill prepare your own feeds to your formula?

**ANSWER:** Usually this is not economical unless you use a large volume of feed and can handle it in bulk form.

**QUESTION:** What can you do to increase the palatability of a ration?

**ANSWER:** Keep feed boxes clean, feed only what horse will clean up, and use good quality feeds.

**QUESTION:** Do you think there is any value in cooked rations?

**ANSWER:** No.

**QUESTION:** Do you have any ideal complete rations to recommend for different ages and classes of horses?

**ANSWER:** I use two basic grain rations. The creep ration is fed to nursing and weanling foals. The mature horses are fed the horse concentrate ration. When we are conditioning show and sale horses, or have a horse that is a poor doer, we will replace part of the horse concentrate ration with the creep ration.

I prefer to feed only good quality alfalfa hay when it is available. In order to cut down on waste we chop most of our alfalfa hay and add about 400 pounds of molasses per ton of hay to reduce dustiness and increase energy value.

Following are the formulas of our two basic rations:

## HORSE CONCENTRATE RATION

| Ingredients | Pounds |
|---|---|
| Rolled corn | 750 |
| Rolled barley | 750 |
| Cottonseed meal (mn-41% protein) | 200 |
| Linseed meal (solvent-extracted) | 125 |
| Molasses | 150 |
| Limestone | 20 |
| Dicalcium Phosphate | 10 |
| Trace-mineralized salt | 8 |
| Sodium Sulfate ($NA_2 SO_4$) | 2.0 |
| Vitamin A (13,620,000 I.U. per lb.) | 0.5 |
| Vitamin D (1,362,000 I.U. per lb.) | 1.0 |
| Vitamin E (20,000 I.U. per lb.) | 1.5 |
| Brewer's yeast | 5.0 |
| Total | 2,023.0 |

Calculated analysis:

| | |
|---|---|
| Crude protein | 14.1% |
| TDN (1.44 Mcal D.E.) | 71.8% |
| Calcium | 0.53% |
| Phosphorus | 0.52% |
| Vitamin A | 3,363 I.U. per lb. |

| Vitamin D | 672 I.U. per lb. |
|-----------|------------------|
| Vitamin E | 14 I.U. per lb. |

## FOAL CREEP (PELLETED) — 3/16″ pellet

| Ingredients | Pounds |
|-------------|--------|
| Ground corn | 650 |
| Ground barley | 600 |
| Soybean meal | 360 |
| Dehydrated alfalfa meal | 100 |
| Wheast | 60 |
| Dried skim milk | 40 |
| Dicalcium Phosphate | 30 |
| Limestone | 10 |
| Trace-mineralized salt | 8 |
| Sodium Sulfate ($NA_2 SO_4$) | 2 |
| Vitamin A (13,620,000 I.U. per lb.) | 0.6 |
| Vitamin D (1,362,000 I.U. per lb.) | 0.8 |
| Vitamin E (20,000 I.U. per lb.) | 1.5 |
| Subtotal | 1,862.9 |
| Molasses | 100 |
| Total Ingredients | 1,962.9 |

Calculated analysis:

| | |
|---|---|
| Crude Protein | 18.2% |
| TDN | 72% |
| Fat | 2.5% |
| Crude Fiber | 6.2% |
| Calcium | 0.70% |
| Phosphorus | 0.73% |
| Lysine | 0.91% |
| Vitamin A | 4,000 I.U. per lb. |
| Vitamin D | 600 I.U. per lb. |
| Vitamin E | 15 I.U. per lb. |

**QUESTION:** How can you recognize the poorly nourished horse that appears fat?

**ANSWER:** Tell-tale signs are smaller size and insufficient muscle development.

**QUESTION:** What are the major causes that make a horse a "poor doer"?

**ANSWER:** Internal parasites, bad teeth, and poor feed.

**QUESTION:** How does good nutrition relate to the susceptibility of the horse to parasites?

**ANSWER:** Poorly nourished horses seem to be more susceptible to the development of heavy parasite loads.

**QUESTION:** What do you feel are the newest, best medications for control of: (a) large strongyles, (b) small strongyles, (c) bots, (d) roundworms?

**ANSWER:** Large strongyles and small strongyles are best controlled by Thiabendazole. Bots are best controlled by Dyrex, and roundworms are best controlled by Piperazine.

**QUESTION:** How frequently do you recommend worming and by what method?

**ANSWER:** Begin worming foals at ten to twelve weeks of age, and worm every eight weeks until three years of age. Older horses should be wormed every two to three months, depending on results of periodic fecal examinations. Until weaning, the foals are wormed via a dose syringe with anthelmintics dispended or dissolved in maple syrup. After weaning, they are wormed via a stomach tube. All older horses should be wormed via a stomach tube.

**QUESTION:** What nutrients do you feel affect breeding performance the most?

**ANSWER:** All nutrients affect breeding performance to some degree. The most important nutrient is the one that is most limiting at that particular point in time. One of the biggest problems I see with nutrition of the average broodmare, is overnutrition, not under-nutrition. The biggest problem with lactating mares is most of them do not receive enough energy in their rations. The lactating mare requires almost twice as much energy as she did before she foaled.

**QUESTION:** How many times per day should a horse be fed under ideal circumstances?

**ANSWER:** At least twice per day. A horse that is working hard and eating large amounts of feed should be fed three times per day, with the largest amount of hay being fed at night so that he has plenty of time to eat it, and not be worked while excessively full.

**QUESTION:** How does grooming affect health, appetite, condition, etc.?

**ANSWER:** Anything that makes the horse feel better is bound to improve all three areas.

**QUESTION:** What special precautions should be taken when horses cannot be fed individually, but must be fed in groups?

**ANSWER:** Horses fed in groups should ideally be provided with individual feeders, spaced well apart. Very aggressive and/or very timid horses should be separated, so that all of the horses will get their proper share.

**QUESTION:** What changes should be made in the horse's diet when his activity is increased or decreased?

**ANSWER:** When the horse's work is increased, his energy intake should be increased accordingly. Increased activity does not increase the protein requirement.

**QUESTION:** Do you feel that it is better to change the feed ration frequently in order to make sure that a variety of nutrients are included, or is it better to stick with a proven formula.

**ANSWER:** It is much better to stick with a proven formula.

**QUESTION:** How long should you leave feed in front of a horse if it is not eaten?

**ANSWER:** Until the next feeding.

# Lucien Laurin

*The powerful Meadow Stable, founded by the late C. T. Chenery has certainly come into its own over the past several racing seasons . . . and one person largely responsible for this success is trainer Lucien Laurin. Lucien Laurin, a transplanted Canadian, has taken to the United States racing scene like a duck to water. Of course, the big guns of recent history, performing for Meadow are Secretariat and Riva Ridge, both millionaires in their own respect. This was the first time in racing history, that one stable owned and campaigned two millionaires simultaneously! Lucien Laurin came into the national limelight by means of these two outstanding individuals, but his reputation for being an excellent trainer was well-known before coming to Meadow Stable. Among his other notable performers was Dike, third-place finisher in the 1969 Kentucky Derby to Majestic Prince and Arts and Letters. Mr. Laurin has also had the privilege of dealing with many other excellent runners, but of course the Meadow Stable duo was the "icing on his cake".*

*Lucien has many training secrets and tricks, like all top quality trainers in the Thoroughbred industry, but he insists that a good nutritional program is the backbone of a successful stable.*

Three feedings per day make up the basis for Lucien Laurin's feeding program. Times of 4 a.m.—10:30 a.m.—and 4 p.m. have been designated by the training dean to be the best times to feed for his particular circumstances. Each of the three daily feedings consist of equal amounts, with the 4 a.m. feeding being composed entirely of top-quality race horse oats; the 10:30 a.m. feeding consisting strictly of sweet feed (Fruen Triple Crown); and the 4 p.m. feeding being a combination of oats, vitamins and sweet feed. Lucien leaves these rations in front of the horse for two hours only, if it is not eaten.

Lucien believes in feeding the best quality hay possible, especially with a high protein content. For horses in race training, he feeds alfalfa and timothy. Horses not in training receive alfalfa and clover. Lucien prefers first-cutting hay. He visually inspects all hay fed to his horses, to ensure he is always feeding top quality. His preference for geographical sources of his hay lies between Pennsylvania, Ohio, Michigan, and Canada.

During the daytime hours, Lucien's horses are fed their hay ration from a rack on the floor. During the night however, the racks are removed from the stalls for safety measures. With the quality horseflesh Lucien Laurin has under his care, even the smallest risks cannot be taken.

**Lucien Laurin, born in Canada, and a former jockey before graduating to the trainer's ranks, has become one of the most popular and prominent Thoroughbred trainers on the entire North American continent.**

Lucien insists on the best quality oats available, and prefers whole oats over processed oats. When asked why he prefers the whole oat, Lucien replied, "It doesn't take as much volume." Lucien also feels that there are definite advantages to oats with clipped ends. And he naturally insists on a very clean oat.

Feeding corn in the fall and winter months is a part of the Laurin method. Corn comprises approximately twenty percent of his daily ration during this period. He prefers that the corn be cracked. Another grain added daily to the evening meal is wheat bran. Lucien feeds three quarts of bran in a mash, to keep his horses "loose."

To ensure ample protein in his rations, Lucien supplements soybean meal in his evening rations. He feeds one cup of this high quality protein feed. He also feeds "one bucket of flaxseed in a big mash."

Lucien feeds four ounces of vitamin supplement per day, plus vitamin E powder. He believes in injectable vitamins "sometimes." He also occasionally mixes a mineral supplement in his rations, depending on the needs of the individual animal. Lucien includes a handful of salt in the cooked mash. He does not feed mineralized salt.

Pure, clean water is very important in the Laurin program. Bottled water is used when traveling to ensure that his horses have a consistent water supply, and will thereby not "go off" water.

When questioned about Lucien's hot mash, he informed us that he feeds the mash in the fall of the year, about three times a week. Lucien also believes in feeding sweet feed because "they love it." One quart per day is included in his rations. (He prefers a medium amount of molasses.) Pellets are definitely not a part of Lucien Laurin's feeding program, because he feels that the "natural" state of feeds are much better for the horse.

Lucien changes his feeding program slightly on nights preceding races by giving "light hay, and cutting down on feed." Some other facets of his feeding program include a special "tonic" for picky eaters, and carrots twice a day as "treats" for the horses in his care. He also grazes his horses that are in training about twenty minutes daily. Lucien also believes in using an electrolyte solution in the feed or water for a horse suffering from dehydration.

We questioned Lucien about horses with problems in their eating habits. He told us that he sometimes finds that it will stimulate a "poor doer's" appetite to lessen the amount of exercise he gets. Our next question evoked the most noteworthy quote of the entire interview, and at the same time possibly offered some insight as to why Lucien Laurin is truly a great trainer, and a very nice individual. We asked Lucien, "What do you give to a particularly nervous horse?" His answer . . . "Love."

Lucien also told us he felt that brushing, rubbing and grooming is an absolute essential to the health, nutrition and overall performance of any horse, and his horses receive forty minutes per day of this attention.

Manure is picked up from all Laurin's stalls three times a day. And if the temperature is no lower than 63 to 64 degrees, his horses receive a daily bath. He always uses heated water. Lucien prefers rye straw bedding at the track, and he uses tanbark bedding at the farm.

Other sound stable management procedures adhered to by Lucien are: (1) One helper for every three horses (whether in training or not). (2) A careful and thorough cleaning of each feed tub after each feeding. (3) A blood analysis on each horse approximately every two months. (4) A daily application of hoof dressing.

We asked Lucien if he had any suggestions on stopping a horse from cribbing. He has two methods: one, a cribbing strap, and two, he paints surfaces the horse might use for this vice with red peppers. Lucien worms his horses every two months with a commercial powder, and has their teeth checked for any dental work that might be necessary three times a year. Another medical measure strictly adhered to by Mr. Laurin is to take a horse's temperature at any time he appears to have something wrong with him.

We have all heard the old saying, at one time or another, "the horse makes the trainer . . . the trainer does not make the horse." Until we can assume that all trainers are as careful, conscientious, and knowledgeable as Lucien Laurin, we are going to have to assume the old saying would be more apt the other way around!

# White Oaks Ranch

*Having graduated from the University of Kentucky with the highest grade-point average in the history of the Department of Animal Science is but one of the many accomplishments of the young, attractive Ginger Hyland of White Oaks Ranch in Lake Hughes, California. The young blond, whose father is Executive Vice-President for Hughes Aircraft and one of the inventors of radar, has owned several outstanding running Quarter Horses, in addition to having bred many very useful campaigners.*

*White Oaks Ranch has been set up as a top-flight market-breeding establishment, composed of numerous quality broodmares, who are bred to outstanding Quarter racing stallions each year. The entire breeding program at White Oaks Ranch has been developed by Miss Hyland, utilizing a highly sophisticated computerized system. Her success, thus far has been phenomenal and Miss Hyland insists that none of it would be possible without a sound, well-planned nutritional program.*

*Some of the more successful horses owned or bred by White Oaks Ranch include Suki Tadre, a multiple stakes winning mare, who accumulated winnings of over $68,000.00 at the track, and Winds of Spring, a currently campaigning two-year-old who has already accounted for one stakes win this season.*

**QUESTION:** How many times per day do you feed?
**ANSWER:** Normally aged horses we feed twice; foals three times per day.
**QUESTION:** At what times of day do you feed?
**ANSWER:** 7 a.m. (noon for foals) and 4 p.m.
**QUESTION:** Do you feed equal amounts at each feeding?
**ANSWER:** Yes, we do for yearlings and milking mares, but not for pregnant or dry mares. The pregnant and dry mares get grain only at night.
**QUESTION:** Do you feed the same things at each feeding?
**ANSWER:** Not exactly. We feed oat hay in the morning, and alfalfa hay at night. We do feed the same grain rations morning and night.
**QUESTION:** How long do you leave the feed out if it is not eaten?
**ANSWER:** Not more than one day. Feed should be fresh, free from mold and drying or bleaching effects.

**QUESTION:** What kinds of hay do you feed?

**ANSWER:** We feed alfalfa and we feed oat hay.

**QUESTION:** Which cutting do you prefer for your alfalfa?

**ANSWER:** Second-cutting.

**QUESTION:** Are there other kinds of hay you would prefer if they were available locally?

**ANSWER:** We would include high quality timothy or good grass hay if they were available.

**QUESTION:** How do you judge your hay to decide if you are getting the quality you desire?

**ANSWER:** If the alfalfa hay is leafy and not stemmy, and cut at about thirty percent bloom, we consider it good enough to have it analyzed at the Santa Ynez Research Farm. Oat hay should be just slightly green with good grains and not just hulls.

**QUESTION:** What parts of the country do you like your hay to come from?

**ANSWER:** Antelope Valley, California.

**QUESTION:** What methods do you use to feed hay (floor, rack, net, manger, etc.)?

**ANSWER:** Racks with bottoms that are flush with the wall.

**QUESTION:** Where do you obtain your oats?

**ANSWER:** We obtain our oats locally, however, we would prefer to have them shipped in because the quality is superior when obtained elsewhere, however I have been unable to have them shipped in.

**QUESTION:** Do you feed whole oats or processed oats?

**ANSWER:** I feed rolled or crimped oats, because I feel that they are digested better.

**QUESTION:** Do you insist upon a standard weight per bushel for your oats?

**ANSWER:** No.

**QUESTION:** Do you insist that your oats be cleaned and then recleaned?

**ANSWER:** Yes.

**QUESTION:** Do you feed any corn?

**ANSWER:** No.

**QUESTION:** Do you feed bran in your ration?

**ANSWER:** Yes.

**QUESTION:** How much?

**ANSWER:** One to two cups per day per ration.

**QUESTION:** Why?

**ANSWER:** It keeps the digestive tract flushed out (less colic) and it is a good source of protein.

**QUESTION:** Does the amount of bran you feed depend on the looseness of the bowels of the individual animal?

**ANSWER:** Sometimes, particularly in mares close to foaling.

**QUESTION:** Do you feel that bran is something that you should feed as much of as you possibly can without making the horse's bowels too loose, or do you feel that bran is something you want to feed only as much of as is absolutely necessary to ensure that there is no constipation?

**ANSWER:** I feed only as much bran as I feel is absolutely necessary to ensure that there is no constipation.

**QUESTION:** Do you feed cottonseed meal in your ration?

**ANSWER:** No.

**QUESTION:** Do you feed linseed meal or soybean meal in your rations?

**ANSWER:** Yes, we feed both.

**QUESTION:** How much do you feed and in what proportions?

**ANSWER:** We mix soybean and linseed meal on a fifty-fifty basis, and feed one cup per day per horse.

**QUESTION:** Do you feed any other types of grain in your ration?

**ANSWER:** Barley. We feed barley because it is a good energy source without being too "hot."

**QUESTION:** Do you use any other supplements in your ration to increase the protein content?

**ANSWER:** Yes, we also use dried skim milk.

**QUESTION:** What percent of protein do you think is necessary in the ration of: (a) foals, (b) yearlings, (c) two and three year olds, and (d) mature horses?

**ANSWER:** Foals, eighteen percent; yearlings, sixteen percent; two and three year olds, fourteen percent; and mature horses, twelve percent.

**QUESTION:** Are there any special activities (such as racing, breeding, etc.) that you think require more protein in the diet?

**ANSWER:** Not in the mature horse. The amount of protein may be increased with more work, but the percentage of the total ration should remain the same. To increase the percentage of protein is an economical waste since the horse will not utilize it, and protein supplements are expensive.

**QUESTION:** Do you feed a vitamin supplement in your ration?

**ANSWER:** Yes.

**QUESTION:** What kind is it, and how much of it do you use?

**ANSWER:** It is formulated for us by the Santa Ynez Research Farm, and we feed one ounce per day.

**QUESTION:** Do you also supplement vitamin E in your ration?

**ANSWER:** Yes.

**QUESTION:** Do you give injectable vitamins?

**ANSWER:** Only if a horse has a definite deficiency.

**QUESTION:** Do you feed a mineral supplement?

**ANSWER:** Yes, mixed in the rations.

**QUESTION:** What mineral supplement do you feed?

**ANSWER:** A formula made up by the Santa Ynez Research Farm.

**QUESTION:** What do you feel is the ideal calcium to phosphorus ratio?

**ANSWER:** 2 parts calcium to 1 part phosphorus.

**QUESTION:** What do you do in your feeding program to ensure that you keep this balance?

**ANSWER:** Alfalfa hay is very rich in calcium in California, so we supplement one-half ounce of Monosodium Tripolyphosphate daily.

**QUESTION:** Do you feel that salt is important in your horse's diet?

**ANSWER:** Yes!

**QUESTION:** By what method or form do you feed salt, and how much?

**ANSWER:** Two ounces of salt mixed in the ration plus salt blocks free-choice.

**QUESTION:** Do you recommend minerals with the salt?

**ANSWER:** Yes.

**QUESTION:** Explain your procedures for ensuring that your horses have constant, pure, clean water supply at all times?

**ANSWER:** We have automatic waterers in all stalls. Our troughs in pastures are checked twice daily and cleaned every week, or more often, as is necessary.

**QUESTION:** Do you ever feed a horse a hot mash?

**ANSWER:** Yes.

**QUESTION:** When, how often, and under what circumstances?

**ANSWER:** Every other day with mares close to foaling, and just after foaling.

**QUESTION:** Do you feed any sweet feed in your ration?

**ANSWER:** Yes.

**QUESTION:** How much?

**ANSWER:** All of our grain we mix ourselves with molasses.

**QUESTION:** How much molasses do you like in your sweet feed — (little, medium, a lot)?

**ANSWER:** A medium amount.

**QUESTION:** Do you feed any kind of pelleted feeds?

**ANSWER:** No.

**QUESTION:** Are there any kinds of pellets that are better than others in your opinion?

**ANSWER:** Grain pellets are alright, but I have good results using natural grains.

**QUESTION:** Could you give us the ingredients and amounts of your complete feeding program?

**ANSWER:** Our basic ingredients are rolled oats, rolled barley, wheat bran, soybean meal and linseed meal, vitamins, minerals, phosphorus, dried skim milk, salt, and molasses. (Wheat germ oil is added to the rations for yearlings, mares in late pregnancy, and lactating broodmares.) Feed is bought fresh every three to four weeks. Then each ration is mixed in fifty pound batches and stored in metal cans. This means that each ration is mixed about every two days. For yearlings and mares in late pregnancy, we feed them at the following rate: yearling fillies we feed two quarts at the morning feeding and two and one-half quarts at the night feeding. Yearling stallions we feed four quarts at the morning feeding, and four and one-half quarts at the night feeding. Mares in late pregnancy (eight to eleven months): at eight months pregnancy we feed one quart at the morning feeding, three and one-half quarts at the night feeding, at nine months pregnancy we feed two quarts at the morning feeding and three and one-half quarts at the night feeding. At ten months pregnancy we feed three quarts at the morning feeding and three and one-half quarts at the night feeding. At ten and one-half months pregnancy we feed three quarts in the morning, and four quarts at the night feeding. Our ration for lactating broodmares includes four and one-half quarts in the morning feeding, four and one-half quarts at the night feeding plus two flakes of oat hay in the morning feeding, and two flakes of alfalfa hay at the night feeding. Foals are creep fed three times daily, one-third quart of our basic ration at each feeding up to three months old, and one-half quart at each feeding up to 6 months old. When foals are weaned, they are fed one and one-half quarts grain daily (three-fourths quart at the morning feeding and three-fourths quart at the night feeding) till December, then we increase the ration one-half quart every two weeks till we hit the normal yearling levels. (Of course there is some individual variation.) Also, I should note that we weigh yearlings and race horses weekly to ensure proper growth and that they are not getting too fat.

**QUESTION:** Do you change your broodmare's rations just before and after foaling?

**ANSWER:** We cut back one-half the amount of grain and increase the bran. We take all feed away after foaling for eight hours, then give a bran mash and one flake of hay. Then she goes back on full feed.

**QUESTION:** Do you have any special tricks for making a horse eat that goes off his feed?

**ANSWER:** Yes, a grain and honey mix seems to work very well.

**QUESTION:** Do you believe in giving your horses little treats?

**ANSWER:** Yes, occasionally we give carrots and apples when they are available.

**QUESTION:** Do you graze your horses at all when they are in training?

**ANSWER:** If grass is available, every afternoon.

**QUESTION:** How many horses per helper do you normally prefer?

**ANSWER:** I prefer three to four horses per helper for horses in training.

**QUESTION:** How often and exactly how do you clean feed tubs?

**ANSWER:** We wash our feed tubs out with water whenever necessary.

**QUESTION:** What kind of hoof dressing do you use?

**ANSWER:** Traileze or Valentine's.

**QUESTION:** How often do you apply hoof dressing?

**ANSWER:** Twice weekly.

**QUESTION:** How often do you have a blood analysis done on your horses?

**ANSWER:** Whenever a horse is "off," and routinely on race horses as needed.

**QUESTION:** What do you look for in a blood test?

**ANSWER:** RBC, WBC, Packed Cell Volume, hemoglobin, neutrophils, lymphocytes, monocytes, and eosinophils.

**QUESTION:** How often do you have your horses wormed?

**ANSWER:** We worm adult horses twice yearly, and foals up to two year olds four times per year.

**QUESTION:** What method do you use?

**ANSWER:** We tube worm with Equizole A and Piperazine.

**QUESTION:** How often do you have dental work done on your horses?

**ANSWER:** Whenever needed.

**QUESTION:** How often do you take a horse's temperature?

**ANSWER:** Whenever they appear to have something wrong with them.

**QUESTION:** Do you inoculate your horses on a periodic basis?

**ANSWER:** Yes, for tetanus, sleeping sickness, and flu.

**QUESTION:** What areas of equine nutrition do you feel are most in need of further research?

**ANSWER:** Vitamin and mineral requirements and assimilation, and amino acid requirements.

**QUESTION:** Are there any points in a good equine nutrition program that you would like to discuss that we have not mentioned?

**ANSWER:** Whatever the feed program, horses should be fed on the same time schedule daily. Feed should be clean and fresh. Horses should be kept in good flesh but should **not** be fat. Drastic changes in the feeding program should be done gradually. Never feed more than one vitamin and/or mineral supplement, nor more than is recommended.

# Meadow Lands Farm

*Standardbreds, the high-spirited trotters of the harness racing world have excited millions of fans across the country for years. One of the major figures of the lucrative, fast-paced Standardbred industry is Mr. Delvin Miller, owner of the beautiful Meadow Land Farm in Meadow Land, Pennsylvania.*

*Mr. Miller has been represented at the trotting races by some of the most famous horses in Standardbred history, while driving many of the trotters himself. Most recently, his Delmonica Hanover was the victress in the International Trot, worth $150,000.00. To date, Delmonica Hanover has won over $400,000.00, quite a total, considering that Miller obtained her for a modest $5,000.00 as a yearling. Other Meadow Land horses include Meadow Flower, leading money-winning trotting filly of 1973; Tarport Adios, and many more.*

**QUESTION:** How many times per day do you feed, and why do you feed this many times?

**ANSWER:** Three times daily. I feed three times daily because, due to the relatively small size of the horse's stomach, it is easier for them to digest, etc.

**QUESTION:** At what times of day do you feed?

**ANSWER:** Approximately 6 a.m.—12 noon—and 6 p.m. "Bad feeders" we may feed four times a day, giving them another feeding at 10 p.m.

**QUESTION:** Do you feed equal amounts at each feeding?

**ANSWER:** This depends on whether the horse is racing, in training, or out of training. Also, it depends on what kind of a feeder the horse is. We usually feed equal amounts to a "good feeder."

**QUESTION:** How long do you leave the feed out if it is not eaten?

**ANSWER:** Not over one hour.

**QUESTION:** What kinds of hay do you feed?

**ANSWER:** Alfalfa, alfalfa and timothy mix, clover, and clover and timothy mix.

**QUESTION:** Which cutting do you prefer for each variety?

**ANSWER:** Second and third-cuttings are better in our part of the country, as we can cure it better.

**QUESTION:** Are there other kinds of hay you would prefer if they were available locally?

**ANSWER:** I would feed alfalfa all the time, the year-round, if it was available!

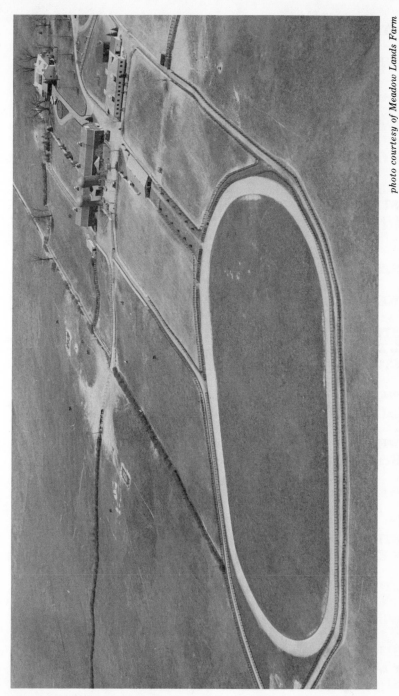

*photo courtesy of Meadow Lands Farm*

Located in Pennsylvania, the beautiful Meadow Lands Farm has bred and campaigned some of the most successful Standardbred horses in the history of the breed.

**QUESTION:** How do you judge your hay to decide if you are getting the quality you desire?

**ANSWER:** By smell, feel, and by knowing we have properly treated the soil upon which it is grown.

**QUESTION:** What parts of the country do you like your hay to come from?

**ANSWER:** From anywhere the soil has been properly treated, and where it is not too wet to get properly cured hay.

**QUESTION:** What methods do you use to feed hay (floor, rack, net, manger, etc.)?

**ANSWER:** Floor, and rack.

**QUESTION:** Why do you use these two methods?

**ANSWER:** The floor is better if they don't waste it, since it is a natural position for a horse to feed. If it is the kind of horse that wastes hay, then we prefer to use racks to help save the hay.

**QUESTION:** Where do you buy your oats? Do you prefer to buy from local feed dealers or have them shipped in?

**ANSWER:** We buy Jockey Club oats by the carload. I do this because it is cheaper and I know exactly what I am receiving.

**QUESTION:** Do you feed whole oats or processed oats?

**ANSWER:** Whole oats. I believe whole oats keep better.

**QUESTION:** Do you insist upon a standard weight per bushel for your oats?

**ANSWER:** Yes, I insist on a minimum 38 to 40 pound per bushel oat.

**QUESTION:** Do you insist that your oats be cleaned and then recleaned?

**ANSWER:** Yes, definitely.

**QUESTION:** Is there a particular company, or companies, whose oats you feel are better than others?

**ANSWER:** There are a number of very good companies, however, I have had good relations with M. T. Pritchard, and their Jockey Club oats.

**QUESTION:** Do you feed any corn?

**ANSWER:** From one-fourth to one-third of our total ration is composed of corn in the winter, but not as much in the summer.

**QUESTION:** Do you prefer your corn in some particular form (whole, shelled, cracked, etc.)?

**ANSWER:** I prefer whole corn because I feel that it is good for their teeth.

**QUESTION:** Do you feed bran in your rations?

**ANSWER:** No.

**QUESTION:** Do you feed cottonseed meal in your rations?

**Adios, by Hal Dale, out of Adioo Volo, has proven to be one of the greatest sires in the history of Standardbreds. This picture shows his outstanding condition in his later years.**

**ANSWER:** No.

**QUESTION:** Do you feed linseed meal in your rations?

**ANSWER:** Not to my race horses, however we might feed small portions of linseed meal to horses that are going to a sale. Linseed meal seems to improve their hair coat.

**QUESTION:** Do you feed soybean meal in your rations?

**ANSWER:** No.

**QUESTION:** Do you feed any other types of grain in your rations?

**ANSWER:** No.

**QUESTION:** Do you supplement the protein content of your rations in any way?

**ANSWER:** No, only with good hay and Stamm.

**QUESTION:** Do you feed a vitamin supplement in your rations?

**ANSWER:** No, just Stamm.

**QUESTION:** Do you give injectable vitamins?

**ANSWER:** Only in cases where it appears to be definitely called for. I leave this up to the vet.

**QUESTION:** Do you feed a mineral supplement?

**ANSWER:** Only Stamm at the track, and we feed free-choice calcium and phosphorus at our farm to broodmares, weanlings and yearlings.

**QUESTION:** Do you feel that salt is important in your horse's diet?

**ANSWER:** Yes.

**QUESTION:** By what method or form do you feed salt, and how much?

**ANSWER:** Free-choice block and loose salt.

**QUESTION:** Do you ever recommend minerals with the salt?

**ANSWER:** Yes, we use mineral salt in blocks.

**QUESTION:** Do you ever feed your horses a hot mash?

**ANSWER:** No.

**QUESTION:** Do you feed any sweet feed in your ration?

**ANSWER:** No.

**QUESTION:** Why?

**ANSWER:** It spoils them from eating other feeds, especially a "bad feeder."

**QUESTION:** Do you think pelleted feeds have any advantages?

**ANSWER:** They have minerals, etc. added and some horses will eat a pelleted feed, like Stamm, better than oats.

**QUESTION:** Could you give us the ingredients and amounts of your complete feeding program?

**ANSWER:** This, of course, fluctuates somewhat depending on the individual animal, however, the average animal we feed hay free-choice, and about three quarts of oats and at least a pint to a quart of Stamm per feeding.

**QUESTION:** Do you change your feeding program in any way before a race?

**ANSWER:** Yes, we cut down on hay in the morning and feed grain at least one hour before warming up for a race.

**QUESTION:** Do you have any special tricks for making a horse eat that is a picky eater?

**ANSWER:** I feed a picky eater more often, and feed him more at night. I try not to overfeed the picky eater at any one meal and keep him just a little bit hungry. Another trick that sometimes works is to turn a picky eater out with a good eater.

**QUESTION:** Do you change your feeding program in any way after a race?

**ANSWER:** No, a good feed is always fed my horses after they are properly cooled out. We may even graze them if there is good grass available.

**QUESTION:** Do you believe in giving your horses little treats like carrots?

**ANSWER:** Yes we do believe in feeding carrots, if they are fresh, at least once a day. Sugar is strictly off limits.

**QUESTION:** Do you graze your horses when they are in training?

**ANSWER:** Yes, often, especially in the evenings or after a jog work or a race. I feel that grazing supplies the horse with needed minerals that they might not otherwise get. Grazing also seems to help the horse's appetite, and they eat their prepared rations better.

**QUESTION:** Do you ever turn your horses out, that are in race training, in a grassy paddock?

**ANSWER:** Yes, quite often, even when they are at the track if there is a suitable paddock available. Also, I often take my horses to my farm between races and allow them to get in as much grazing and rest as possible.

**QUESTION:** What, if any, differences are there in the way you feed two year olds in training and aged horses in training?

**ANSWER:** Two year olds trotting, need as much feed as aged horses.

**QUESTION:** Do you feed any of the commercially prepared hair conditioners in your ration?

**ANSWER:** No.

**QUESTION:** What do you do to help stimulate a horse's appetite when he goes off his feed after a race?

**ANSWER:** We turn them in a paddock if possible, and give them a rest away from the track.

**QUESTION:** Do you ever use an electrolyte solution in the feed or water of your horses?

**ANSWER:** Yes we do, especially a horse that has been raced hard. It seems to help them recuperate from a hard race much quicker.

**QUESTION:** Do you supplement your feeding or injection program with anything for a particularly nervous horse?

**ANSWER:** No, we just pamper and baby them more than the average horse.

**QUESTION:** Do you have any other hints to help a particularly nervous horse?

**ANSWER:** A good top groom, that really cares for the horse.

**QUESTION:** Have you found that you can sometimes stimulate a poor doer's appetite by lessening the amount of exercise he gets?

**ANSWER:** Yes, definitely.

**QUESTION:** What is your exercise program for an average trotter getting ready for an average race?

**ANSWER:** We always walk the horse the day after the race, jog three to four miles daily between races, and usually at least three miles jogging and two heats of a mile each two to three days before the race.

**QUESTION:** How important do you feel that brushing, rubbing, and grooming are to the health, nutrition and performance of your horses?

**ANSWER:** Very important. A clean, well-groomed horse performs at his very best.

**QUESTION:** How much time per day do you spend on each horse's grooming?

**ANSWER:** It depends on whether or not they were bathed that day. If they were not bathed, it takes a good groom at least forty to sixty minutes to groom properly.

**QUESTION:** How often do you pick up manure from each stall?

**ANSWER:** If possible, every time there is manure to be picked up.

**QUESTION:** How often do you give your horses a bath?

**ANSWER:** Every time they work up a good sweat, if the weather is not too cool. We never like to bathe in a drafty place.

**QUESTION:** Do you use heated water?

**ANSWER:** Yes, always.

**QUESTION:** What type of material do you prefer for bedding your stalls?

**ANSWER:** We use good clean straw when available, and sawdust or shavings when straw is not available. Also, we may use sawdust and shavings for a horse we want to cut down on hay, to keep him from eating his straw bedding.

**QUESTION:** How deeply do you bed your stalls?

**ANSWER:** At least six to ten inches deep when we use straw, and four to six inches deep when we use shavings or sawdust.

**QUESTION:** How many horses per helper do you prefer when your horses are in training?

**ANSWER:** We use one man to a horse when racing and shipping, and two horses to one man when training or racing at one track.

**QUESTION:** How often do you clean up feed tubs?

**ANSWER:** After every meal.

**QUESTION:** How often do you apply hoof dressing?

**ANSWER:** Daily.

**QUESTION:** How often do you have a blood analysis done on your horses?

**ANSWER:** At least every four months.

**QUESTION:** How often do you have your horses wormed?

**ANSWER:** At least every six months.

**QUESTION:** What method do you use?

**ANSWER:** My horses are tubed by a veterinarian.

**QUESTION:** How often do you have dental work done on your horses?

**ANSWER:** We have them checked two to three times a year.

**QUESTION:** How often do you take a horse's temperature?

**ANSWER:** Every morning before jogging, and always before a race.

**QUESTION:** Do you inoculate your horses on a periodic basis?

**ANSWER:** Yes, for flu, distemper and abortion.

# Newt Keck

*One of the most successful trainers in the history of the running Quarter Horse, Newt Keck resides with his wife, Flo, on the couple's beautiful ranch in north central Texas. Since Mr. Keck is not only a trainer, but a successful breeder as well, his approach to equine nutrition covers a broad scope.*

*At the present time, his ranch is the home of many top-producing broodmares, as well as numerous weanlings and yearlings. The success of Mr. Keck's feeding program has been evidenced many times over by his continuing high-ranking among Quarter Horse trainers across the country. One hallmark achieved in his success is a goal reached by no other trainer. Newt Keck has trained three separate individuals who have won the World's richest horse race, the All-American Futurity at Ruidoso Downs, New Mexico. In fact, Newt Keck-trained horses won three of the first five runnings of this prestigious event. His All-American winners were Galobar in 1959, Pokey Bar in 1961, and Goetta in 1963.*

*Other great running Quarter Horses Mr. Keck has trained are, Ruby Charge, winner of the 1965 Kansas Futurity, Nippy Bars, winner of the 1965 Rainbow Derby, Jet Too, winner of the 1966 Sunland Park Fall Futurity, and the outstanding runner, Mr. Jet Moore, winner of over $340,000, and named World Champion Quarter Running Horse in 1972.*

According to Mr. Keck's theories on feeding programs, his main stress lies in punctuality. Newt states, "What you feed, and how often you feed, are obviously important, but one often overlooked and truly critical factor in horse feeding, is the **times** at which you feed. Scheduling is essential and must be followed to the most minute detail. The horse has a fairly delicate digestive tract, and inconsistencies in feeding times can throw the whole system completely out of coordination.

Newt feeds his horses twice per day, hay and grain, five a.m. and five p.m. When asked why he feeds twice per day, instead of three times, Newt replied, "I feel they do better with only two feedings, as they have more time to rest and relax." Newt's morning feeding consists of one gallon of oats and a half gallon of sweet feed. The evening feeding consists of one and one-half gallons of oats, one-half gallon of sweet feed, one gallon of bran, one measure of Calf Manna, vitamins and minerals, and about two ounces of mineral salt. "This I feed in a hot mash, just moist enough so that when I grab up a handful it will just stick together."

*photo courtesy of Ruidoso Downs*

Newt Keck, outstanding Quarter Horse race trainer, is pictured with one of his most successful pupils, Pokey Bar, winner of the 1961 All-American Futurity, and winner of over $160,000.00.

Following his punctual methods, Newt believes in leaving feed out for his horses approximately two hours. He feels this time limit keeps the horse's appetite stimulated by allowing an ample but consistent amount of time, in which the horse knows he has to finish his ration. The very highest quality hay and oats available make up the basis for Mr. Keck's feeding program. His preference for hays are timothy and alfalfa. He prefers timothy from the Ellensburg, Washington area, and second or third-cutting alfalfa from the San Joaquin valley in California. He prefers the kind of alfalfa commonly referred to as "rabbit hay." Hay is fed from a floor manger, "so the horse can eat with his head down, in a natural position, and also prevent him from getting hay in his eyes and nostrils as otherwise might happen." Newt also feels that it is extremely important that hay be cut and baled at proper times, and that it be properly cured.

Newt prefers high quality whole oats to be fed to his horses, because he feels, that more "strength" is retained in the oat, which is often lost when processed oats are stored for any length of time. Newt also feels that oats should be well-cleaned. Further, he feels that oats with clipped ends have definite advantages. Newt does not include any corn in his rations.

When asked what brand and what quantity of vitamin supplements he feeds, Newt replied, "What's available, and the amount the particular brand suggests." Newt also includes vitamin E supplementation in his rations. Further, he includes a mineral supplement in the ration. He uses any available commercial mix marketed by reputable companies. Newt mixes about two ounces of mineral salt in his ration as well.

When asked about his procedures for watering horses, he replied, "I keep water buckets clean at all times, and refill when necessary. I keep them placed away from the hay manger to lessen the amount of trash entering the water. A pure, fresh, constant water supply is essential to a good feeding program." Newt does, however, withhold water the night before a horse is to race.

Newt definitely believes in a hot mash for race horses. And he likes a sweet feed with a medium amount of molasses.

Another change Newt makes in his feeding program, starting the night before a horse is to race, is to diminish the proportions of the ration. "I give a light feeding the night before a race." A slight change he makes after a race is to feed the horse a "mash that's a little more moist."

Newt does not believe in "nibblers" at all. However, an evening "graze" for each horse is recommended whenever possible.

Some other helpful hints on horse care offered by Newt are as follows:

*photo courtesy of Newton Keck*

The winner's circle was a happy occasion after the inaugural running of the All-American Futurity at Ruidoso Downs, New Mexico in 1959. The world's richest horse race had a gross purse of over $129,000.00 in its first running and is now worth over $1,000,000.00. The winner pictured above was Galobar, a 1957 filly owned by Hugh Huntley of Madera, California, and trained by Newt Keck.

(1) He prefers clean wheat straw for bedding. (2) He has a minimum of one helper for every three horses he has in training. (3) He washes and cleans thoroughly every feed tub with a brush each morning. (4) He has a blood analysis done on his horses "when they're not doing as well as I think they should, and feel it is necessary." (5) He only applies fly repellent to horses in extreme cases, and usually manages to combat any fly problems with a commercial fly killer on wet grain sacks placed around the barn. (6) Newt worms his horses usually three times a year. His horses are always tube wormed by a veterinarian. (7) He takes a horse's temperature at any time the horse appears to have anything wrong with him.

(Editor's Note: Although not covered in the interview, Newt places great emphasis on the values of grooming, rubbing, and personal attention. His reputation among knowledgeable Quarter Horsemen in this regard is without equal.)

# Dr. William J. Tyznik

*Scientist, professor, writer, lecturer and highly regarded member of the teaching staff at Ohio State University, Dr. Tyznik is a leading authority on the subject of equine nutrition. Among Dr. Tyznik's many and varied contributions to the field of equine nutrition, he is presently Chairman of the Subcommittee on Horse Nutrition for the highly regarded National Research Council.*

The following question and answer session was conducted by a staff member of Equine Research Publications. Answers were provided by Dr. Tyznik.

**QUESTION:** What areas in the field of equine nutritional research do you feel are most in need of further study?

**ANSWER:** Almost all areas, with special emphasis on mineral and amino acid balances . . . but the entire area of nutritional interdependence.

**QUESTION:** What do you think are the particular advantages or disadvantages of the different popular grains being fed today?

**ANSWER:** It is difficult to evaluate feedstuffs, because value is relative to economics. Availability of a specific cereal grain is by far the most critical factor. If all grains are equally available, the following relative value per pound can be used as a guide:

| Corn | 100% |
|------|------|
| Oats | 60-90% |
| Barley | 80-85% |
| Milo | 90% |
| Wheat | 110% |
| Rye | 100% |

**QUESTION:** How valid are the USDA standards for judging grains?

**ANSWER:** The USDA standards, indicating weight per bushel, and absence of foreign materials are good guides.

**QUESTION:** What do you feel a minimum weight should be for a good quality oat?

**ANSWER:** A good quality oat should weigh at least 36 pounds per bushel.

**QUESTION:** Are there any particular geographical areas which you think excel in the production of certain grains?

**ANSWER:** Certain areas do excel in producing certain grains, and interestingly enough, this is primarily the result of climatic conditions.

**QUESTION:** Which grains generally have the highest palatability factor for horses?

**ANSWER:** Palatability seems to be more a matter of physical state of the grain, (i.e. dusty, coarse, etc.), and what a horse becomes accustomed to eating.

**QUESTION:** How quickly may grains be fed after harvest?

**ANSWER:** Grain can be fed anytime after harvest if one remembers that moisture content changes as the grain heats and stablizes in condition. This change constitutes an adjustment for a horse which may result in minor digestive disturbances.

**QUESTION:** When would you recommend using processed grains, rather than natural grains?

**ANSWER:** Processing of grain should result in cracking the hull especially for young horses, and horses who have a tendency to "bolt" their feed.

**QUESTION:** What method of processing is most valuable for oats?

**ANSWER:** Crimping is the best treatment for oats.

**QUESTION:** What method of processing is most valuable for corn?

**ANSWER:** Crimping.

**QUESTION:** What about "race horse" oats? Are they worth the additional expense for the average horse?

**ANSWER:** Race horse oats are nothing more than a heavy oat that has been screened and sometimes clipped. They are expensive because of limited supply, as well as extensive processing. Nutritionally, for the average horse, they are not always worth the additional cost.

**QUESTION:** Which cutting of hay is usually highest in quality?

**ANSWER:** Quality of hay is generally determined by the stage of maturity, rather than whether it is a first, second, or later cutting. Practically any quality forage will make good hay if it is cut young enough.

**QUESTION:** What are the advantages of mixing grass and legume hays? What proportions are ideal?

**ANSWER:** Mixing of grasses and legumes has the tendency of increasing yield. The type and proportion are best determined by the County Agent or agronomist of the area.

**QUESTION:** What varieties of hay available in your area, are highest in nutritional value?

**ANSWER:** Alfalfa, or alfalfa and orchardgrass mixed.

**QUESTION:** What is the minimum amount of hay necessary for a balanced diet?

**ANSWER:** Minimum hay is determined on the basis of boredom and economics. No one has established the fact that horses require roughage, but they usually will become wood chewers if not given coarse material.

**QUESTION:** How long should hay be cured before feeding?

**ANSWER:** There really is no time limit, but again, as hay cures, it changes and will stabilize in about two weeks of storage.

**QUESTION:** Should hay be fed free-choice or in measured amounts?

**ANSWER:** Free-choice is more desirable, but is often a wasteful procedure. If I had a choice, I would provide all they want.

**QUESTION:** Do you feel that it is best to feed hay from a manger, in a net, on the ground, or how?

**ANSWER:** How hay is fed is a matter of opinion. The important factor is that the horse has easy access to it.

**QUESTION:** Is pasture important to a complete ration?

**ANSWER:** No.

**QUESTION:** How do you decide what are the best types of pasture to plant?

**ANSWER:** The forage that grows best in the locale.

**QUESTION:** When horses are turned out to pasture all day, or when pasture is a primary part of the total ration, how many acres should you allow per horse?

**ANSWER:** Two acres per horse.

**QUESTION:** What do you feel is the most practical method for preventing the spread of parasites in pastures?

**ANSWER:** Keep pastures clipped, drag the pasture, and follow a regular worming program.

**QUESTION:** Is there much danger from toxic plants or weeds if pasture is well-cultivated?

**ANSWER:** Horses consume toxic weeds only as a last resort.

**QUESTION:** What, if any, are the advantages of feeding nibblers, such as carrots, apples, sugar, etc.?

**ANSWER:** There are no nutritional values in nibblers. The advantage would appear to be a psychological one for the horse owner.

**QUESTION:** What about the psychological effects of nibblers on stalled horses? Do the bad habits outweigh the good?

**ANSWER:** I feel that the bad habits definitely outweigh the good.

**QUESTION:** What are the relative advantages of soybean meal, linseed meal and cottonseed meal?

**ANSWER:** Soybean meal is the best protein source, followed by cotton-seed, linseed, and peanut.

**QUESTION:** How can you determine which of these concentrates is the most advantageous for a particular need, and how much to feed?

**ANSWER:** You should be guided by the protein requirement of the animal.

**QUESTION:** Are commercial protein supplements valuable and worthwhile?

**ANSWER:** They usually are fortified with vitamins as well minerals, so the cost is somewhat greater. They are usually worthwhile when fed as supplements to cereal grains.

**QUESTION:** Which commercial supplements are the best to use?

**ANSWER:** Any reputable company will make good supplements.

**QUESTION:** Should protein supplements be added to the diet routinely, or only under special circumstances?

**ANSWER:** Supplements are needed for growing horses and lactating mares.

**QUESTION:** What are your suggestions as to protein needs?

**ANSWER:** Weanlings, 20 to 22 percent of the grain mix should be protein, yearlings 16 to 18 percent, two year olds 16 percent, three year olds 14 percent, mature horses 12 percent, lactating mares 16 percent.

**QUESTION:** Is it preferable to feed mineralized salt, plain salt, or both?

**ANSWER:** It is preferable to feed mineralized salt.

**QUESTION:** Do you prefer loose salt or block salt?

**ANSWER:** Block salt is a better choice for stalled horses, but in some parts of the country, the humidity is so high that block salt disintegrates. Loose salt is a very acceptable method of providing salt.

**QUESTION:** Is it more advantageous to feed free-choice, or in measured amounts mixed into the feed?

**ANSWER:** Salt should always be provided free-choice.

**QUESTION:** Are there any times when water should be withheld?

**ANSWER:** Water should be withheld only when the horse has been seriously overheated, and then give only limited amounts until he is thoroughly "cooled out."

**QUESTION:** What do you feel is the best method for inducing a horse to drink more water if he is drinking insufficient amounts?

**ANSWER:** Providing free access to cool (45 degrees Farenheit) and clean water is the best method I know. Water consumption is highly correlated with dry matter consumption.

**QUESTION:** What are the physiological results of allowing a hot horse unlimited amounts of water?

**ANSWER:** If hot horses are allowed unlimited amounts of water, they will usually colic, and they may founder and die.

**QUESTION:** In your opinion, what is the role of vitamin E in body function? Do you feel that it can have a beneficial effect on racing, working, or breeding performance? Can any of its effects be harmful?

**ANSWER:** Vitamin E is involved with muscle maintenance and reproduction in other species, and may be with horses. No harmful effects have been reported.

**QUESTION:** Are vitamin supplements necessary if the diet is well-balanced?

**ANSWER:** No.

**QUESTION:** Are there any special activities that could necessitate vitamin supplementation, such as strenuous work or foaling? If so, what vitamins and under what circumstances?

**ANSWER:** The B-complex may need to be supplemented when horses are stressed, such as in heavy training or racing.

**QUESTION:** Do you feel that injected supplements are superior to oral vitamins?

**ANSWER:** No. Injected vitamins should be used only when horses do not consume feed.

**QUESTION:** Is the average horse owner today too concerned with supplements, not concerned enough, or does he usually have the proper attitude?

**ANSWER:** Supplements in general have been seriously oversold.

**QUESTION:** If a balanced diet is fed, are mineral supplements necessary?

**ANSWER:** Free-choice trace-mineralized salt and dicalcium phosphate are desirable supplements.

**QUESTION:** What do you feel is the ideal calcium to phosphorus ratio?

**ANSWER:** 1.1 to 1 for growing foals and 2 to 1 for mature horses.

**QUESTION:** What are the easiest methods of balancing the calcium-phosphorus ratio, and how can you tell if the balance is correct?

**ANSWER:** By analysis, but it must be appreciated that only about forty to fifty percent of the phosphorus in plant materials is available to the horse.

**QUESTION:** Do you consider the relationship of zinc and selenium to be significant?

**ANSWER:** Not presently.

**QUESTION:** Do you believe that mineral supplements should be fed free-choice, forced, or not at all?

**ANSWER:** Free-choice.

**QUESTION:** Do you think that the Total Digestible Nutrient (TDN) system of balancing a ration is practical and valid?

**ANSWER:** Yes.

**QUESTION:** What factors do you think are most important to consider in preparing the complete balanced diet?

**ANSWER:** Addressing oneself to the importance of nutrient interplay. All nutrients are of equal importance.

**QUESTION:** Do sweet feeds have any advantages or disadvantages?. Are they of special benefit at any time?

**ANSWER:** Sweet feeds do not have any advantages.

**QUESTION:** Are there any commercial feeds that you feel are especially good?

**ANSWER:** Not specifically.

**QUESTION:** Are pelleted rations of value in a normal feeding program?

**ANSWER:** Yes.

**QUESTION:** Are there any times when it would be advantageous to feed a completely pelleted ration?

**ANSWER:** Yes, when only one or two horses are being fed in a confined area.

**QUESTION:** Is pelleted hay an adequate substitute for loose hay?

**ANSWER:** Yes (one inch pellets).

**QUESTION:** In your opinion, what is the major advantage of pelleted feeds?

**ANSWER:** The horse has no opportunity to sift and sort.

**QUESTION:** In your experience, have you found commercial feed mixes from a reputable feed company to be usually adequate in quality.

**ANSWER:** Yes.

**QUESTION:** How can you judge the worth of a commercial feed?

**ANSWER:** By the label of analysis and ingredients.

**QUESTION:** In your opinion, is it ever worthwhile to have a commercial mill prepare your own feeds to your formula? Do the costs outweigh the advantages?

**ANSWER:** Depends on amount. Generally, it costs more to have a special mix than to buy those being commercially marketed.

**QUESTION:** What is the best way to increase the palatability of a ration?

**ANSWER:** Eliminate fines and dustiness.

**QUESTION:** Do you think that there is any value in cooked rations.

**ANSWER:** There is no advantage in cooked rations.

**QUESTION:** What are the danger signs that show an inadequate feeding program?

**ANSWER:** Loss of condition, appetite, growth and performance.

**QUESTION:** Can you give us ideal, complete rations for different ages and classes of horses?

**ANSWER:** There are no ideal, complete rations for horses, since the type of grain ration will be dependent on the type of hay that is used. Any horse that is over three years of age will do very well on a ration of early-cut hay, plus any grain, such as corn, oats, etc. The minerals would, of course, be provided on a free-choice basis. Weanlings and nursing foals need to be provided with rations that contain: forty percent corn or other grain, thirty percent soybean meal, twenty percent oats, one percent brewer's grain, five percent limestone, five percent biofos or dynafos, one percent trace-mineralized salt. Rations should also contain two thousand to five thousand I.U. of vitamin A per pound of feed, and two hundred to five hundred I.U. of vitamin D, and twenty I.U. of vitamin E. Most mature horses that are in good condition and are eating well will usually be fine.

**QUESTION:** How can you recognize the poorly nourished horse that appears fat?

**ANSWER:** In young horses, poor growth rate and/or poor appetite would give indications.

**QUESTION:** What are the major causes that make a horse a poor doer?

**ANSWER:** Usually parasitism or teeth that need to be floated.

**QUESTION:** What precautions would you take on a day-to-day basis to prevent the occurrence of laminitis (founder)?

**ANSWER:** Prevent rapid changes in quantity of feed.

**QUESTION:** What are your feelings about the use of medicated feeds?

**ANSWER:** Generally, medications should be given for a specific infection rather than on a shotgun basis.

**QUESTION:** Are there any "best" times of day to feed?

**ANSWER:** Time of day is not nearly as important as regularity.

**QUESTION:** What changes should be made in a horse's diet when his overall activity is increased?

**ANSWER:** Usually, an increase in energy intake, and possible B vitamin supplementation.

**QUESTION:** Do you feel that it is better to change the ration frequently in order to make sure that a variety of nutrients are included, or is it better to stick with a proven formula?

**ANSWER:** It is best to stay with a proven formula. Horses are creatures of habit, and will consume best that which they are accustomed to eating.

**QUESTION:** How long should you leave feed in front of a horse if it is not eaten?

**ANSWER:** In my opinion, grain should be removed from mature horses no later than one hour after feeding.

**QUESTION:** How long should you leave hay in front of a horse if it is not eaten?

**ANSWER:** Hay should always be present.

**QUESTION:** What do you think about the average level of equine nutrition as it is practiced in the United States today?

**ANSWER:** Relatively, not as good as it could be. Much effort is expended on "exotics," rather than good nutrition.

**QUESTION:** If you have conducted any research or special study on any factors related to equine nutrition, not covered in this interview, we would be interested in a brief summary of your results and conclusions.

**ANSWER:** A. Early weaning, (two months) indicates that young horses grow better and are more capable of "going to work" and remaining sound. B. Use of two to three ounces of corn oil per day will improve hair coat. C. Horses can tolerate up to thirty percent added fat in their rations without difficulty. D. Soybean protein is fully as good as milk protein for horses, with linseed meal running a poor fourth in the field of high protein supplements. Urea at levels of five percent of the ration is not harmful.

# Meadow Stud

*The Meadow Stud, home of Secretariat and Riva Ridge located near Doswell, Virginia has been the foaling place of many of the most outstanding runners in recent American turf history.*

*In addition to Secretariat and Riva Ridge, Meadow Stud has produced such notables as Cicada, named Champion Filly during her career; First Landing, an outstanding runner, who is the sire of Riva Ridge; and Sir Gaylord, a half brother to Secretariat, who was a very successful campaigner during his brief career. The facilities at Meadow Stud are second to none, and Mr. Howard Gentry, farm manager, has developed an outstanding nutritional program to enhance the overall success of the operation. Mr. Gentry was kind enough to take time out of his very busy schedule and answer a few questions for us, about this program.*

**QUESTION:** How many times per day do you feed?

**ANSWER:** Older horses twice per day; growing stock, three times.

**QUESTION:** At what times of day do you feed?

**ANSWER:** Older horses at 5 a.m. and 4 p.m.; others 5, 11 and 4.

**QUESTION:** Do you feed equal amounts at each feeding?

**ANSWER:** For growing horses, I feed a lighter ration at midday.

**QUESTION:** Do you feed the same things at each feeding?

**ANSWER:** For all practical purposes, yes.

**QUESTION:** How long do you leave the feed out if it is not eaten?

**ANSWER:** Any feed not eaten is removed quickly, for several reasons. The chief reason is so as not to get a horse in the habit of having stale food at his disposal, which is apt to get him off his feed.

**QUESTION:** What kinds of hay do you feed?

**ANSWER:** Alfalfa, and mixed hay which consists of orchardgrass, clover, and timothy.

**QUESTION:** Which cutting do you prefer for each variety of hay?

**ANSWER:** For clover, first cutting. For alfalfa, second and third cuttings.

**QUESTION:** Are there other kinds of hay you would prefer if they were available locally?

**ANSWER:** No.

**QUESTION:** How do you judge your hay to decide if you are getting the quality you desire.

**ANSWER:** I look for properly cured hay, which has a good color and good smell.

**QUESTION:** What parts of the country do you like your hay to come from?

**ANSWER:** We grow our own.

**QUESTION:** What methods do you use to feed hay, (floor, rack, net, manger, etc.)?

**ANSWER:** Floor. The foreign matter and dust sift out best when hay is fed from the floor.

**QUESTION:** Where do you buy your oats?

**ANSWER:** We buy our oats locally, and most are Western oats.

**QUESTION:** Do you feed whole oats or processed oats?

**ANSWER:** Crushed oats to young horses, and whole oats to older ones.

**QUESTION:** Do you insist upon a standard weight per bushel for your oats?

**ANSWER:** I do when this is possible.

**QUESTION:** What weight?

**ANSWER:** 42 to 44 pounds.

**QUESTION:** Do you insist that your oats be cleaned and recleaned?

**ANSWER:** Yes.

**QUESTION:** Do you think there is any advantage to oats with clipped ends?

**ANSWER:** Yes.

**QUESTION:** Do you feed corn?

**ANSWER:** Only what comes in prepared sweet feed.

**QUESTION:** How much of your total ration is composed of corn?

**ANSWER:** About two to three percent.

**QUESTION:** Do you feed bran in your ration?

**ANSWER:** Bran is in our sweet feed. Also, in winter, we feed four to five quarts of bran mash in our rations, two or three times a week to stallions and horses in training.

**QUESTION:** Why do you feed bran?

**ANSWER:** To increase body heat, and help elimination of wastes.

**QUESTION:** Does the amount of bran you feed depend on the looseness of the bowels of the individual animal?

**ANSWER:** Yes.

**QUESTION:** Do you feed cottonseed meal in your ration?

**ANSWER:** No.

**QUESTION:** Do you feed linseed meal in your ration?

**ANSWER:** Only what is in the sweet feed.

**QUESTION:** Do you feed soybean meal in your ration?

**ANSWER:** Only what is in the sweet feed.

**QUESTION:** Do you feed any other types of grain in your ration?

**ANSWER:** No.

Meadow Stud, birthplace of Secretariat, Riva Ridge, Cicada, First Landing, Sir Gaylord and many others, has become one of the most successful Thoroughbred breeding farms in the entire industry.

**QUESTION:** Do you supplement the protein content of your ration?
**ANSWER:** Yes.
**QUESTION:** What do you use for this purpose?
**ANSWER:** Winn.
**QUESTION:** Are there any special activities (such as racing, breeding, etc.) that you think requires more protein in the diet?
**ANSWER:** Yes, racing.
**QUESTION:** Do you feed a vitamin supplement in your ration?
**ANSWER:** Yes.
**QUESTION:** What kind do you feed, and how much of it do you use?
**ANSWER:** A vitamin and mineral powder, fed in the recommended dosage.
**QUESTION:** Do you supplement your rations with vitamin E? If so, in what form, and how much?
**ANSWER:** Yes, we do. During breeding season we give stallions one-half ounce of wheat germ per day, in liquid form.
**QUESTION:** Do you give injectable vitamins?
**ANSWER:** Only when indicated.
**QUESTION:** What kinds do you give, and how much of each?
**ANSWER:** Only the kinds recommended by our veterinarian, usually $B_{12}$.
**QUESTION:** Do you feed a mineral supplement?
**ANSWER:** Yes.
**QUESTION:** Do you mix it in your ration, or feed it free-choice?
**ANSWER:** We mix it in our rations.
**QUESTION:** Do you use a commercial mineral supplement, or do you have your own formula?
**ANSWER:** We use a commercial mix.
**QUESTION:** What do you do in your feeding program to ensure that you maintain a proper calcium to phosphorus ratio?
**ANSWER:** We have pasture, hay, etc. analyzed.
**QUESTION:** By what method do you feed salt, and how much?
**ANSWER:** Fresh supply in stalls at all times; special boxes in pastures which refill as used.
**QUESTION:** Do you recommend minerals with the salt?
**ANSWER:** Yes.
**QUESTION:** How much sweet feed do you utilize in your rations?
**ANSWER:** About one-fifth of our ration is composed of sweet feed for older horses, and about one-third for growing stock.
**QUESTION:** Why do you feed sweet feed?
**ANSWER:** Sweet feed adds flavor, as well as nutritional value, and acts as an appetizer and a laxative.

*photo courtesy of The Blood-Horse*

Secretariat glides to the wire in the 1973 running of the Belmont Stakes, a race which he won by over 30 lengths in record time. After his victory, many turf experts were calling him the horse of the decade and possibly the horse of the century. Secretariat retired from the 1973 season with total earnings of over $1,300,000.00.

**QUESTION:** What brand of sweet feed do you prefer?

**ANSWER:** Eshelman's Super Horse Feed.

**QUESTION:** How much molasses do you like in your sweet feed?

**ANSWER:** A medium amount.

**QUESTION:** Do you feed any kinds of pellets?

**ANSWER:** Some of our supplements are pelleted, and that is all.

**QUESTION:** Do you think pelleted feed has any advantages?

**ANSWER:** We have never been very interested in trying pelleted feed, consequently our knowledge of it is minimal.

**QUESTION:** Could you give us the ingredients and amounts of your complete feeding rations for: (a) horses in training, (b) broodmares, (c) lactating mares, (d) stallions in off season, (e) stallions in service, (f) weanlings, and (g) yearlings?

**ANSWER:** Yes, I can. For horses in training, we feed eight to eleven pounds of oats per day, ten to fifteen pounds of hay per day, two pounds of sweet feed per day, and one-half pound of supplement. For broodmares, we feed four to eight pounds of oats per day, twenty to twenty-five pounds of hay per day, one pound of sweet feed per day, and one pound of supplement. For lactating mares, we feed six to eight pounds of oats per day, twenty to twenty-five pounds of hay per day, two pounds of sweet feed per day, and one pound of supplement per day. For stallions in off season, we feed seven to nine pounds of oats per day, twenty to twenty-five pounds of hay per day, one-half pound of sweet feed per day, and one pound of supplement per day. For stallions in service, we feed seven to eleven pounds of oats per day, twenty to twenty-five pounds of hay per day, one pound of sweet feed per day, and one pound of supplement. For weanlings, we feed four to seven pounds of oats per day, five to ten pounds of hay per day, two pounds of sweet feed per day, and one-half pound of supplement per day. For yearlings, we feed five to eight pounds of oats per day, eight to twelve pounds of hay per day, three pounds of sweet feed per day, and one pound of supplement per day.

**QUESTION:** Do you creep feed foals?

**ANSWER:** Yes, we do. Our creep feed is composed of sweet feed, crushed oats, and supplement.

**QUESTION:** Do you change a broodmare's ration just before and after foaling?

**ANSWER:** Yes, we lighten the feed ration awhile before, and go back to normal as soon as possible.

photo courtesy of The Blood-Horse

The 1972 Kentucky Derby ended in victory for Meadow Stable's Riva Ridge, a son of First Landing - Iberia by *Heliopolis. It was the first time in over a decade that a two-year-old champion Thoroughbred had returned to win the "derby" in his three-year-old season.

**QUESTION:** Do you have any special tricks for making a horse eat, that goes off his feed?

**ANSWER:** Yes, I let him fast for a day, then resume light feedings and give him a tonic.

**QUESTION:** Do you have any special tricks for making a horse eat that is a picky eater?

**ANSWER:** Yes, give him small servings often, and **never** leave feed in box after first chance at it.

**QUESTION:** Do you believe in giving your horses any little treats, like carrots, lettuce, etc.

**ANSWER:** No.

**QUESTION:** Do you graze your horses at all when they are in training?

**ANSWER:** Yes, once a day.

**QUESTION:** Is there any type of pasture that you prefer?

**ANSWER:** Mixed pasture, (clover, bluegrass, orchardgrass, fescue, and other native grasses).

**QUESTION:** What, if any, differences are there in the way you feed two year olds in training, and aged horses in training?

**ANSWER:** The younger horses eat slightly more.

**QUESTION:** Do you feed any of the commercially prepared hair conditioners in your ration?

**ANSWER:** No.

**QUESTION:** Do you change your feeding program in any way with the change of the seasons?

**ANSWER:** Yes, I feed a little more hay in winter.

**QUESTION:** Do you ever use an electrolyte solution in the feed or water?

**ANSWER:** Yes, in extremely hot weather.

**QUESTION:** Do you feel that brushing, rubbing, and grooming are important to the health, nutrition, and performance of your horses?

**ANSWER:** Our horses in training are groomed thoroughly and regularly.

**QUESTION:** How often do you pick up the manure out of each stall?

**ANSWER:** At least daily.

**QUESTION:** How often do you give your horses a bath?

**ANSWER:** Horses in heavy training are given baths daily when the outside temperature is 80 to 90 degrees, or inside when the temperature is 70 to 80 degrees.

**QUESTION:** Do you use heated water?

**ANSWER:** For horses in training I use warm water, for others I use tap water.

**QUESTION:** What substance do you prefer to use for stall bedding?
**ANSWER:** Straw.
**QUESTION:** What are the requirements for the straw you use?
**ANSWER:** Clean wheat straw, well-cured.
**QUESTION:** How many horses per helper do you prefer to use?
**ANSWER:** Three horses per helper with horses in training, and six to eight horses per helper when not in training.
**QUESTION:** How often do you clean out feed tubs?
**ANSWER:** We clean feed tubs thoroughly on a daily basis.
**QUESTION:** What kind of hoof dressing do you use?
**ANSWER:** Molumentun.
**QUESTION:** How often do you apply hoof dressing?
**ANSWER:** Two to three times per week.
**QUESTION:** How often do you have a blood analysis done on your horses?
**ANSWER:** As often as is recommended by our veterinarian.
**QUESTION:** What do you look for in a blood test?
**ANSWER:** We usually do a Complete Blood Count.
**QUESTION:** Do you ever have a hair analysis done on your horses?
**ANSWER:** Yes.
**QUESTION:** Do you ever have your water tested?
**ANSWER:** Yes.
**QUESTION:** Do you ever have your soil tested?
**ANSWER:** Yes.
**QUESTION:** What steps do you take during the warm months to combat the fly problem?
**ANSWER:** We use a stall spray system.
**QUESTION:** How often do you have your horses wormed?
**ANSWER:** Four or five times per year.
**QUESTION:** What method do you use?
**ANSWER:** Tube.
**QUESTION:** How often do you have dental work done on your horses?
**ANSWER:** Annually.
**QUESTION:** Do you do the dental work, or do you have your veterinarian do it?
**ANSWER:** We use an equine dental specialist.
**QUESTION:** How often do you take a horse's temperature?
**ANSWER:** For horses in training we take the temperature daily, for other horses we take the temperature only when indicated.
**QUESTION:** Do you inoculate your horses on a periodic basis?
**ANSWER:** Yes.
**QUESTION:** For what dieseases?
**ANSWER:** Tetanus, encephalomyelitis, flu, virus abortion.

# Buena Suerte Ranch

*Owning outstanding horses, both Thoroughbred and Quarter Horses, has become a habit with Mrs. Harriett Peckham, owner of the beautiful Buena Suerte Ranch in Roswell, New Mexico. Buena Suerte was designed and built as the home of Go Man Go, one of the truly great running Quarter Horse stallions of all time, and the leading living sire of Quarter racing horses. In addition to Go Man Go, Buena Suerte's stallion roster includes, Sparkling Native, a Thoroughbred son of the great Raise A Native; Fleet Kirsch, a beautifully-bred Thoroughbred stallion by Fleet Nasrullah; Tony B Deck, a stakes-winning Quarter stallion by the illustrious Jet Deck; and St. Bar, a Quarter Horse stallion by the immensely popular Three Bars.*

*Naturally, a breeding operation which boasts five outstanding stallions to its credit, will house many outside mares during the heavy breeding season. In keeping all the outside mares and active stallions in top condition, an extremely efficient and effective feeding program must be in use. Buena Suerte's nutritionally designed feeding program was formulated by Mrs. Peckham and her resident veterinarian, Dr. Leonard Blach. In addition to all the high quality grains, supplements, etc., which comprise a large portion of the daily rations, the Buena Suerte feeding program is highlighted by the richness of its home-grown alfalfa, some of the richest grown in the entire southwest.*

Mrs. Peckham definitely believes that the little minute details, which are sometimes overlooked, are extremely important in the overall nutritional adequacy of a feeding program. Getting the **very** best quality grains and supplements are the "little things" horsemen often overlook. Harriet feels these steps are well worth the extra expense and effort. She theorizes that if you are feeding your horses any substance which is not the best quality available over an extended period of time, the effects can be overwhelming on the growth rate of foals, weanlings and yearlings, as well as the performance of horses at the track. To help with the quality control standards of her feeding program, Harriet has designed the Buena Suerte feeding program around Fruen feeds, which she feels have very strict quality control measures for all their products. These particular feeds make up a large proportion of the three daily feedings for Buena Suerte horses, even when at the track.

Feeding times of 7 a.m.—12 noon—and 5 p.m. are standard for the popular owner's horses. And, although there are exceptions, the general

Mrs. Harriett Peckham, owner of the beautiful Buena Suerte Ranch in Roswell, New Mexico is pictured with the pride of her stallion roster, Go Man Go. The powerful, roan Quarter Horse stallion captured "World Championships" for three straight years during his running career and has proven to be equally successful at stud, being the leading sire of Quarter racing money earners.

rule for her horses in training is to receive one-half gallon of ration in the morning, one gallon at noon, and two gallons at night. All supplementations, such as vitamins, minerals, bran, etc. are added during the evening ration, to give more time for complete assimilation.

Harriet does not feed corn. She includes bran in her ration to ensure looseness of the bowels, and soybean meal to ensure the proper amount of protein for each individual. Harriet also includes cottonseed meal in her rations, and, for further protein supplementation, so that she gets the benefits of several different amino acids, she also uses the commercial product Sleek. Buena Suerte horses are always fed a minimum of eighteen percent protein for foals and yearlings, and fourteen percent for two year olds and older.

Buena Suerte horses have vitamin supplements added to their rations, and the supplement most often used is Visorbin Clovite. Harriet also believes in vitamin E supplementation. Injectable vitamins are given only when necessary, and only on the advice of Mrs. Peckham's veterinarian, Dr. Blach.

Mineral supplements on a free-choice basis are available for Buena Suerte horses, as is salt. Hot mashes are sometimes prepared for sick horses or picky eaters. Pelleted feeds are not a part of the feeding program at the Buena Suerte ranch.

Maintaining a proper ratio of calcium to phosphorus is an integral part of Buena Suerte's program. Mrs. Peckham is cognizant of the importance of the calcium-phosphorus ratio in developing and maintaining proper bone development.

"Nibblers" are given daily to all horses in training to alleviate boredom, and also, a certain amount of grazing is incorporated into the program for the same reason. Mrs. Peckham believes that the little daily "pleasures" will prove beneficial in the overall performance of the individual. Grooming, brushing, and rubbing are considered to be "very important" aspects of the overall Buena Suerte program. Approximately one hour per day per horse is dedicated to this procedure.

Scrupulously clean stalls are a "must" at Buena Suerte. Manure is picked up from stalls as often as necessary, "all day long." Baths are given to horses in training on a daily basis in an enclosed area with heated water. Mrs. Peckham prefers wood shavings for bedding. Feed tubs are thoroughly cleaned after each feeding. Lanolin is applied to hooves on a daily basis. And a blood analysis is run on every horse "as needed."

Young horses are wormed every two months at Buena Suerte, and older horses every three to four months. Tube worming is always the method, and Dr. Blach does the worming. Dental checkups are on an annual basis, and naturally, Dr. Blach takes care of this as well. Other health measures include taking the temperature of every horse in training twice daily, and annual inoculations for encephalomyelitis, tetanus, and flu.

# Hobeau Farm

The title of farm manager, especially for a very large breeding operation, includes many and varied duties. Elmer Heubeck, the talented, hard-working farm manager for Hobeau Farm in Ocala, Florida performs a myriad of activities on this very successful farm. Among his most important duties is setting up the proper nutritional program for the high-quality horses under his care.

Hobeau Farm has long been prominent in American racing circles, both as an outstanding breeding operation, and as a successful campaigner at the major tracks across the country. The list of notable runners either owned or bred by the Jack Dreyfus facility include Beau Purple, conqueror of the mighty Kelso several times in his career; Beaupy, stakes winner of over $200,000.00; Blessing Angelica, stakes winner of over $350,000.00 and Onion, recent victor of the Whitney Stakes over Secretariat. A 1973 acquisition by Hobeau has proven to be quite a success story . . . Prove Out, a beautiful son of Graustark, was purchased by Hobeau from the King Ranch, and is the only horse to have outrun both the "greats" of the Meadow Stable, Secretariat and Riva Ridge. To have outrun each of these outstanding individuals on separate occasions gives Prove Out enough credentials to be a history maker in his own right.

**QUESTION:** How many times per day do you feed?
**ANSWER:** It may vary from not at all, for a fat barren mare on good pasture, to four times in twenty-four hours for a "poor doer" in training.
**QUESTION:** How long do you leave the feed out if it is not eaten?
**ANSWER:** This varies. Some fillies we may leave in all night, reason: to get enough feed into the horse.
**QUESTION:** What kinds of hay do you feed?
**ANSWER:** On the farm we feed all Coastal Bermuda hay.
**QUESTION:** Which cutting do you prefer for your hay?
**ANSWER:** On the farm, we cut our highly-fertilized Coastal Bermuda four or five times per year. The horses get all but the first-cutting. The cows get the first one.
**QUESTION:** Are there any kinds of hay you would prefer if they were available locally?
**ANSWER:** We would feed alfalfa if we could grow it, or buy it from a good source at a fair price. Freight costs prohibit this.

*photo courtesy of The Blood-Horse*

Hobeau Farm near Ocala, Florida has bred and campaigned some of the best runners to ever come out of the "Sunshine State". Among their more popular performers have been Beau Purple, Handsome Boy, and Beaupy.

**QUESTION:** How do you judge your hay to decide if you are getting the quality you desire?

**ANSWER:** We judge our hay in this order: (a) the way the horse eats it, (b) it must be clean and cured right with a good color, (c) should be at least ten percent protein by analysis.

**QUESTION:** What parts of the country do you like your hay to come from?

**ANSWER:** We like to grow our own hay or buy from our neighbors where we know the soil that produces it.

**QUESTION:** What methods do you use to feed hay (floor, rack, net, manger, etc.)?

**ANSWER:** We feed on the floor. We sprinkle the hay with salt (mineralized) water. This gives the horse a chance to pick out what he wants, and eat with his head down as if he were grazing. We use molasses and water if the horse is a "poor hay doer."

**QUESTION:** Where do you buy your oats?

**ANSWER:** We buy our oats from the elevators of Illinois Grain Corporation in Tampa.

**QUESTION:** Do you feed whole oats or processed oats?

**ANSWER:** We crimp our oats three times a week.

**QUESTION:** Why do you prefer crimped oats over other types?

**ANSWER:** We feel our oats go further crimped, and young horses utilize them better.

**QUESTION:** Do you insist upon a standard weight per bushel for your oats?

**ANSWER:** Yes, we buy a #2 white, thirty-eight to forty pound test oat.

**QUESTION:** Do you insist that your oats be cleaned and then recleaned?

**ANSWER:** We clean our oats and run them over a magnet to pick up any metal before we crimp them.

**QUESTION:** Do you think there is any advantage to oats with clipped ends?

**ANSWER:** Not on the farm — if they are crimped.

**QUESTION:** Do you feed any corn?

**ANSWER:** Yes, we do feed some corn, mostly in cooler months.

**QUESTION:** How much of your total ration is composed of corn?

**ANSWER:** Never more than twenty percent of the total ration.

**QUESTION:** What quality of corn do you insist on?

**ANSWER:** Clean yellow.

**QUESTION:** What variety of corn do you like?

**ANSWER:** We like a good yellow hard dent.

**QUESTION:** In what form (whole, shelled, cracked, etc.)?

**ANSWER:** We prefer cracked corn, and in the winter we steam it and feed it warm.

**QUESTION:** Do you feed bran in your rations?

**ANSWER:** Yes — we go to every effort to get a high quality, large flake bran. The only place we have found it lately is in Tennessee.

**QUESTION:** How much bran do you feed?

**ANSWER:** We feed up to ten percent bran, and in some cases more. It is a good insurance against sand impaction.

**QUESTION:** Does the amount you feed depend on the looseness of the bowels of the individual animal?

**ANSWER:** Yes, to some extent.

**QUESTION:** Do you feel that bran has any value outside of its laxative effect?

**ANSWER:** Yes — bulk and phosphorus.

**QUESTION:** Do you feed cottonseed meal in your rations?

**ANSWER:** We use cottonseed meal at a rate of ten percent of the total ration. Cottonseed meal is a good source of amino acids.

**QUESTION:** Do you feed linseed meal in your rations?

**ANSWER:** Yes, it is a good grade of horse protein. It also does a good job of regulating bowels.

**QUESTION:** How much linseed meal do you feed?

**ANSWER:** About thirty percent of our total protein mixture is composed of linseed meal.

**QUESTION:** Do you feed soybean meal in your rations?

**ANSWER:** Yes, it is a good source of protein, it is easy to digest, and the horses like it.

**QUESTION:** How much soybean meal do you feed?

**ANSWER:** About thirty percent of the protein ration mix is composed of soybean meal.

**QUESTION:** Do you feed any other types of grain in your rations?

**ANSWER:** Yes, we feed steam-rolled barley.

**QUESTION:** How much, and why?

**ANSWER:** Up to twenty percent of the total ration, because it puts a nice hard finish on a horse, and horses like it.

**QUESTION:** What is the total formula of your protein mixture?

**ANSWER:** Twenty-eight percent Calf Manna, thirty percent soybean meal, thirty percent linseed oil meal, ten percent cottonseed oil meal (old process), and two percent gelatin. (We replace some of this with dry milk for weanlings.)

**QUESTION:** What percent of protein do you think is necessary in the ration of: (a) foals, (b) yearlings, (c) two and three year olds, and (d) mature horses?

**ANSWER:** Foals — 15 percent plus, with mare's milk. Yearlings — fifteen to sixteen percent. Two to three year olds — twelve to fourteen percent, and mature horses — twelve percent.

**QUESTION:** Are there any special activities that you think would require more protein in the diet?

**ANSWER:** Yes, racing, breeding and lactating mares require more protein — up to eighteen percent.

**QUESTION:** Do you feed a vitamin supplement in your ration?

**ANSWER:** When needed, but not often. We do feed an ounce of Kelp regularly.

**QUESTION:** Do you feed vitamin E?

**ANSWER:** Yes, we feed wheat germ oil during breeding season to the studs and mares.

**QUESTION:** Do you give injectable vitamins?

**ANSWER:** Only when needed.

**QUESTION:** How often is this?

**ANSWER:** Very seldom.

**QUESTION:** What kinds do you give, and how much of each?

**ANSWER:** Whatever kind we have on hand that we think is called for. We would rather get our vitamins out of feed, sun and grass.

**QUESTION:** Do you feed a mineral supplement?

**ANSWER:** Yes.

**QUESTION:** Do you mix it in your ration, or feed it free-choice?

**ANSWER:** We mix our mineral supplements in our ration.

**QUESTION:** What do you feel is the ideal calcium to phosphorus ratio?

**ANSWER:** 1 to 1.

**QUESTION:** What do you do in your feeding program to ensure that you keep this balance?

**ANSWER:** We have to add phosphorus, as our water and soil are very high in calcium.

**QUESTION:** Do you feel that salt is important in your horse's diet?

**ANSWER:** Yes, particularly so in Florida.

**QUESTION:** By what method or form do you feed salt, and how much?

**ANSWER:** We use a heaping tablespoonful of mineralized salt in each ration daily. We also have free-choice salt blocks.

**QUESTION:** Explain your procedures for ensuring that your horses have a constant, pure, clean water supply at all times.

**ANSWER:** Our stalled horses have clean buckets with fresh water regularly (even at night, we have a night watchman). Pastures have deep tanks for coolness with automatic floats. The tanks should be cleaned regularly. Use small amount of copper sulfate or goldfish to keep down algae.

**QUESTION:** Do you ever withhold water? Under what circumstances and for how long?

**ANSWER:** Only if a horse comes in hot or has been deprived of water for some time, and then we "water them off" slowly, just as we do when a horse comes off the race track after exercise.

**QUESTION:** Do you ever feed your horses a hot mash?

**ANSWER:** Yes, almost every night.

**QUESTION:** Do you feed any sweet feed in your rations?

**ANSWER:** We include four to eight ounces of blackstrap molasses in each ration every day.

**QUESTION:** Why?

**ANSWER:** Because it is a very good conditioner and appetizer. It is a good source of iron, it regulates bowels, and horses like it.

**QUESTION:** Do you feed any kinds of pellets in your rations?

**ANSWER:** Calf Manna always, and sometimes sun-cured alfalfa pellets if I can get good, fresh ones.

**QUESTION:** Are there any kinds of pellets that are better than others in your opinion?

**ANSWER:** If I were to use pelleted feeds, I would like them larger and harder than the average.

**QUESTION:** Do you think pelleted feed has any particular advantages or disadvantages?

**ANSWER:** We have trouble in this area with pellets taking on moisture and spoiling.

**QUESTION:** What is your overall opinion of pelleted feeds?

**ANSWER:** I do not like pelletized feed because I do not trust the quality of the feedstuff that is used. I think with the poor labor of today, this could be even more of a problem with pellets.

**QUESTION:** Have you personally ever had any bad experiences with pelleted feeds?

**ANSWER:** Yes.

**QUESTION:** Could you relate those to us?

**ANSWER:** I have had horses go off of feed, I have had problems with storing pellets, and I am unable to change my rations to individual needs when I feed pellets.

**QUESTION:** From what you hear from other trainers and owners, do you feel that pelletized feed is a coming thing? Or just the reverse?

**ANSWER:** I think the use of pelleted feeds will increase because it is easier to feed, but I do not think the best horseman will use them entirely.

**QUESTION:** Do you prefer a particular size of pellet?

**ANSWER:** I do not like pellets, but if I used them I would use a larger size than the average.

**QUESTION:** Could you give us the ingredients and amounts of your complete feeding program?

**ANSWER:** We probably have the most unorthodox feeding program in the country. In our three training barns of twenty-two horses each, our rations will differ more throughout the barn than it will between the different groups and ages. Basically, we try to plan our rations taking into consideration; the amount of work or the age and purpose of the horse, the amount and quality of pasture, and the amount, quality and protein content of our hay. Our best Coastal hay is put into the barn at about fifteen percent protein. These are good closed hay barns, but the hay will lose about one percent protein for every month stored for the first six months.

Our feeding program is my responsibility, but I try to train each foreman of every barn to take an interest in the feeding of every individual horse in his care, and he is to report any horse that does not clean up or has a dislike to some type of feed. The feed is hand-mixed just before feeding. The early morning feed that the night watchman feeds is mixed in tubs outside the stable door in the evening, and the night watchman adds molasses in early morning before he feeds.

Oats are our main bulk. To that we add one quart or more of bran. Our protein mixture is added in the amount necessary to bring our protein to our desired level. Our protein mixture generally runs around thirty-five percent of the ration. Salt and Kelp are added along with one ounce of wheat germ oil if we are using it. Our barley and corn have been soaked for several hours in very hot water. We now add the amount of barley and corn we desire, put on the blackstrap molasses, stir up well, and feed. This procedure does take more time than using a definite measure of a mixed feed, but throughout the years, I have become convinced it is worth the effort, as long as you can get competent foremen to watch over the feeding.

We do not creep feed foals. They are brought in twice a day with their mothers. After they start eating well with their mothers, we tie the mare and let them eat all they want before we turn the mares loose. The advantage that I see in creep feeding is a labor-saving item, but I would much rather have my foals handled and inspected twice a day.

**QUESTION:** Do you change your feeding program in any way before a horse is to receive exercise?

**ANSWER:** When we have work days on the training track, we are careful not to have our horses full of hay at the time they breeze. Their morning feed is not often changed as they are fed at 3 a.m.

**QUESTION:** Do you have any special tricks for making a horse eat that is a picky eater?

**ANSWER:** Sometimes we hold back a few meals from a picky eater, trying to make him hungry. Other times we will take the feed out after one hour. Most of the time we try and offer a picky eater something he wants, being satisfied to get most any foodstuff into the horse.

**QUESTION:** Do you change a broodmare's ration just before and after foaling?

**ANSWER:** We do lower the protein content of a foaling mare about thirty days prior to foaling, and increase it slowly after foaling. We also cut back on the entire ration at this time.

**QUESTION:** Do you have any special tricks for making a horse eat that goes off his feed?

**ANSWER:** Our horses that go off feed are always checked for parasites, and most of the time given a good drench, and then we try to bring the horse back on feed gradually. In some extreme cases, we use a stimulant, or a product such as Caco-Copper, Nux Vomica and sometimes the juice of ragweed will work when nothing else does.

**QUESTION:** Do you change your feeding program in any way after a race or hard exercise?

**ANSWER:** After a hard work-out or race, we will give a larger amount of hot mash, molasses or linseed meal, to loosen the tension of the digestive system. We also add Glauber salts for kidneys. Any added electrolytes will prove beneficial.

**QUESTION:** Do you believe in giving your horses any little treats like carrots, etc.?

**ANSWER:** This varies from barn to barn. I do not object, but do not like to see a horse get dependent on these "extras."

**QUESTION:** Do you graze your horses at all when they are in training?

**ANSWER:** We graze as much as possible, not so much for the benefit from the grass, but for the relaxation. If you graze in a confined area, you must check parasites more often.

**QUESTION:** Do you ever turn your horses in training out on grass or dry paddocks?

**ANSWER:** As often as we can, without danger of getting them hurt.

**QUESTION:** Is there any type of pasture that you prefer?

**ANSWER:** Any good, clean, tender pasture. We use Coastal Bermuda or Pensacola Bahia.

**QUESTION:** What, if any, differences are there in the way you feed two year olds in training, and aged horses in training?

**ANSWER:** Here again, we feed strictly as individuals, but the two year old will generally take more feed with a higher level of protein than the older horse.

**QUESTION:** Do you feed any of the commercially prepared hair conditioners in your ration?

**ANSWER:** No. Sometimes wheat germ oil, linseed oil, and a trace of sulphur are fed to improve the hair coat.

**QUESTION:** Do you change your feeding program in any way with the change of the seasons?

**ANSWER:** Yes. We feed heavier in the cooler months and less grass.

**QUESTION:** Do you supplement your feeding or injection program with anything for a particularly nervous horse?

**ANSWER:** We have had good results with Diphenylhydantoin.

**QUESTION:** Do you do anything else to help a particularly nervous horse?

**ANSWER:** Time, patience, and we make sure that the nervous horse has a good, quiet groom.

**QUESTION:** Have you found that you can sometimes stimulate a poor doer's appetite by lessening the amount of exercise he gets?

**ANSWER:** Only in extreme cases.

**QUESTION:** What is your exercise program for colts getting ready for the track?

**ANSWER:** Our average horse in training usually takes about ninety days from the time it is broken till it is ready to run — sometimes longer. The last three weeks is usually done at the race track where it will run. We stress long gallops (up to three miles) and slow works.

**QUESTION:** How important do you feel that brushing, rubbing, and grooming are to the health, nutrition and performance of your horses?

**ANSWER:** We feel that grooming is very important. It is often worth several quarts of good feed.

**QUESTION:** How much time per day do you spend on each horse's grooming?

**ANSWER:** We try to spend at least thirty minutes per day on horses in training, and our "turn-outs" get five to ten minutes with a rubber shedder.

**QUESTION:** How often do you pick up the manure out of each stall?

**ANSWER:** Daily.

**QUESTION:** How often do you give your horses a bath?

**ANSWER:** We give our training horses a bath after exercising anytime they get hot enough to need it. Here in Florida, we seldom have to worry about temperature.

**QUESTION:** Do you use heated water?

**ANSWER:** We use lukewarm water.

**QUESTION:** What material do you prefer for stall bedding?

**ANSWER:** We use some straw, but mostly clean grass clippings for bedding, which makes good cow feed after we clean the stalls. I do not like shavings, hulls, or sawdust as there is often a dust problem.

**QUESTION:** What are your requirements for the bedding you use?

**ANSWER:** We require bedding to be clean and free from mold.

**QUESTION:** How many horses per helper do you prefer when your horses are in training?

**ANSWER:** In a training barn of twenty-two horses, we have a foreman, five exercise riders that ride in the morning, and groom and care for the horses in the afternoon. I employ girls for riders. There are also two grooms that help on the ground and muck stalls. In the turn-out barns of twenty-two horses, I have a foreman and one helper.

**QUESTION:** How often do you clean your feed tubs?

**ANSWER:** We wash our feed tubs at least once a day in hot water. And we place them in the sun when we can.

**QUESTION:** How often do you have a blood analysis done on your horses?

**ANSWER:** Whenever we think we need it. Also before and after any operation.

**QUESTION:** What do you look for in a blood test?

**ANSWER:** We pay attention to the packed blood cell count, white count, and red count differential, hemoglobin and a number of different types of cells.

**QUESTION:** What kind of hoof dressing do you use?

**ANSWER:** We alternate from pine tar, castor oil, and lanolin.

**QUESTION:** How often do you apply hoof dressing?

**ANSWER:** As often as we think necessary. It depends on the dryness and the condition of the hoof.

**QUESTION:** Do you ever have your grain or hay analyzed by a lab?

**ANSWER:** Yes, whenever changes are made.

**QUESTION:** Do you ever have your water or soil tested?

**ANSWER:** Yes, yearly.

**QUESTION:** Do you ever have problems with horses that chew wood, cribbers, wind suckers, stall weavers, etc.?

**ANSWER:** Yes.

**QUESTION:** What do you think causes them to do this?

**ANSWER:** Nervousness or monotony.

**QUESTION:** What do you do to stop them?

**ANSWER:** We use cribbing straps, sometimes another horse next to them works, sometimes a pet, like a dog or a goat works. A radio or most anything they will like is also occasionally used.

**QUESTION:** How often do you have your horses wormed?

**ANSWER:** We worm our foals every twenty-one days, our weanlings and yearlings every thirty days, and our older horses at least every two months.

**QUESTION:** What method do you use?

**ANSWER:** We always use a stomach tube.

**QUESTION:** How often do you have dental work done on your horses?

**ANSWER:** We have dental work performed twice per year, and more often if we have a problem.

**QUESTION:** Do you do the dental work, or do you have your veterinarian do it?

**ANSWER:** We have a resident veterinarian.

**QUESTION:** How often do you take a horse's temperature?

**ANSWER:** We take a horse's temperature when we think we need to or if we have an outbreak in a barn, then we take all horse's temperatures in the barn twice per day.

**QUESTION:** Do you inoculate your horses on a periodic basis?

**ANSWER:** Yes, for Eastern and Western encephalomyelitis and tetanus.

**QUESTION:** What areas of equine nutrition do you feel are most in need of further research?

**ANSWER:** Nutrition to help soundness problems and breeding problems.

**QUESTION:** Are there any points in a good equine nutritional program that you would like to discuss that we have not mentioned?

**ANSWER:** Personally, I think the success of any nutritional program depends largely on regularity, the quality of your feedstuff, and **the quality of your personnel.**

# Yale Freed

*Mr. Yale Freed has the outstanding honor to have been elected as President of the International Arabian Association. His many years of experience in the Arabian industry have set up the basis for this position. Operating from his Briarwood Arabian Farm in Solvang, California, Mr. Freed has been a definite leader in the growing Arabian horse industry, not only in this country, but over the entire world. In his own behalf, he has had dealings with some extremely successful Arabians, most notable Bolero\*, Hassa\* and Mr. Miracle\*. All of these horses are Legion of Merit earners, with Bolero\* and Hassa\* being named Reserve National Champion and National Champion respectively.*

**QUESTION:** How many times per day do you feed?
**ANSWER:** Two to three times per day, depending on the individual animal. We have free-choice feed for foals.
**QUESTION:** At what times of day do you feed?
**ANSWER:** 7 a.m.—5 p.m. (noon for some).
**QUESTION:** Do you feed equal amounts at each feeding?
**ANSWER:** Normally, we feed an equal amount at each feeding, but it still depends on the individual animal.
**QUESTION:** Do you feed them the same things at each feeding?
**ANSWER:** Yes.
**QUESTION:** How long do you leave the feed out if it is not eaten?
**ANSWER:** Until the next feeding.
**QUESTION:** What kind of hay do you feed?
**ANSWER:** Alfalfa.
**QUESTION:** Which cutting do you prefer?
**ANSWER:** Third-cutting.
**QUESTION:** Are there any other kinds of hay you would prefer if they were available locally?
**ANSWER:** No.
**QUESTION:** How do you judge your hay to decide if you are getting the quality you desire?
**ANSWER:** Color, blossom, texture and smell.
**QUESTION:** What parts of the country do you like your hay to come from?
**ANSWER:** Lancaster, California.
**QUESTION:** What methods do you use to feed hay (floor, rack, net, manger, etc.)?

**ANSWER:** Manger.

**QUESTION:** Do you buy your oats from local feed dealers or have them shipped in?

**ANSWER:** I would prefer to buy from local feed dealers, however I have them shipped in because of cost.

**QUESTION:** Do you feed whole oats or processed oats?

**ANSWER:** We feed cracked oats and rolled oats, because they are easier to digest and have less waste.

**QUESTION:** What quality oats do you insist upon?

**ANSWER:** We insist upon the very highest quality recleaned oats.

**QUESTION:** Do you think that there is any advantage to oats with clipped ends?

**ANSWER:** No.

**QUESTION:** Is there any particular company or companies whose oats you feel are better than others?

**ANSWER:** Kruse in El Monte, California.

**QUESTION:** Do you feed any corn?

**ANSWER:** Yes, thirty percent of our grain rations are composed of cracked corn on a year-round basis.

**QUESTION:** What quality of corn do you insist on?

**ANSWER:** The very best!

**QUESTION:** Do you feed bran in your ration?

**ANSWER:** Yes, about twenty percent of our grain ration is composed of bran.

**QUESTION:** Do you feed cottonseed meal, linseed meal or soybean meal in your rations?

**ANSWER:** Yes, we feed a combination of these three, and they total 7.3 percent of our total ration.

**QUESTION:** Do you feed any other types of grain in your ration?

**ANSWER:** Yes, barley.

**QUESTION:** Do you use any commercial supplements to supplement the protein content of your ration?

**ANSWER:** Yes, Calf Manna.

**QUESTION:** What percent of protein do you think is necessary in the ration of (a) foals, (b) yearlings, (c) two and three year olds, and (d) mature horses?

**ANSWER:** Foals, fourteen percent; yearlings, twelve to fourteen percent; two and three year olds, ten to twelve percent; and mature horses, it depends on the amount of work they do, and if they are broodmares.

**QUESTION:** Do you feed a vitamin supplement in your ration?

**ANSWER:** Yes, we feed Clovite as per instructions on the label.

**QUESTION:** Do you supplement vitamin E in your rations?

**ANSWER:** Yes, we use soybean oil, one ounce per feeding.

**QUESTION:** Do you give injectable vitamins?

**ANSWER:** No.

**QUESTION:** Do you feed a mineral mix?

**ANSWER:** Yes, we mix it in our rations.

**QUESTION:** What mineral supplement do you feed?

**ANSWER:** A special mix prepared by our feed dealer.

**QUESTION:** What do you feel is the ideal calcium to phosphorus ratio?

**ANSWER:** 2 to 1.

**QUESTION:** Do you feel that salt is important in your horses' diet?

**ANSWER:** Yes, we use mineralized salt blocks.

**QUESTION:** Do you ever feed your horses a hot mash?

**ANSWER:** Yes, to horses that have suffered from colic.

**QUESTION:** Do you feed any sweet feed in your ration?

**ANSWER:** Yes, varying amounts. It depends on the animal.

**QUESTION:** What brand of sweet feed do you prefer?

**ANSWER:** A special mix prepared by our feed dealer.

**QUESTION:** How much molasses do you like in your sweet feed?

**ANSWER:** As little as possible.

**QUESTION:** Do you feed any kinds of pellets?

**ANSWER:** Yes, a limited amount in special situations, however, we have found that feeding of pellets tends to create wood chewing.

**QUESTION:** Do you think pelleted feed has any advantages?

**ANSWER:** Yes, they are cleaner, less waste, and easier to store.

**QUESTION:** Could you give us the ingredients and amounts of your complete feeding program?

**ANSWER:** For an average horse, fifteen to twenty pounds of hay, four pounds of grain. For horses in training, twenty pounds of hay, six to eight pounds of grain. Horses laying-up in stalls, fifteen pounds of hay, no grain. Broodmares, fifteen pounds of hay, four to six pounds of grain. Lactating mares, fifteen pounds of hay, six pounds of grain. Stallions in off season, fifteen pounds of hay, four pounds of grain. Stallions in service, twenty pounds of hay, six to eight pounds of grain. Weanlings and yearlings are fed on a free-choice basis. Foals are creep fed on a free-choice basis.

**QUESTION:** Do you change a broodmare's ration just before and after foaling?

**ANSWER:** Yes, we increase the rations.

**QUESTION:** Do you change your feeding program in any way before a

horse is entered in an arena event, or after he has partici-
pated?

**ANSWER:** No.

**QUESTION:** Do you believe in giving your horses any little treats like
carrots, etc.?

**ANSWER:** No.

**QUESTION:** Do you graze your horses at all when they are in training?

**ANSWER:** No.

**QUESTION:** What, if any, differences are there in the way you feed
two year olds in training, and aged horses in training?

**ANSWER:** We give more grain to the two year olds.

**QUESTION:** Do you feed any of the commercially prepared hair conditioners in your ration?

**ANSWER:** No.

**QUESTION:** Do you change your feeding program in any way with the
change of the seasons?

**ANSWER:** No.

**QUESTION:** Do you ever use an electrolyte solution in the feed or
water of a horse?

**ANSWER:** Yes, in cases where dehydration is a problem.

**QUESTION:** Do you supplement your feeding or injection program
with anything for a particularly nervous horse?

**ANSWER:** We do not have any nervous horses!

**QUESTION:** Have you found that you can sometimes stimulate a poor
doer's appetite by lessening the amount of exercise he
gefs?

**ANSWER:** No.

**QUESTION:** What is your exercise program for an average horse getting ready for average riding, or an average arena event?

**ANSWER:** One-half hour to one hour work daily.

**QUESTION:** How important do you feel that brushing, rubbing and
grooming are to the health, nutrition and performance of
your horses?

**ANSWER:** Major!

**QUESTION:** How much time per day do you spend on each horse's
grooming?

**ANSWER:** Whatever is necessary to assure that the horse is clean and
well-groomed.

**QUESTION:** How often do you pick up manure out of each stall?

**ANSWER:** Daily.

**QUESTION:** How often do you give your horses a bath?

**ANSWER:** Whenever necessary.

**QUESTION:** What material do you prefer for stall bedding?

**ANSWER:** I prefer straw, but sometimes use sawdust.

**QUESTION:** What are your requirements for the straw you use?

**ANSWER:** It must be very clean, no dust or mold.

**QUESTION:** How often, and exactly how, do you clean up feed tubs?

**ANSWER:** Once per week with scrub brush and disinfectant.

**QUESTION:** What kind of hoof dressing do you use?

**ANSWER:** Hooflex, as needed.

**QUESTION:** How often do you have a blood analysis done on your horses?

**ANSWER:** Only when necessary.

**QUESTION:** What do you look for in a blood test?

**ANSWER:** Red cell count.

**QUESTION:** What steps do you take during the warm months to combat the fly problem?

**ANSWER:** We utilize fogging, wipes, and include one tablespoon of vinegar in our grain rations.

**QUESTION:** How often do you have your horses wormed?

**ANSWER:** We worm horses as needed on the basis of a check of the fecal material, but in no case less often than once per year.

**QUESTION:** What method do you use?

**ANSWER:** Wonder Wormer and tubing.

**QUESTION:** How often do you take a horse's temperature?

**ANSWER:** Only when they appear to have something wrong with them.

**QUESTION:** Do you inoculate your horses on a periodic basis?

**ANSWER:** Yes, for tetanus, flu, VEE, and sleeping sickness.

**QUESTION:** What areas of equine nutrition do you feel are most in need of further research?

**ANSWER:** Supplement analysis.

# Paul R. Weyerts, D.V.M., Ph.D.

*A practicing veterinarian and Professor of Animal Science at Sul Ross University, Alpine, Texas, Dr. Paul R. Weyerts comes into contact with every problem associated with the horse population as far as nutritional inadequacies are concerned. His Ph.D. in the field of Range Nutrition provides a firm foundation for his vast field experiences in the south Texas area.*

*Studying at the University of Wyoming and Texas A&M University, Dr. Weyerts has established himself as one of the leading veterinarians in the southwest, especially in nutritionally related problem areas. Through his findings as a practicing professional, Dr. Weyerts has concluded that actual research on digestion and absorption from the cecum and colon are the areas most in need of further study in the field of equine nutrition. These particular fields have been the basis for much of his research.*

**QUESTION:** What do you think are the particular advantages or disadvantages of the following grains? (a) oats, (b) corn, (c) wheat, (d) barley, (e) milo.

**ANSWER:** Oats seem to be the best all-around grain for horses because of the blend of qualities of both a concentrate and a roughage. (Well-balanced). Corn naturally contains the highest nutritional value of all grains. It is a good grain for horses if it is cracked or rolled. Wheat in bran form is an excellent supplement in the horse's diet. It is a good laxative. Barley is good in "hot" rations, or adjunct to other grains. Milo is less desirable than corn and in some cases may cause kidney disorders.

**QUESTION:** What factors do you look for in judging grains?

**ANSWER:** Grains should be free of mold and excessive dust, they should be properly cured when cut, and stored in clean facilities.

**QUESTION:** What do you feel a minimum weight should be for a good quality oat?

**ANSWER:** Thirty-three to thirty-four pounds per bushel.

**QUESTION:** Which grains generally have the highest palatability factor for horses?

**ANSWER:** Oats, barley, wheat bran and corn.

**QUESTION:** What do you feel are the advantages or disadvantages of processed grains over whole grains?

**ANSWER:** The advantages of processed grains are increased digestibility, and the disadvantages are cost.

**QUESTION:** What methods of processing are most valuable for oats?

**ANSWER:** Rolled or screened.

**QUESTION:** What methods of processing are most valuable for corn?

**ANSWER:** Cracked or flaked.

**QUESTION:** What proportions of legume hays to grass hays do you recommend?

**ANSWER:** I recommend approximately one-third legume to two-thirds grass, up to one-half legume to one-half grass.

**QUESTION:** What varieties of hay available in your area tend to be most palatable?

**ANSWER:** Alfalfa, grama (if available), green sprangletop, sudan, and Bermuda.

**QUESTION:** Would you prefer other varieties if available locally?

**ANSWER:** I feel that oat hay is the most desirable, but it is usually not available.

**QUESTION:** What is the minimum amount of hay necessary for a balanced diet?

**ANSWER:** One-half of the total ration.

**QUESTION:** What proportion of hay to grain is best in the average diet?

**ANSWER:** Two-thirds hay to one-third grain.

**QUESTION:** How long should hay be cured before feeding?

**ANSWER:** Alfalfa should be cured one month, since this lessens the chance of colic.

**QUESTION:** Should hay be fed free-choice or in measured amounts?

**ANSWER:** Alfalfa should be fed in measured amounts since a lot of people tend to overfeed alfalfa.

**QUESTION:** Do you feel that it is best to feed hay from a manger, in a net, on the ground, or how?

**ANSWER:** Anything except on the ground.

**QUESTION:** Is pasture important to a complete ration?

**ANSWER:** Pasture is not essential but it certainly helps maintain a healthy horse.

**QUESTION:** How useful do you feel the protein concentrates soybean meal, linseed meal, and cottonseed meal are?

**ANSWER:** I feel that soybean meal is excellent to the point needed in maintaining the proper protein level for younger animals.

**QUESTION:** Are there any commercial protein supplements that you feel are better than others?

**ANSWER:** Any good, reputable company will usually produce an adequate supplement.

**QUESTION:** Should protein supplements be added to the diet routinely, or only under special circumstances?

**ANSWER:** Protein supplements should be added routinely for younger horses.

**QUESTION:** What are the protein requirements for the following: (a) weanlings, (b) yearlings, (c) growing horses, (d) mature horses, (e) old horses, (f) broodmares, (g) stallions, (h) race horses, (i) performance horses, and (j) pleasure horses?

**ANSWER:** Weanlings, fifteen to eighteen percent; yearlings, twelve to fourteen percent; growing horses, twelve percent; mature horses, ten percent; old horses, twelve percent; broodmares, twelve percent; stallions, twelve percent; race horses, twelve percent; performance horses, twelve percent; pleasure horses, ten to twelve percent. (Note: protein requirements for mature horses are less than most people think. However, my personal views are, that the addition of one or two percent more protein may be valuable to cover all the essential amino acids in sufficient amounts. The value may easily outweigh the additional expense.)

**QUESTION:** Is it preferable to feed mineralized salt, plain salt, or both?

**ANSWER:** Iodized salt should be fed in iodine deficient areas.

**QUESTION:** Is it more advantageous to feed salt free-choice or in measured amounts mixed into the feed?

**ANSWER:** Free-choice, block or loose.

**QUESTION:** Are there any times when water should be withheld from the horse?

**ANSWER:** Yes, prior to abdominal surgery or castration.

**QUESTION:** What do you feel is the best method for inducing a horse to drink more water if he is drinking insufficient amounts?

**ANSWER:** Be certain that you are offering the animal proper amounts of salt and minerals.

**QUESTION:** What precautions should normally be taken when watering the hot horse?

**ANSWER:** Let the animal drink small amounts, often, (every ten to fifteen minutes).

**QUESTION:** In your opinion, what is the role of vitamin E in body function?

**ANSWER:** Vitamin E is excellent for strengthening muscles, and it is also good for the treatment of azoturia.

**QUESTION:** Do you feel that vitamin E supplementation can be beneficial in racing, working, or breeding performance?

**ANSWER:** Yes, definitely.

**QUESTION:** Can any vitamin E effects be harmful?

**ANSWER:** None that I am aware of.

**QUESTION:** Are vitamin supplements necessary if the diet is well-balanced?

**ANSWER:** Yes, I think there is a need in the diet of the lactating mare and the growing foal and yearling.

**QUESTION:** Do you feel that injected vitamin supplements are superior to oral vitamins?

**ANSWER:** Not for everyday use, however in rare cases, injected supplements may become necessary if the animal is unable to absorb oral vitamins properly.

**QUESTION:** Is the average horse owner today too concerned with supplements, not concerned enough, or does he usually have the proper attitude?

**ANSWER:** In my opinion, the average horse owner is not to be found. The owners either do not care at all, or they are absolute "nuts" on the subject of giving supplements.

**QUESTION:** If a balanced diet is fed, are mineral supplements necessary?

**ANSWER:** I think that a good free-choice mineral supplement should be available at all times.

**QUESTION:** What do you feel is the ideal calcium to phosphorus ratio?

**ANSWER:** 1.5 calcium to 1 phosphorus (with ample vitamin D).

**QUESTION:** Do you think that the Total Digestible Nutrient (TDN) system of balancing a ration is practical and valid?

**ANSWER:** I think that it is a fair method, and I think it is a reasonable approach for the average horseman. However, I think that energy requirements are more accurate.

**QUESTION:** What factors do you think are most important to consider in preparing the complete balanced diet?

**ANSWER:** (1) essential amino acids, (2) essential fatty acids, (3) energy. These three factors, combined with meeting the vitamin and mineral needs, with an overall consideration of palatability.

**QUESTION:** Do sweet feeds have any advantages or disadvantages?

**ANSWER:** They are high in palatability, and due to the different grain ingredients, they may also aid as a broad source of natural proteins.

**QUESTION:** Do you feel that there are times when it would be advantageous to feed pelleted feeds?

**ANSWER:** Yes, when it is difficult to secure good, clean, high quality hay and grain.

**QUESTION:** In your experience, have you found commercial feed mixes from a reputable company to be usually adequate in quality?

**ANSWER:** Yes.

**QUESTION:** How do you judge the worth of a commercial feed?

**ANSWER:** Taste, smell, texture, and the performance of the horses to which the commercial feed is fed.

**QUESTION:** In your opinion, is it worthwhile to have a commercial mill prepare your own feeds to your formula?

**ANSWER:** Yes.

**QUESTION:** Do the costs outweigh the advantages?

**ANSWER:** Not usually.

**QUESTION:** What do you normally do if you feel that the palatability of a ration needs to be increased?

**ANSWER:** I either add sweet feed and/or molasses.

**QUESTION:** Do you think there are any advantages in feeding cooked rations?

**ANSWER:** There is probably an advantage in palatability. However, cooked rations should be fed only by an experienced horseman who can observe amount eaten and prevent moldy feed from collecting in the feed trough.

**QUESTION:** What are the hallmarks of a good feeding program?

**ANSWER:** A vigorous, healthy animal.

**QUESTION:** What are the danger signs that show an inadequate feeding program?

**ANSWER:** Lack of appetite, dull coat, listless, etc.

**QUESTION:** What do you feel is the most worthwhile use of laboratory testing?

**ANSWER:** To ensure that you have a proper calcium to phosphorus balance.

**QUESTION:** How can the average person recognize the poorly nourished horse that appears fat?

**ANSWER:** The activity of the horse, the results of a blood test, and the appearance of the hair coat.

**QUESTION:** What do you feel are the major causes of a "poor doer"?

**ANSWER:** Bad teeth and parasites.

**QUESTION:** What can you do to stimulate a "poor doer's" appetite?

**ANSWER:** A change of feed and the addition of possible needed minerals.

**QUESTION:** How frequently do you recommend worming, and by what method?

**ANSWER:** A horse should be tubed at least once per year, and worming powder should be included in the feed ration two or three times per year.

**QUESTION:** How do stimulants affect a horse's health and appetite?

**ANSWER:** Stimulants can have an adverse effect on a horse's health and appetite if not used for specific treatment.

**QUESTION:** Although drugs are generally outlawed in racing programs, do you feel that they could ever be of value?

**ANSWER:** Yes, in some limited cases of illness or lameness.

**QUESTION:** What do you feel is the minimal number of times a horse should be fed daily under ideal circumstances?

**ANSWER:** Twice daily.

**QUESTION:** What are the best times of day to feed?

**ANSWER:** This doesn't really matter if the meals are spaced evenly.

**QUESTION:** How should the total daily ration be divided up among feedings?

**ANSWER:** They should be divided about equally, however this should be adjusted according to the amount of exercise the horse gets.

**QUESTION:** How does grooming affect health, appetite, condition, etc.?

**ANSWER:** Grooming affects the horse's disposition and thereby his general condition.

**QUESTION:** What special precautions should you take when horses cannot be fed individually, but must be fed in a group?

**ANSWER:** Spread rations adequately, so all horses can get a reasonable share.

**QUESTION:** How long should you leave feed in front of a horse if it is not eaten?

**ANSWER:** This depends on the individual animal, however a "good rule of thumb" would be about one hour.

**QUESTION:** How long should you leave hay in front of a horse if it is not eaten?

**ANSWER:** I like to feed small amounts of hay free-choice.

**QUESTION:** Do you think that the life expectancy of the average horse could be lengthened if most owners were to change their feeding programs?

**ANSWER:** Yes, particularly in the case of the stalled horse.

**QUESTION:** How do you feel the average level of equine nutrition is in the United States today?

**ANSWER:** Only fair.

Special Note: "As a practicing veterinarian for thirteen years and one still in an active part-time practice, I must conclude with the following thoughts: (1) Horse owners as a rule, either grossly overfeed or underfeed their animals. (Mostly overfeed). (2) As a rule — sanitation procedures to reduce internal parasites are largely ignored. (3) The average horseman who feeds his horses high level rations and is exercising his animals properly, does not realize the importance of reducing feed consumption at times when his horses are unable to get proper exercise.

# M and M Ranch

*Owning and operating a large successful Quarter Horse breeding operation has qualified Mike and Millie Leonard to become extremely familiar with, and authoritative on the subject of equine nutrition. Their operation houses many horses each year, including many outside broodmares, which are sent to them for expert care, as well as to be bred to their resident stallions.*

*What higher compliment could be paid to a particular facility, than to have a mare sent for proper care and nutrition during the crucial gestation and foaling period. The Leonards have gained the reputation of being outstanding horsepeople, both as breeders and as nutritionists through many years of experience and hard work, which has paid off many times during the past seasons. In addition to their current outstanding stallion roster, M and M Ranch was the home of Major King, a stallion whose siring accomplishments have had a phenomenal impact on the entire Quarter Horse industry. Major King's name appears on both the "Leading Sires of American Quarter Horse Association Champions" list and "Leading Sires of Arena Register Of Merit" list.*

**QUESTION:** How many times per day do you feed?
**ANSWER:** At least two.
**QUESTION:** At what times of day do you feed?
**ANSWER:** 8 a.m. and 6 p.m.
**QUESTION:** Do you feed equal amounts at each feeding?
**ANSWER:** Yes.
**QUESTION:** Do you feed the same things at each feeding?
**ANSWER:** Mostly . . . yes.
**QUESTION:** How long do you leave the feed out if it is not eaten?
**ANSWER:** Two hours usually, and maybe more depending on the individual.
**QUESTION:** What kinds of hay do you feed?
**ANSWER:** Alfalfa, Coastal Bermuda, prairie hay, and good quality johnsongrass.
**QUESTION:** Which cutting do you prefer for each variety?
**ANSWER:** Second.
**QUESTION:** Are there any kinds of hay you would prefer if they were available locally?
**ANSWER:** Timothy, and high quality prairie hay.
**QUESTION:** How do you judge your hay to decide if you are getting the

quality you desire?

**ANSWER:** Look, smell, feel, and laboratory analysis.

**QUESTION:** What parts of the country do you like your hay to come from?

**ANSWER:** North and Northwest.

**QUESTION:** What methods do you use to feed hay (floor, rack, net, manger, etc.)?

**ANSWER:** Rack, bottom of rack is eighteen inches from ground.

**QUESTION:** Where do you get your oats?

**ANSWER:** We grow our own.

**QUESTION:** Do you feed whole oats or processed oats?

**ANSWER:** We feed whole oats which we feel is more natural for the animal, unless of course you have problems with bad teeth or very old age, then it is okay to process the oats.

**QUESTION:** Do you insist upon a standard weight per bushel for your oats?

**ANSWER:** Thirty-six pounds or more.

**QUESTION:** How many times do you feel that oats should be cleaned and recleaned?

**ANSWER:** Twice.

**QUESTION:** Do you think there is any advantage to oats with clipped ends?

**ANSWER:** No.

**QUESTION:** Other than the oats you grow yourself, is there any particular variety you prefer?

**ANSER:** We prefer red, heavy oats from the northern part of the United States.

**QUESTION:** Do you feed any corn?

**ANSWER:** Yes, cracked, #1 yellow dent corn on a year-round basis.

**QUESTION:** How much of your total ration is composed of corn?

**ANSWER:** Generally, ten percent.

**QUESTION:** Do you feed bran in your ration?

**ANSWER:** Yes, about ten percent of our rations are composed of bran.

**QUESTION:** Why?

**ANSWER:** Loose bowels, energy, and amino acids.

**QUESTION:** Do you feed cottonseed meal in your ration?

**ANSWER:** Yes, about five percent of the total ration is cottonseed meal.

**QUESTION:** Why?

**ANSWER:** The overall protein content and the amino acids in particular.

**QUESTION:** Do you feed linseed meal in your ration?

**ANSWER:** Yes, for the same reasons we feed cottonseed meal.

**QUESTION:** How much linseed meal do you feed?

**ANSWER:** Five percent of the total ration.

**QUESTION:** Do you feed soybean meal in your ration?

**ANSWER:** Yes, for the same reasons we feed cottonseed meal and linseed meal.

**QUESTION:** How much?

**ANSWER:** Five percent of the total ration.

**QUESTION:** Do you feed any other types of grain in your ration?

**ANSWER:** Yes. We feed about five percent barley at times.

**QUESTION:** What percent of protein is necessary in the ration of: (a) foals, (b) yearlings, (c) two and three year olds, (d) mature horses?

**ANSWER:** Foals, eighteen to twenty percent; yearlings, sixteen to eighteen percent; two and three year olds, twelve to fourteen percent; and mature horses, twelve percent.

**QUESTION:** Are there any special activities that you think would require more protein in the diet, such as racing, breeding, etc.?

**ANSWER:** A slight increase in protein may be called for for breeding horses.

**QUESTION:** Do you feed a vitamin supplement in your ration?

**ANSWER:** Yes.

**QUESTION:** What kind is it?

**ANSWER:** Vitamins A, D and E made by the Pfizer Company.

**QUESTION:** Do you use vitamin E supplementation?

**ANSWER:** Yes, in feed and also in injectable form.

**QUESTION:** What is your injectable vitamin program?

**ANSWER:** About two cc's of A, D, and E every forty-five to ninety days.

**QUESTION:** Do you feed a mineral supplement?

**ANSWER:** Yes.

**QUESTION:** Do you mix it in your ration or feed it free-choice?

**ANSWER:** Both.

**QUESTION:** What do you feel is the ideal calcium to phosphorus ratio?

**ANSWER:** 1 to 1.

**QUESTION:** Do you feel that salt is important in your horses' diets?

**ANSWER:** Yes, we feed loose salt, free-choice.

**QUESTION:** Do you recommend minerals with the salt?

**ANSWER:** No.

**QUESTION:** Do you ever feed your horses a hot mash?

**ANSWER:** No.

**QUESTION:** Do you feed any sweet feed in your ration?

**ANSWER:** Yes, enough to keep down fines and dust.

**QUESTION:** How much molasses do you like in your sweet feed?

**ANSWER:** Not over twenty percent.

**QUESTION:** Do you feed any kinds of pelleted feeds?

**ANSWER:** Moorman's alfalfa pellets.

**QUESTION:** Could you give the ingredients and amounts of your complete feeding program?

**ANSWER:** Our number one feed mix consists of the following: thirty-six pound minimum per bushel clean oats — twenty percent, shelled #1 yellow corn, cracked — ten percent, wheat bran — ten percent, linseed meal — five percent, soybean meal or cottonseed meal — five percent, alfalfa #1 leafy (rabbit hay) — twenty percent, prairie, Coastal Bermuda, or johnsongrass hay — twenty percent, Calf Manna (or equal), five percent, loose salt, three percent, mineral, (red) two percent, and enough molasses to keep down fines and dust. This "#1" feed mix is for breeding stallions and broodmares. Other horses in pasture we mix one-half oats with one-half of the "#1" feed mix. Working horses we mix one-third oats with two-thirds of the "#1" feed mix. Our creep feed mix for suckling foals, we add ten percent milk replacer (pellets preferred, powder okay), to the "#1" feed mix. Also, salt is provided free-choice, a good mineral mix is provided free-choice, and steamed bone meal is provided free-choice.

**QUESTION:** Do you believe in giving your horses any little treats like carrots, etc.?

**ANSWER:** No, it creates too many bad habits.

**QUESTION:** Do you graze your horses when they are in training?

**ANSWER:** Yes, as much as possible.

**QUESTION:** Is there any type of pasture that you prefer?

**ANSWER:** Good native grasses.

**QUESTION:** What, if any, differences are there in the way you feed two year olds in training, and aged horses in training?

**ANSWER:** We feed the younger horses more protein.

**QUESTION:** Do you change your feeding program in any way with the change of the seasons?

**ANSWER:** We cut down on carbohydrate content in the warmer months.

**QUESTION:** What do you do to help stimulate a horse's appetite when he goes off his feed after a performance event or heavy exercise?

**ANSWER:** We have found that rest, bran, and sweet feed are our three best tools for dealing with this problem.

**QUESTION:** How important do you feel that brushing, rubbing, and grooming are to the health, nutrition, and performance of your horses?

**ANSWER:** Very!

**QUESTION:** How much time per day do you spend on each horse's grooming?

**ANSWER:** Stalled horses receive at least fifteen minutes grooming time per day. Also, in warm weather, horses are bathed.

**QUESTION:** How often do you pick up the manure out of each stall?

**ANSWER:** Daily.

**QUESTION:** What material do you prefer for stall bedding?

**ANSWER:** Straw is economical, but you have to be careful that the horse does not eat the straw. Sawdust is okay.

**QUESTION:** What are your requirements for the straw you use?

**ANSWER:** Bright, dry, oat straw.

**QUESTION:** How often do you clean up feed tubs?

**ANSWER:** After every feeding.

**QUESTION:** What kind of hoof dressing do you use?

**ANSWER:** We only use hoof dressings that do not seal the hoof.

**QUESTION:** How often do you apply hoof dressing?

**ANSWER:** Seldom. We prefer to use mud and water.

**QUESTION:** How often do you have your horses wormed?

**ANSWER:** Two to three times per year.

**QUESTION:** What method do you use?

**ANSWER:** Tube method and also the drench method.

**QUESTION:** How often do you have dental work done on your horses?

**ANSWER:** When it appears necessary.

# Elliott Burch

A man who certainly needs no introduction to fellow members of the Thoroughbred industry is Mr. Elliott Burch, long regarded as one of the leading trainers in United States Thoroughbred racing circles. His list of past performers reads like a "who's who" of the racing industry. Horses such as Arts and Letters, Fort Marcy, and Sword Dancer were all trained by Mr. Burch, and all three had the distinction of being voted Horse of the Year in their respective seasons. He has also had the good fortune to have trained Key To The Mint, named Champion Three Year Old Colt of 1972; Bowl Of Flowers, named Champion Two Year Old, and Champion Three Year Old Filly of her years, in addition to many other outstanding individuals.

Mr. Burch currently trains for one of the most powerful stables in the entire country, Rokeby Stable, owned by Mr. Paul Mellon. Of course, Key To The Mint was one of the most consistent performers in the Rokeby string until his retirement. The highlight of his career came when he was voted Champion Three Year Old Colt in 1972.

*photo courtesy of The Blood-Horse*

**Elliott Burch is one of the most successful and consistently good Thoroughbred trainers at the major tracks across the country.**

## ROKEBY STABLE

BELMONT PARK RACE TRACK

P. O. Box 356

ELMONT, N. Y. 11003

September 13, 1973

Mr. John M. Brown
Public Relations Director
Equine Research Publications
P.O. Box 347
Grapevine, Texas   76051

Dear Mr. Brown:

Thank you for your letter of September 7th.  The following information is in answer to your questionnaire.

In our barn we feed three times a day; at 11:00 in the morning,
4:00 in the afternoon, and 3:00 a.m.  The reason for dividing the
feed in this way is that the horse has a small stomach, and, in this
way, he can get a full ration at these feedings.  We generally feed
a little heavier feed at the 4:00 p.m. feedings.  If we are going to
"mash", which we do about three times a week, this is done at the
4:00 p.m. feeding.  In cold weather we give a warm mash, in warm
weather we give a cold mash.  The mash is not too watery.

The only time we leave feed in the tub, would be at the evening
meal.  Then we would leave the tub in for an hour (at most), after
feeding time.

We feel that the best type of hay for horses in training is a
heavy clover mix.  Personally, I don't think it can be too heavy.
I don't like to feed new hay, as it scours horses.  Also, I have
found many horses "bleed" when they are being fed new hay.  On some
of our heavier horses who are in light training, we feed straight
timothy hay to keep them from getting too fat.

The best hay I have seen is the California pea hay, which is
not obtainable in the East.  Horses love it, and thrive on it.  The
way we judge our hay is by color, consistency, and smell.  Also, a
way of judging your hay is by the way that horses eat it.  The best
hay obtainable is usually from Ohio, Michigan, Canada, and New York
state.

We don't feed hay in racks other than nets placed in front of
each stall, as we feel it is more natural for a horse to eat off the
ground.  In the training stable, we feed whole oats of the best

Mr. John M. Brown

quality obtainable, and we judge these by the cleanliness of the feed, and the weight. For the most part, we feed Jockey Club oats.

As to any other grain feeds; if we are stabling in cold weather, and the horses are in light training, we feed corn on the cob which has been soaked in molasses. Corn is a heater, and therefore, not a good feed to feed when a horse is in heavy training. We feed bran in our mashes in small measure, first, for the variety of taste, and secondly, because it is a good source of iron. The laxative effect of bran is negligible. At times, Spring and Fall usually, we will mix in a little pure linseed oil meal, as it's terribly good for a horse's coat. In feeding linseed oil meal, the horse must get used to the taste, and you increase the proportion as you go along.

We have a very good vitamin supplement which is mixed in their feed, and our horses have thrived on this. As I am not doing a commercial for this vitamin supplement, it shall remain nameless. We have found that massive doses of vitamin E are very good for nervous horses, and for horses that suffer from tying up.

Our horses have salt available to them at all times in the form of salt bricks in their stall. When the weather is intensely hot, we give them loose salt as well. We also sprinkle salt in their mashes. Water is available to the horses at all times through buckets which are changed at least three times a day, and they are scrubbed out at frequent intervals. Some of our top horses are put on Mt. Valley water for the reason that they have to move around a good deal, and that insures that they have the same quality water wherever they go.

I don't believe in feeding horses sweet feed, as it is a completely unnatural feed, and you are forcing the horse to eat by giving him something sweet.

Personally, I don't think that pellets are a good feed, as long as hay and oats are available. Our only experience with pelleted feed has been with broodmares that we had sent to a certain farm in Florida, and, after having been fed pellets, they came back looking like hell.

The only change we make in our feeding program before a race is to take most of the hay away the night before the race, then feed them about half ration at their noon feeding. We also take their water away about two hours before the race.

The only tricks I know to get a horse to eat after he has gone off his feed is to sweeten the hay with a sugar-water solution. There are also some tonics on the market that will pick up a horse's appetite.

I spoil my horses by giving them lump sugar when they are out of their stalls, and they come to know me, and look for it every time they see me. I don't give it to them in the stall, as they would get to pawing every time they see me.

We feed carrots when they are in good condition, and economical. At the present, the price is exhorbitant, and the carrots aren't that good.

I don't believe in grazing horses while they are in training, as it leads to bleeding, and, also, they pick up a great many bloodworms from the heavily infested areas around the barns. If a horse needs grass, we turn him out at the farm for six weeks to two months.

Our exercise program at Rokeby is to walk a horse one day, gallop him for two days, breeze him, if it's a fast breeze, he will walk the next day, gallop, gallop, and breeze.

I think good grooming of a horse is essential, and by good grooming I mean that the stall should be kept as clean as possible of droppings, and that his coat, and equipment, should be kept spotless. We bathe our horses in hot weather after a strong gallop, or breeze, but in cold weather we merely sponge them off. Also, we give them alcohol and Absorbine washes in hot or cold weather.

I prefer straw for a bedding for a horse, but, sometimes use wood shavings for a heavy doer. Also, for a horse that has been injured, wood shavings are easier for a horse to stand in. I prefer rye straw. Must be absolutely clean, free from chiggers, etc.

Each of our grooms are assigned three horses, and they take care of these horses all the time except on their day off, when our "swing man" takes their horses. We do not use hoof dressings, nor do I believe in them.

We do blood analyses about once a month on most of our horses, and they are checked for worms at least every six weeks. We try to keep our barn free of flying insects by spraying frequently, keeping the barn clean, and by keeping our feed covered.

Our horses teeth are done about once every two months. Our horses are inoculated as foals, yearlings, and as two-year olds for all the various diseases.

Yours truly,

J. Elliott Burch

# Dr. E. R. Barrick

*Eight years of involvement and research in animal nutrition has brought Dr. E. R. Barrick of Raleigh, North Carolina into constant contact with all developments in the fairly exclusive area of equine nutrition. During a period of the last ten years, most of the truly significant findings in equine nutrition research have come to the fore, placing Dr. Barrick "right in the middle" of the most noteworthy studies in this field.*

*Professor of Animal Science at North Carolina State University, Dr. Barrick has concluded that the field of equine nutrition has definitely made outstanding progress over the past few years, but that there is truly a need for intensive research in all aspects of the highly specialized field. His personal findings have brought him to the conclusion that the one main area, which is extremely crucial as far as equine nutrition is concerned, is the area of nutritionally oriented diseases and their prospective cures.*

**QUESTION:** What do you think are the particular advantages or disadvantages of the popular grains fed today?

**ANSWER:** Any of the popular grains can be used, when it is economically desirable, and if rations are balanced for essential nutrients, bulk, and palatability.

**QUESTION:** How valid are the USDA standards for judging grains?

**ANSWER:** They are very useful since they are understood in the market place.

**QUESTION:** What do you feel a minimum weight should be for a good quality oat?

**ANSWER:** This is not a critical factor if more grain like corn is used along with light oats.

**QUESTION:** Which grains generally have the highest palatability factor for horses?

**ANSWER:** Corn and oats.

**QUESTION:** What methods of processing do you feel are most valuable for oats?

**ANSWER:** If oats are not fed whole, then crimping is probably the most valuable processing method.

**QUESTION:** What method of processing is most valuable for corn?

**ANSWER:** Rolled or cracked.

**QUESTION:** What about "race horse" oats? Are they worth the additional expense for the average horse?

**ANSWER:** No, in my opinion, they are not necessary to prepare an adequate diet.

**QUESTION:** Which cutting is the highest in quality for average hays?

**ANSWER:** Second and later cuttings.

**QUESTION:** What are the advantages of mixing grass and legume hays?

**ANSWER:** A better calcium to phosphorus ratio and, also, this reduces the laxative properties of the straight legume hays.

**QUESTION:** What proportions of legumes and grass hays are ideal?

**ANSWER:** Half and half.

**QUESTION:** What varieties of hay available in your area are highest in nutritional value for that part of the country?

**ANSWER:** Orchardgrass and clover mixed, and Bermuda.

**QUESTION:** What varieties of hay available in your area tend to be most palatable?

**ANSWER:** Orchardgrass.

**QUESTION:** Would you prefer other varieties of hay if they were available locally?

**ANSWER:** Yes, alfalfa.

**QUESTION:** How long should hay be cured before feeding?

**ANSWER:** Hay should only be cured a sufficient length of time to reduce moisture to the proper level.

**QUESTION:** Should hay be fed free-choice or in measured amounts?

**ANSWER:** Feeding hay free-choice is okay for idle horses.

**QUESTION:** Do you feel that it is best to feed hay from a manger, in a net, on the ground, or how?

**ANSWER:** From a manger.

**QUESTION:** Is pasture important to a complete ration?

**ANSWER:** Pasture is important to a complete ration only from an economic standpoint.

**QUESTION:** How do you decide what are the best types of pasture to plant?

**ANSWER:** This is decided upon by the soil and climatic conditions of the particular area.

**QUESTION:** When horses are turned out to pasture, or when pasture is the primary part of the total ration, how many acres should you allow per horse?

**ANSWER:** One to two acres per horse.

**QUESTION:** What do you feel is the most practical method for preventing the spread of parasites in pastures?

**ANSWER:** Rotational grazing with cattle, and treatment.

**QUESTION:** Is there much danger from toxic weeds or plants if pasture is well cultivated?

**ANSWER:** No.

**QUESTION:** How useful do you feel soybean meal, linseed meal and cottonseed meal are in the horse ration?

**ANSWER:** These meals are good sources of protein if they are needed to meet protein needs.

**QUESTION:** How can you determine which of these concentrates is the most advantageous for a particular need, and how much to feed?

**ANSWER:** The determining factors are cost per unit of protein, and the amino acid needs (especially where foals are concerned).

**QUESTION:** Are commercial protein supplements valuable and worthwhile?

**ANSWER:** They are when they provide an economical source of protein, and they meet the protein requirements.

**QUESTION:** Should protein supplements be added to the diet routinely, or only under special circumstances?

**ANSWER:** Protein supplements should be added to the diet only if the diet is deficient in protein.

**QUESTION:** Is it preferable to feed mineralized salt, plain salt, or both?

**ANSWER:** I feel that plain salt should be fed free-choice and mineralized salt should be included in the ration.

**QUESTION:** How much salt do you feel should be included in the ration?

**ANSWER:** A limited amount (one-half to one percent).

**QUESTION:** In your opinion, what is the role of vitamin E in body function?

**ANSWER:** Enzyme function.

**QUESTION:** Do you feel that vitamin E can have a beneficial effect on racing, working, or breeding performance?

**ANSWER:** Not in amounts in excess of requirements.

**QUESTION:** Can any of the effects of vitamin E be harmful?

**ANSWER:** No.

**QUESTION:** Are vitamin supplements necessary if the diet is well-balanced?

**ANSWER:** No.

**QUESTION:** Are there any special activities that could necessitate vitamin supplementation?

**ANSWER:** Not with a good diet.

**QUESTION:** Is the average horse owner today too concerned with supplements, not concerned enough, or does he usually have the proper attitude?

**ANSWER:** I feel that the average horse owner today is too concerned with supplements.

**QUESTION:** If a balanced diet is fed, are mineral supplements necessary?

**ANSWER:** No.

**QUESTION:** What do you feel is the ideal calcium to phosphorus ratio?

**ANSWER:** 1.2 to 1.

**QUESTION:** When mineral supplements are needed, do you feel that they should be fed free-choice or included in the ration?

**ANSWER:** They should be included in the ration.

**QUESTION:** Do you think that the Total Digestible Nutrient (TDN) system of balancing a ration is practical and valid?

**ANSWER:** Yes.

**QUESTION:** What factors do you think are most important to consider in preparing the complete balanced diet?

**ANSWER:** There is no one important factor, all nutrient needs must be met.

**QUESTION:** Do sweet feeds have any advantages or disadvantages?

**ANSWER:** Sweet feeds are an aid to palatability for some horses.

**QUESTION:** Are pelleted rations of value in a normal feeding program?

**ANSWER:** Yes, they prevent sorting ingredients and they minimize dustiness.

**QUESTION:** In your experience, have you found most commercial feed mixes from reputable companies to usually be adequate in quality?

**ANSWER:** Yes.

**QUESTION:** How can you judge the worth of a commercial feed?

**ANSWER:** The best guide is the reputation of the company.

**QUESTION:** What can you do to increase the palatability of a ration?

**ANSWER:** The quality of the ingredients is the most important measure. Molasses is also an efficient aid.

**QUESTION:** Do you think there is any value in cooked rations?

**ANSWER:** No.

**QUESTION:** How can you tell if your feeding program is adequate?

**ANSWER:** Feed analysis, and the condition of the animals you are feeding.

**QUESTION:** Under what circumstances do you recommend using the various laboratory tests?

**ANSWER:** When you are involved with high-performance horses.

**QUESTION:** What precautions would you take on a day to day basis to prevent the occurrence of laminitis (founder)?

**ANSWER:** Regular feeding and watering with a balanced exercise program.

**QUESTION:** How does good nutrition relate to the susceptibility of the horse to parasites?

**ANSWER:** With good nutrition, the horse has more resistance to parasites and suffers less.

**QUESTION:** How many times a day should a horse be fed under ideal circumstances?

**ANSWER:** Three to four times per day if the animal is at hard work.

**QUESTION:** What changes should be made in the horse's diet when his activity is increased or decreased?

**ANSWER:** The most important, is to regulate the energy intake with the activity.

# Tom Warren

Tom Warren is a transplant to the running Quarter Horse industry from the performance horse faction of the industry. He has been immensely successful in both.

Having trained such successful running Quarter Horses as Sea Nymph, Miss Three Wars, Jet Charger, Twelve Five, and many others, have helped place Tom Warren near the top of the list as a leading trainer year after year. He has consistently qualified many of his better runners for the top futurities and stakes races across the country. All four of the above-mentioned horses qualified for the finals of the All-American Futurity at Ruidoso Downs, New Mexico. Of course, the All-American is the "world's richest horse race," therefore, qualifying four individuals for this prestigious race is an extremely noteworthy accomplishment. When being interviewed about his feeding program, Mr. Warren professed, that there is absolutely no means for a horse to perform to the best of his capabilities unless placed on a proper diet to ensure all the vital nutrients required for adequate body functions.

**QUESTION:** How many times per day do you feed your horses?

**ANSWER:** It varies. Twice here at the training track, and three times at the race track.

**QUESTION:** What times?

**ANSWER:** We feed at 5 a.m. — 11 a.m. — and 5 p.m.

**QUESTION:** Do you feed equal amounts to each horse?

**ANSWER:** No, I feed what each horse will clean up.

**QUESTION:** Do you divide your feed evenly between the feedings?

**ANSWER:** No, the big meal is at night. They get about four gallons a day, and we usually feed a gallon in the morning, a half gallon at noon, and two and one-half gallons at night. We feed more if they eat more.

**QUESTION:** Do you feed the same things at each feeding?

**ANSWER:** No, we just feed whole oats in the morning. In the evening we feed bran and sweet feeds, vitamins, bone supplement meal, other supplements, and Super Endurance powder.

**QUESTION:** How long do you leave the feed out?

**ANSWER:** No more than one and one-half hours.

**QUESTION:** What kinds of hay do you feed?

**ANSWER:** Coastal and alfalfa here, (Coastal in the morning and alfalfa at night), at the track, whatever we can get.

**QUESTION:** Which cutting?

**ANSWER:** Third or fourth cutting is better hay, has lower moisture content and is easier to cure properly.

**QUESTION:** Do you prefer Coastal hay or timothy hay?

**ANSWER:** Timothy is the best, but I can't always get it.

**QUESTION:** How do you judge the quality of hay?

**ANSWER:** In alfalfa I like "rabbit hay," the kind with a lot of foliage in it, and it must be dry. Moisture in it will colic a horse. You want it to be pretty green, and you don't want the stems to be coarse.

**QUESTION:** How do you feed hay?

**ANSWER:** From a manger, about two feet high.

**QUESTION:** Why?

**ANSWER:** It keeps excess weight off the neck of a horse. If he gets his head up and down, he exercises his neck more. I like a horse to get plenty of exercise in his neck.

**QUESTION:** Do you buy your oats locally?

**ANSWER:** No, I have them shipped in from Minnesota.

**QUESTION:** Do you feed whole oats?

**ANSWER:** We feed whole oats till we get to the track, then we usually feed crimped oats in a mash, hot bran mashes.

**QUESTION:** Do you insist on any particular weight per bushel?

**ANSWER:** I like oats that test forty pounds per bushel at least.

**QUESTION:** Do you insist that they be cleaned and recleaned?

**ANSWER:** Yes, that's all I buy, and I like oats with clipped ends.

**QUESTION:** What company do you feel is best?

**ANSWER:** Fruen.

**QUESTION:** Do you feed any corn?

**ANSWER:** Yes, a little chopped corn, in the winter.

**QUESTION:** How much of your ration is composed of corn when you do feed it?

**ANSWER:** Two percent.

**QUESTION:** Do you feed bran?

**ANSWER:** Yes, from one-half gallon to one gallon per horse per day.

**QUESTION:** Why do you feed bran?

**ANSWER:** For its laxative effects.

**QUESTION:** Do you feed any cottonseed meal?

**ANSWER:** No.

**QUESTION:** Linseed meal?

**ANSWER:** Yes, sometimes, to improve the hair coat of some individuals.

**QUESTION:** What about soybean meal?

**ANSWER:** No.

**QUESTION:** Do you feed any other kinds of grains?

**ANSWER:** A little rolled barley sometimes.

**QUESTION:** Do you use a protein supplement?

**ANSWER:** No, not ordinarily.

**QUESTION:** Do you think vitamin supplements are necessary in a good balanced ration?

**ANSWER:** Yes, I do.

**QUESTION:** What kind of supplements do you use?

**ANSWER:** Stamin-Atom is good, and Super Endurance powder.

**QUESTION:** Do you ever feed vitamin E to your horses.

**ANSWER:** No, I inject it about once per week.

**QUESTION:** Do you usually feed a mineral supplement?

**ANSWER:** I use mineralized salt blocks in the stalls at all times.

**QUESTION:** What do you do to make sure that your horses have good clean water at all times?

**ANSWER:** Change it twice a day.

**QUESTION:** How often do you feed a hot mash?

**ANSWER:** Usually just after a race. If you feed it all the time they get too "hot."

**QUESTION:** What do you put in it?

**ANSWER:** Bran and supplements.

**QUESTION:** Do you ever use sweet feed?

**ANSWER:** Yes, every night.

**QUESTION:** Why?

**ANSWER:** You get a good variety of grains in it.

**QUESTION:** What brand?

**ANSWER:** Omolene most of the time.

**QUESTION:** How much molasses do you like in it?

**ANSWER:** Not much, about ten percent.

**QUESTION:** Do you ever feed pellets?

**ANSWER:** No.

**QUESTION:** Why not?

**ANSWER:** You don't know what you're getting. They may be good, but you don't know what you're feeding.

**QUESTION:** Do you change your feeding program before a race?

**ANSWER:** No.

**QUESTION:** After a race?

**ANSWER:** I sometimes put them on a mash to keep them "loose."

**QUESTION:** Do you ever give little treats like carrots?

**ANSWER:** No, carrots are for rabbits.

**QUESTION:** Do you graze your horses in training?

**ANSWER:** Yes.

**QUESTION:** How long?

**ANSWER:** Ten or fifteen minutes every day.

**QUESTION:** Do you ever turn your horses out on grass?

**ANSWER:** Only during the "off" season.

**QUESTION:** Is there any kind of pasture you prefer?

**ANSWER:** Coastal Bermuda.

**QUESTION:** Are there any differences in the hay you feed your two year olds and your older horses?

**ANSWER:** I usually feed the older horses a little more feed, but the same proportions and ingredients.

**QUESTION:** Do you ever feed any commercial coat conditioners in your ration?

**ANSWER:** No, the best thing for their coats is "elbow grease."

**QUESTION:** Do you ever do anything special for a particularly nervous horse to calm him down?

**ANSWER:** I put a goat with him. It really helps.

**QUESTION:** Do you find that lessening a poor doer's exercise will stimulate his appetite?

**ANSWER:** Somewhat, but it depends on the horse. Some get off their feed if you work them, and some get off their feed if you don't.

**QUESTION:** How important do you think brushing and rubbing are to the appetite, health, and general nutrition of the horse?

**ANSWER:** I'm sure it has a lot to do with good health; I don't really think it has anything to do with their appetite.

**QUESTION:** How much time do you usually spend grooming your horses every day?

**ANSWER:** That would really be hard to say. Sometimes it seems like all day. We just work on them till they look good, and then we quit.

**QUESTION:** What do you include when you groom a horse, what steps do you take?

**ANSWER:** We brush, rub, vacuum, clip when necessary, clean and treat hooves, lubricate their nose to keep dust out, etc.

**QUESTION:** How often do you clean out hooves with a hoof pick?

**ANSWER:** Twice a day, each time they come back in from working.

**QUESTION:** How often do you clean manure out of stalls?

**ANSWER:** Twice a day.

**QUESTION:** How often do you give your horses a bath?

**ANSWER:** We don't in the winter. Just at the track, every time we run one.

**QUESTION:** Do you heat the water each time?

**ANSWER:** Yes, just so it feels hot to your hand.

**QUESTION:** What do you use for bedding?

**ANSWER:** I like good, bright, clean straw, but it is hard to find good straw, especially at the track.

**QUESTION:** Ever use anything else?

**ANSWER:** I don't really like shavings, they are too dusty. Wouldn't consider using sand, a horse will get it in his stomach.

**QUESTION:** How many horses per helper do you prefer?

**ANSWER:** About four.

**QUESTION:** What do you think a good groom should be like?

**ANSWER:** Have a lot patience, get along well with horses, and like horses. I think girls are a lot better. They get along with horses better than men, they are cleaner, and they are more reliable.

**QUESTION:** What is your pet peeve about the average person working around the stable?

**ANSWER:** They are lazy, they play around with the horses, and they don't come to work on time.

**QUESTION:** How often do you clean your feed tubs?

**ANSWER:** Once a day when we feed twice; twice a day when we feed three times.

**QUESTION:** How do you clean them?

**ANSWER:** With water, disinfectant, and scrub brush.

**QUESTION:** How often do you clean up brushes, rub rags, etc.?

**ANSWER:** Every day, in the morning, with water and disinfectant.

**QUESTION:** What kind of hoof dressing do you use?

**ANSWER:** I mix up my own, with Hooflex and Valentine's, as a base.

**QUESTION:** How often do you apply it?

**ANSWER:** Every day, unless the ground is moist, then two to three times per week.

**QUESTION:** Do you ever have a blood analysis done on your horses?

**ANSWER:** Yes, often.

**QUESTION:** What do you look for?

**ANSWER:** What the red cell count is.

**QUESTION:** How often do you have your horses wormed?

**ANSWER:** Usually every sixty to ninety days.

**QUESTION:** What method do you use?

**ANSWER:** I have the vet tube them.

**QUESTION:** Do you use anything else?

**ANSWER:** Shell Equi-Guard. I put it in the feed because I can't really tube them at the track. It puts them off feed for too long. I use it every two to three weeks.

**QUESTION:** How often do you have dental work done on your horses?

**ANSWER:** I have their wolf teeth pulled, and I have the vet look at their teeth every time he checks them.

**QUESTION:** How often do you have your horses shod or reset?

**ANSWER:** About every thirty days.

**QUESTION:** How often do you take a horse's temperature?

**ANSWER:** Whenever he looks sick, and usually if I'm going to run one, I check his temperature.

**QUESTION:** Do you inoculate your horses on a regular basis?

**ANSWER:** All kinds, Fluvac, distemper and everything.

**QUESTION:** Do you X-ray your two year old's knees?

**ANSWER:** Yes.

**QUESTION:** Do you insist they be completely closed?

**ANSWER:** No. It depends on the horse's age. If they are where they should be for his age (short or long), then we put them in training. It depends on what the owner wants.

# Gordon Shillingburg

*Teaching and conducting intensive research projects for the past 22 years has qualified Gordon Shillingburg of Scottsdale, Arizona to be considered as one of the truly outstanding equine nutritionists in the southwest.*

*Holding the position of Consulting Nutritionist for the San Marcos Research Center in Scottsdale, Mr. Shillingburg is placed in contact with the latest research developments in all phases of nutrition, whether conducted at his own facility or at other major research centers across the country. His studies have primarily been centered around the fields of minerals, vitamins, protein, and energy contents of feedstuffs for horses.*

**QUESTION:** What areas in the field of equine nutritional research do you feel are most in need of further study?

**ANSWER:** Minerals, vitamins, protein and energy.

**QUESTION:** What do you think are the particular advantages or disadvantages of the following grains: (a) oats, (b) corn, (c) wheat, (d) barley, (e) milo, and (f) rye?

**ANSWER:** Oats — bulk, corn — energy, wheat — poorest of grains for horse, barley — bulk energy, milo — energy, rye — too light.

**QUESTION:** How valid are the USDA standards for judging grains?

**ANSWER:** Moderate.

**QUESTION:** Are there other factors that you look for?

**ANSWER:** Palatability.

**QUESTION:** How long should grain be allowed to ripen before feeding?

**ANSWER:** Grain should be mature, but not flinty.

**QUESTION:** When would you recommend using processed grains rather than natural grains?

**ANSWER:** Always.

**QUESTION:** What are the advantages of processed grains?

**ANSWER:** Palatability, and availability of nutrients.

**QUESTION:** What method of processing is most valuable for oats?

**ANSWER:** Crimping.

**QUESTION:** What method of processing is most valuable for corn?

**ANSWER:** Steam-rolled.

**QUESTION:** What about "race horse" oats? Are they worth the additional expense for the average horse?

**ANSWER:** No, with proper processing of other grains, particularly barley, and proper mixing, race horse oats are not necessary. Energy is the important factor in rations.

**QUESTION:** Which cutting is highest in quality for: (a) alfalfa, (b) clover hays, (c) timothy, (d) Bermuda?

**ANSWER:** Alfalfa, first and second cutting; clover hays, first and second cutting; timothy, first cutting; Bermuda, first cutting.

**QUESTION:** What proportions are ideal for mixing grass hays and legume hays?

**ANSWER:** Half and half.

**QUESTION:** What varieties of hay available in your area are highest in nutritional value?

**ANSWER:** Alfalfa.

**QUESTION:** Would you prefer other varieties if they were available locally?

**ANSWER:** No.

**QUESTION:** What is the minimum amount of hay necessary for a balanced diet?

**ANSWER:** There is no set amount, it depends on the quality of the hay and the productivity of the animal.

**QUESTION:** How long should hay be cured before feeding?

**ANSWER:** It takes thirty days, to go through an adequate "sweat" period.

**QUESTION:** Should hay be fed free-choice or in measured amounts?

**ANSWER:** In measured amounts.

**QUESTION:** How much?

**ANSWER:** Depends on the productivity of the animal.

**QUESTION:** Do you feel that it is best to feed hay from a manger, in a net, on the ground, or how?

**ANSWER:** Hay should be fed from a manger.

**QUESTION:** Is pasture important to a complete ration?

**ANSWER:** Yes, if possible.

**QUESTION:** How do you decide what are the best types of pasture to plant?

**ANSWER:** Production, nutrition, and acceptability.

**QUESTION:** When horses are turned out to pasture all day, or when pasture is a primary part of the total ration, how many acres would you allow per horse?

**ANSWER:** Four acres per horse.

**QUESTION:** Do you feel that the psychological advantages of "nibblers" such as carrots or lettuce, for stalled horses are worth the possibility of developing bad habits?

**ANSWER:** Yes, I feel that "nibblers" are a plus point in an overall horse care program.

**QUESTION:** Do you feel that the addition of soybean meal, linseed meal or cottonseed meal are advantageous to a nutritious feeding program?

**ANSWER:** All three of these concentrates are useful from a protein content standpoint, and also to balance the amino acid content of the feed.

**QUESTION:** Do you feel that commercial protein supplements are generally valuable and worthwhile?

**ANSWER:** Yes.

**QUESTION:** Should protein supplements be added to the diet routinely, or only under special circumstances?

**ANSWER:** Only under special circumstances . . . depending on the needs of the horse.

**QUESTION:** What do you feel is the desirable protein content of rations for: (a) weanlings, (b) yearlings, (c) growing horses, (d) mature horses, (e) old horses, (f) broodmares, (g) stallions, (h) race horses, (i) performance horses, and (j) pleasure horses?

**ANSWER:** Weanlings, fifteen percent; yearlings, thirteen percent; growing horses, twelve percent; mature horses, eleven percent; old horses, eleven percent; broodmares, twelve percent; stallions, twelve percent; race horses, twelve percent; performance horses, twelve percent; and pleasure horses, eleven percent.

**QUESTION:** Is it preferable to feed mineralized salt, plain salt, or both?

**ANSWER:** Plain salt.

**QUESTION:** Do you prefer loose salt or block salt?

**ANSWER:** Block salt.

**QUESTION:** In your opinion, what is the role of vitamin E in body function?

**ANSWER:** Vitamin E aids in the utilization of vitamin A and also in food metabolism.

**QUESTION:** Do you feel that vitamin E can have beneficial effects on racing, working, or breeding performance?

**ANSWER:** Yes.

**QUESTION:** Can any of the effects of vitamin E be harmful?

**ANSWER:** No.

**QUESTION:** Do you feel that injected supplements are superior to oral vitamins?

**ANSWER:** No.

**QUESTION:** Do you feel that the average horse owner today is too concerned with supplements, not concerned enough, or does he usually have the proper attitude?

**ANSWER:** The average horseman today is not concerned enough.

**QUESTION:** What do you feel is the ideal calcium to phosphorus ratio?

**ANSWER:** 1.5 to 1.

**QUESTION:** Do you feel that mineral supplements should be fed free-choice, forced, or not at all?

**ANSWER:** Forced.

**QUESTION:** What factors do you think are most important when considering the preparation of the complete balanced diet?

**ANSWER:** Palatability, available protein, and energy.

**QUESTION:** In your experience, have you found commercial feed mixes from reputable companies to usually be adequate in quality?

**ANSWER:** Yes.

**QUESTION:** How can you judge the worth of a commercial feed?

**ANSWER:** Visual inspection, and feed analysis.

**QUESTION:** What can you do to increase the palatability of a ration?

**ANSWER:** High quality, proper feeds, and occasionally the addition of molasses.

**QUESTION:** Do you think there is any value in cooked rations?

**ANSWER:** Yes, I think grains are better utilized.

**QUESTION:** How frequently do you recommend worming, and by what method?

**ANSWER:** I recommend both tube and oral worming methods, one to three times per year.

**QUESTION:** Although drugs are generally outlawed in racing programs, do you feel that they could ever be of value?

**ANSWER:** Yes.

**QUESTION:** How many times a day should a horse be fed under ideal circumstances?

**ANSWER:** Three times per day.

**QUESTION:** What changes should be made in a horse's diet when his activity is increased or decreased?

**ANSWER:** Energy should be increased or decreased according to the activity, and possibly the amount also.

**QUESTION:** Do you feel that it is better to change a ration frequently in order to make sure that a variety of nutrients are included, or is it better to stick with a proven formula?

**ANSWER:** It is better to stick with a proven formula.

**QUESTION:** How long should you leave feed in front of a horse if it is not eaten?

**ANSWER:** Twelve hours.

**QUESTION:** How long should you leave hay in front of a horse if it is not eaten?

**ANSWER:** Twelve hours.

**QUESTION:** Do you think the life expectancy of the average horse could be lengthened if most owners were to improve their feeding programs?

**ANSWER:** Yes.

**QUESTION:** How good do you feel the average level of equine nutrition is in the United States today?

**ANSWER:** Poor.

# Al-Marah Arabians

Owner of the largest Arabian farm in the world is the title which can be bestowed on Mrs. Bazy Tankersley, head of the Al-Marah Arabians in Barnesville, Maryland. Mrs. Tankersley is one of the best known and most successful people in the entire Arabian industry.

In addition to owning this huge and beautiful Arabian establishment, she has had the distinction of having owned and bred many outstanding Arabian performers over the years. Among the more successful individuals under her name have been Al-Marah Ralla and Al-Marah El Hezzez, both National High Score Award Winners. Also, she has owned Count Bazy, National Champion Arabian Stallion, and Al-Marah Silver Sparrow, National Western Pleasure Arabian Champion.

The fact that Mrs. Tankersley has met with such success in all her endeavors in the field of Arabians, has focused national attention on her operation in Maryland. Naturally the nutritional aspects of her overall program are of great interest.

**QUESTION:** How many times per day do you feed?

**ANSWER:** Twice per day, except with horses we are trying to fatten, or horses in intensive training such as for endurance rides.

**QUESTION:** At what times of day do you feed?

**ANSWER:** Normally 7:30 a.m. and 5 p.m. for horses that are fed twice per day. Horses that are fed three times per day are fed at 7:30 a.m., noon, and 5 p.m. Horses that are fed four times per day are fed at 7:30 a.m., noon, 5 p.m., and midnight.

**QUESTION:** Do you feed equal amounts at each feeding?

**ANSWER:** Yes.

**QUESTION:** Do you feed the same things at each feeding?

**ANSWER:** Normally, however we occasionally feed alfalfa in the morning and timothy at night for horses in training.

**QUESTION:** How long do you leave the feed out if it is not eaten?

**ANSWER:** Until the next feeding.

**QUESTION:** What kind of hay do you feed?

**ANSWER:** Mostly alfalfa, but also mixed, or timothy.

**QUESTION:** Which cutting do you prefer for each variety?

**ANSWER:** We prefer second or third cutting for our legumes.

**QUESTION:** Are there any other kinds of hay you would prefer if they were available locally?

**ANSWER:** No.

**QUESTION:** What method do you use to feed hay?

**ANSWER:** In a closed, low manger.

**QUESTION:** Where do you get your oats?

**ANSWER:** We grow them ourselves to ensure consistent quality control standards.

**QUESTION:** Do you feed whole oats or processed oats?

**ANSWER:** We feed crimped oats, as we feel they will be better digested.

**QUESTION:** Do you feed any corn?

**ANSWER:** Yes, we feed cracked corn, year-round.

**QUESTION:** How much of your total ration is composed of corn?

**ANSWER:** It varies with the individual animal.

**QUESTION:** Do you feed bran in your ration?

**ANSWER:** Yes, because it keeps bowels in good order, and it has a good phosphorus content.

**QUESTION:** Do you feed cottonseed meal in your ration?

**ANSWER:** Sometimes, for coat appearance.

**QUESTION:** Do you feed linseed meal in your ration?

**ANSWER:** No.

**QUESTION:** Do you feed soybean meal in your ration?

**ANSWER:** No.

**QUESTION:** Do you feed any other types of grain in your ration?

**ANSWER:** Yes, speltz. Speltz is higher in protein than oats, and I get a higher yield per acre.

**QUESTION:** Do you supplement the protein content of your ration?

**ANSWER:** Yes.

**QUESTION:** What do you use for this purpose, and how much of it do you use?

**ANSWER:** I use a milk-base, 21 percent protein supplement, enough to bring the total ration up to an average of sixteen percent.

**QUESTION:** What percent of protein do you think is necessary in the ration of: (a) foals, (b) yearlings, (c) two and three year olds, (d) mature horses?

**ANSWER:** Foals, sixteen percent; yearlings, sixteen percent; two and three year olds, fourteen percent; mature horses, fourteen percent.

**QUESTION:** Are there any special activities such as heavy performance work, or breeding that you think would require more protein in the diet of the mature horse?

**ANSWER:** Yes, such activities would require that the protein level be raised to sixteen percent.

**QUESTION:** Do you give injectable vitamins?

**ANSWER:** Only occasionally and then just for our endurance horses.

photo courtesy of Al-Marah Arabians

*Count Dorsaz by Rissalix, out of Shamnar, is owned by Al-Marah Arabian Farm headed by Mrs. Bazy Tankersley. The beautiful stallion was imported from England, and this picture was taken at the age of 26. This proves what proper nutrition can do to increase the longevity and productivity of horses.

**QUESTION:** Do you feel that salt is important in your horses' diet?

**ANSWER:** Yes, we feed salt in free-choice, block form.

**QUESTION:** Do you ever recommend minerals with the salt?

**ANSWER:** Yes.

**QUESTION:** Do you ever feed your horses a hot mash?

**ANSWER:** Yes, after foaling or after certain maladies.

**QUESTION:** Do you feed any sweet feed in your ration?

**ANSWER:** Yes.

**QUESTION:** Do you feed any kind of pellets?

**ANSWER:** Occasionally we feed alfalfa pellets.

# E. R. Beddo

Many trainers go for lengthy periods of time without having even one stakes winner to their credit, but our subject of discussion, Mr. E. R. Beddo, has had the good fortune and great skill to have trained two Quarter Horses, who have been named "Champion Quarter Running Horses" in their respective seasons. Howdy Jones, under Mr. Beddo's tutelage was named "Champion Quarter Running Two Year Old Gelding" in 1969 and "Champion Quarter Running Three Year Old Gelding" in 1970. Another student of the Beddo barn, Gallant Jet, was recently named "Champion Quarter Running Two Year Old Colt" of 1972. The training of these two superstars would be enough to place any trainer near the top of his category, not to mention that Beddo has had several other outstanding runners to his credit over the past several years.

His feeding program exemplifies the effort, which has been put into the carefully formulated training schedules he has set up for each individual under his care.

QUESTION: How many times a day do you feed?
ANSWER: Three.
QUESTION: Why?
ANSWER: They seem to do better on three feedings.
QUESTION: What times of day?
ANSWER: 5 a.m. — 11 a.m. — and 5 p.m.
QUESTION: Do you feed equal amounts or vary it?
ANSWER: I feed straight oats in morning and at noon, all vitamins, supplements, sweet feeds, and mash at night.
QUESTION: How long do you leave feed out at each feeding?
ANSWER: About one and one-half hours.
QUESTION: Why?
ANSWER: Because mashes will sour, and I don't like slow eaters.
QUESTION: What kinds of hay do you feed?
ANSWER: Washington timothy, alfalfa, and prairie hay at the races, here (Ross Downs, Colleyville, Texas), just alfalfa and prairie.
QUESTION: Why is there a difference at the races?
ANSWER: Timothy is not usually available here.
QUESTION: Which cutting do you prefer?
ANSWER: Third on alfalfa, second or third on prairie.

**QUESTION:** Do you feed different types of hay at different times, or mix them?

**ANSWER:** I feed timothy or prairie at 5 and 11, and mix alfalfa with them at night.

**QUESTION:** Any particular parts of the country you want your hay to come from?

**ANSWER:** Northern hay, and Washington timothy.

**QUESTION:** Why is it better?

**ANSWER:** The climate.

**QUESTION:** How do you feed your hay?

**ANSWER:** I use a hay rack about three feet tall.

**QUESTION:** Do you buy your oats locally or have them shipped in?

**ANSWER:** I have them shipped in from Minnesota.

**QUESTION:** Why do you buy that particular kind?

**ANSWER:** The best oats there are! They are a clean, heavy oat, a full oat, they have been clipped, and they are just excellent.

**QUESTION:** Why do you think clipped oats are better?

**ANSWER:** Because you get more kernel out of the oats and less fiber.

**QUESTION:** What brand do you buy?

**ANSWER:** Fruen.

**QUESTION:** Do you feed corn?

**ANSWER:** No.

**QUESTION:** Do you feed bran?

**ANSWER:** Yes, at night in a mash.

**QUESTION:** Why?

**ANSWER:** It helps to keep a horse "loose."

**QUESTION:** Do you feed cottonseed meal?

**ANSWER:** Yes, because it is a good hair conditioner.

**QUESTION:** Linseed meal?

**ANSWER:** Yes, for their coats and also to keep bowels loose.

**QUESTION:** Do you feed soybean oil meal?

**ANSWER:** No.

**QUESTION:** Why not?

**ANSWER:** You can give a horse too many things, and I don't think that's good.

**QUESTION:** Do you feed any other grains?

**ANSWER:** I sometimes feed steam-rolled barley.

**QUESTION:** Do you use a commercial protein supplement?

**ANSWER:** Yes.

**QUESTION:** How do you feed it?

**ANSWER:** I feed it at night, in the mash.

**QUESTION:** Do you think race horses require more protein than the average horse?

**ANSWER:** Yes, I do.

**QUESTION:** Do you feed a vitamin supplement?

**ANSWER:** Yes, I do. I mix it in the bran mash.

**QUESTION:** Do you ever inject vitamins?

**ANSWER:** Not usually, just when I have horse with a specific problem, low blood count, etc.

**QUESTION:** Do you ever feed vitamin E?

**ANSWER:** Yes.

**QUESTION:** Do you think it has special benefits?

**ANSWER:** It certainly seems to help their condition.

**QUESTION:** Do you have a particular brand of vitamin supplement you like to use?

**ANSWER:** Stamin-Atom, and Calf Manna. I also feed a half cup of honey every day mixed in the feed.

**QUESTION:** What do you feel are the benefits of honey?

**ANSWER:** I think honey has a lot of energy, and it is very palatable.

**QUESTION:** Do you feed a mineral supplement?

**ANSWER:** No, unless they show up deficient in a blood analysis.

**QUESTION:** Do you feed minerals with your salt?

**ANSWER:** Yes, I feed a mineralized salt, mixed with the ration at night.

**QUESTION:** How do you make sure that your horses have a constant clean water supply?

**ANSWER:** By washing the buckets out every day.

**QUESTION:** How often do you change the water?

**ANSWER:** Twice a day.

**QUESTION:** Have you ever used an automatic watering device?

**ANSWER:** No, I think they are fine for a brood farm, but a race horse should be in a stall with an exact amount, so that you can tell exactly how much water he's drinking, otherwise you can't check this. If a race horse is not drinking his water, you need to do something about it right away.

**QUESTION:** How often do you feed your horses a hot mash?

**ANSWER:** Every night.

**QUESTION:** Do you use sweet feed?

**ANSWER:** At night.

**QUESTION:** How much?

**ANSWER:** A gallon per horse.

**QUESTION:** Why do you like sweet feed?

**ANSWER:** It has a good variety of grains and the horses find it very palatable.

**QUESTION:** How much molasses do you like in your sweet feed?

**ANSWER:** A medium amount, not dry, and not sticky.

**QUESTION:** Do you ever feed pellets?

**ANSWER:** No.

**QUESTION:** Why not?

**ANSWER:** You can't tell what the horse is getting.

**QUESTION:** Do you change your rations before or after a race?

**ANSWER:** No.

**QUESTION:** Do you believe in giving your horses treats such as carrots?

**ANSWER:** Yes, I like to give them carrots every once in a while. Sometimes I cut them up in the feed, and sometimes I walk by the stall and give them.

**QUESTION:** When your horses are in training do you graze them?

**ANSWER:** When I can.

**QUESTION:** How long?

**ANSWER:** Ten minutes at the most, usually just five.

**QUESTION:** Do you ever turn them out on grass or in dry paddock?

**ANSWER:** No.

**QUESTION:** Is there any type of pasture you prefer?

**ANSWER:** I like oat pasture or wheat pasture.

**QUESTION:** Do you work with Thoroughbreds?

**ANSWER:** Yes, I've run Thoroughbreds.

**QUESTION:** Do you feed them differently than Quarter Horses?

**ANSWER:** No, not at all.

**QUESTION:** Are there differences in the way you feed two year olds, and older horses?

**ANSWER:** No.

**QUESTION:** Do you ever use an electrolyte solution in the feed or water for a horse?

**ANSWER:** Once in a while if I have a horse not drinking enough water.

**QUESTION:** Have you found that you can stimulate a poor doer's appetite by lessening the amount of exercise he gets?

**ANSWER:** No, I haven't.

**QUESTION:** What is your average exercise program for the average horse getting ready for the average race?

**ANSWER:** There really isn't anything close to an average. It depends on the horse, and his condition, entirely.

**QUESTION:** How much time do you spend grooming each horse every day?

**ANSWER:** About forty-five minutes. Fifteen in the morning before he goes out, and fifteen when he comes back in, and more later.

**QUESTION:** What do you use to groom them?

**ANSWER:** We have two vacuums. We go over the horse with a curry-comb, vacuum, and brush and then rub him, and then send him out for his morning work, then bring him back in and he's recleaned.

**QUESTION;** How often do you clean your horse's hooves with a hoof pick?

**ANSWER:** Twice a day.

**QUESTION:** How often do you pick up the manure out of each stall?

**ANSWER:** As often as we can. We go in in the morning and pick it out, then when the horse comes out, his stall is completely cleaned and raked, and the straw is re-laid and clean straw is put on top. Then pick it up as often as we see manure. Then in the afternoon when they go out again, we clean the stalls again.

**QUESTION:** How often do you give your horses a bath?

**ANSWER:** Every time we send them to the track, in the summer.

**QUESTION:** Do you give it out in the open or inside?

**ANSWER:** Out in the open.

**QUESTION:** Do you use heated water?

**ANSWER:** Lukewarm.

**QUESTION:** Have you ever used rice hulls for bedding?

**ANSWER:** Yes I have, but I don't like them.

**QUESTION:** What about sand for bedding?

**ANSWER:** I don't like sand, it's cold and dirty, and they can get sand in their stomachs.

**QUESTION:** What kind of straw do you look for?

**ANSWER:** I want my bedding just as clean as my feed. No weeds, just clean straw.

**QUESTION:** Do you have problems with horses eating their bedding?

**ANSWER:** Very little.

**QUESTION:** How many horses per helper do you prefer?

**ANSWER:** I have a helper for every three horses.

**QUESTION:** What attributes do you insist upon in a person working for you around horses?

**ANSWER:** I'd rather have women, they are better around horses than men. They will take care of the barn and their horses like a house. They have pride in their work.

**QUESTION:** What is your pet peeve about the average person who works around stables?

**ANSWER:** About half of the men are drunks, and they just want to "get through" and get away.

**QUESTION:** How often and how do you clean up your feed tubs?

**ANSWER:** We use water and a scrub brush every day.

**QUESTION:** How about your brushes, rub rags, etc.?

**ANSWER:** They're washed about every two days with hot soapy water.

**QUESTION:** What kind of material do you like for your rub rags to be made out of?

**ANSWER:** Wool, it gets the dust out of their coats, and puts gloss on their hair.

**QUESTION:** What kind of hoof dressing do you use?

**ANSWER:** Valentine's.

**QUESTION:** How often do you apply it?

**ANSWER:** About every other day.

**QUESTION:** About how often do you have a blood analysis done?

**ANSWER:** Depends. The horse's condition will tell you when it is needed.

**QUESTION:** Do you have problems with horses that chew wood?

**ANSWER:** Yes.

**QUESTION:** What do you do for them?

**ANSWER:** Paint the wood with creosote.

**QUESTION:** What do you think causes them to chew wood in the first place?

**ANSWER:** Nerves. It's the same as a person chewing his fingernails.

**QUESTION:** What about cribbers, stump suckers, etc.?

**ANSWER:** I've been awfully fortunate; I haven't had any.

**QUESTION:** What about stall weavers?

**ANSWER:** Putting a dog next to the stall door will stop that.

**QUESTION:** Do you think horses catch bad habits from each other?

**ANSWER:** Definitely.

**QUESTION:** How often do you have your horses wormed?

**ANSWER:** About every ninety days.

**QUESTION:** What method?

**ANSWER:** We always have our horses tubed by a veterinarian.

**QUESTION:** How often do you have dental work done on your horses?

**ANSWER:** Three times a year.

**QUESTION:** How often do you have your horses shod or reset?

**ANSWER:** It depends on the horse, but an average of every three weeks.

**QUESTION:** How often do you take a horse's temperature?

**ANSWER:** When they appear sick.

**QUESTION:** Do you inoculate your horses on a periodic basis for anything?

**ANSWER:** Fluvac, sleeping sickness, strangles, distemper — we give all the shots there are.

**QUESTION:** Do you X-ray all of your two year old's knees before you put them into training?

**ANSWER:** Yes.

**QUESTION:** Do they have to be completely closed before you start them?

**ANSWER:** Yes.

**QUESTION:** What areas of equine nutrition do you feel are in need of further research?

**ANSWER:** Colitis X, and colds and coughs of colts.

# BIBLIOGRAPHY

Bailey, Herbert, **Vitamin E: Your Key to a Healthy Heart,** Arc Books, Inc., New York, (1970)

Bullard, T. L., D.V.M., "Nutrition — Some Basic Thoughts on Horse Feeding," Paper presented to Southwestern Planning Conference for Livestockmen, Waco, Texas, March 1973.

Catcott, E. J., D.V.M., Ph.D., and Smithcors, J. F., D.V.M., Ph.D., Editors, **Equine Medicine and Surgery.** American Veterinary Publications, Inc., Wheaton, Illinois, (1972)

Catcott, E. J., D.V.M., Ph.D., and Smithcors, J. F., D.V.M., Ph.D., Editors, **Progress in Equine Practice, Volume Two.** American Veterinary Publications, Inc., Wheaton, Illinois, (1970)

Crampton, E. W., and Harris, L. E., **Applied Animal Nutrition.** W. H. Freeman and Company, San Francisco, (1969)

Cunha, T. J., Ph.D., "Vitamins and Minerals for Horses," **Feedstuffs.** Vol 38 (33): 62-66, (1966)

Donahue, Roy L., Shickluna, John C., and Robertson, Lynn S., **Soils: An Introduction to Soils and Plant Growth.** Prentice-Hall, Inc. Englewood Cliffs, New Jersey, (1971)

Dunn, Angus M., Ph.D., M.R.C.V.S., **Veterinary Helminthology.** Lea and Febiger, Philadelphia, (1969)

Ensminger, M. E., Ph.D., **Horses and Horsemanship.** Interstate Printers and Publishers, Inc., Danville, Illinois, (1969)

Guthrie, Helen Andrews, **Introductory Nutrition.** The C. V. Mosby Company, Saint Louis, (1971)

Hafez, E. S. E., and Dyer, I. A., **Animal Growth and Nutrition.** Lea and Febiger, Philadelphia, (1969)

Hayes, M. Horace, F.R.C.V.S., **Stable Management and Exercise.** Arco Publishing Company, Inc., New York, (1968)

Hodges, R. J., "Keys to Profitable Small Grain Production in the North Central Texas Area," United States Department of Agriculture, Agricultural Extension Service.

Jones, William E., D.V.M., Ph.D., Editor, **The Teeth of the Horse.** Caballus Publishers, East Lansing, Michigan, (1972)

Jones, William E., D.V.M., Ph.D., Editor, **Anatomy of the Horse.** Caballus Publishers, East Lansing, Michigan, (1972)

Miller, Wm. C., F.R.C.V.S., F.R.S.E., **Practical Essentials in the Care and Management of Horses on Thoroughbred Studs.** The Thoroughbred Breeders Association, London, (1965)

Montgomery, E. S., **The Thoroughbred.** Arco Publishing Company, Inc., New York, (1971)

Morris Animal Foundation, "Zinc Requirements of the Horse," Paper Morris Animal Foundation, Denver, Colorado, March 1972

Morrison, Frank B., **Feeds and Feeding, Abridged, Ninth Edition.** The Morrison Publishing Company, Claremont, Ontario, Canada, (1958)

National Research Council, **Nutrient Requirements of Horses.** National Academy of Sciences — National Research Council, Washington, D.C., (1973)

Pike, Ruth L., and Brown, Myrtle, L., **Nutrition: An Integrated Approach.** John Wiley and Sons, Inc., New York, (1967)

Potter, Gary D., Ph.D., "Horse Feeding Management," Paper presented at Texas Agricultural Extension Service Research Center, Renner, Texas, May 1973

Pratt, J. N., and Novosad, A. C., "Keys to Profitable Hay Production," United States Department of Agriculture, Agricultural Extension Service

Rooney, James R., D.V.M., **Autopsy of the Horse, Technique and Interpretation.** The Williams and Wilkins Co., Baltimore, (1970)

Rossdale, Peter D., M.A., F.R.C.V.S., **The Horse.** The California Thoroughbred Breeders Association, California, (1972)

Schalm, Oscar W., D.V.M., Ph.D., **Veterinary Hematology.** Lea and Febiger, Philadelphia, (1965)

Seiden, Dr. Rudolph, **The Handbook of Feedstuffs.** Springer Publishing Company, Inc., New York (1957)

Siegmund, O. H., Editor, **The Merck Veterinary Manual.** Merck and Company, Inc., Rahway, New Jersey, (1967)

Simmons, Hoyt, **Horseman's Veterinary Guide.** The Western Horseman, Colorado Springs, Colorado, (1963)

Smith, A. F., D.V.M., "The Teeth of the Horse," Paper presented to Southwest Planning Conference for Livestockmen, Waco, Texas, March, 1973.

Smythe, R. H., M.R.C.V.S., **The Mind of the Horse.** The Stephen Greene Press, Brattleboro, Vermont, (1965)

Straiton, E. C., **The Horse Owner's Vet Book.** J. B. Lippincott Co., Philadelphia, (1973)

Summerhays, Reginald S., **The Problem Horse.** A. S. Barnes and Company, New York, (1959)

Teeter, S. M., D.V.M., Stillions, Merle C., Ph.D., and Nelson, W. E., Ph.D., "Calcium and Phosphorus Requirements," **Journal of the American Veterinary Medical Association.** Vol. 151 (12): 1625-1628, (1967)

The Blood-Horse, **Feeding the Horse.** The Blood-Horse, Lexington, Kentucky, (1969)

The Borden Company, **Guide to the Care and Feeding of Orphan and Early Weaned Foals.** Borden Chemical Division, Norfolk, Virginia, (1972)

United States Department of Agriculture, **Crops in Peace and War, the Yearbook of Agriculture, 1950-1951.** Government Printing Office, Washington, D.C., (1951)

Weikel, Bill, Editor, **Know Practical Horse Feeding.** The Farnam Horse Library, Omaha, Nebraska, (1971)

Wilson, Eva D., Fisher, Katherine H., and Fuqua, Mary E., **Principles of Nutrition.** John Wiley and Sons, Inc., New York, (1965)